ARAMCO HANDBOOK

Oil and the Middle East

ARABIAN AMERICAN OIL COMPANY

Dhahran, Saudi Arabia

Library of Congress Catalog Card Number 68-24022

Revised Edition, published July 1, 1968,
by Arabian American Oil Company,
Dhahran, Saudi Arabia

Printed in the Netherlands
by Joh. Enschedé en Zonen-Haarlem

Part 1

BACKGROUND OF SAUDI ARABIA AND THE MIDDLE EAST—Highlights of the long history of the Arab world, and of the establishment and development of the Kingdom of Saudi Arabia.

Part 2

THE OIL INDUSTRY AND ITS GROWTH IN THE MIDDLE EAST—A brief account of the beginnings of the oil industry, its growth in importance throughout the world and its development in the Middle East.

Part 3

THE ARAMCO VENTURE—The story of its inception and development of the oil fields both in the desert and offshore in the company's concession area.

Part 4

SAUDI ARABIA: THE GOVERNMENT, THE PEOPLE AND THE LAND—Facts about the country in which Aramco is operating.

Part 5

THE CULTURE AND CUSTOMS OF THE ARABS—Sketches of the religion, literature, calendar and the social and other customs of the Arab people.

Contents

Part 4

SAUDI ARABIA: THE GOVERNMENT, THE PEOPLE AND THE LAND

Part 5

THE CULTURE AND CUSTOMS OF THE ARABS

PICTURE CREDITS

Photographs in this volume were taken by Aramco photographers Burnett H. Moody, S. M. Amin, A. A. Al-Khalifa, A. M. Al-Khalifa, S. M. Al-Ghamdi, A. A. Al-Mentakh and A. L. Yousif, except as noted below:

Part 1: Pages 4, 8 (two bottom), 10—from *The Ancient Near East in Pictures Relating to the Old Testament* by James B. Pritchard, published by Princeton University Press, 1954. Pages 9, 14—United Press International. Page 18—from *Oars, Sails and Steam* by Edward Tunis, published by World Publishing Company, 1952. Page 19—Culver. Pages 20 (top), 21, 36, 43 (top), 44, 45, 64—Ewing Galloway. Page 20 (bottom), Brainerd S. Bates. Pages 24, 25, 26 (top)—American Foundation for the Study of Man. Page 27—K. Lankester Harding. Page 29—Arab Information Center. Page 30—Bahrain Petroleum Company. Page 33—T. F. Walters. Page 40—Joe Covello from Black Star. Page 42—from *Islamic Metalwork in the British Museum* by Douglas Barrett, published by the Trustees of the British Museum, 1949. Page 67 (top)—U.S. Signal Corps from United Press International. Page 67 (bottom)—Associated Press.

Part 2: Pages 74, 75 (top)—Standard Oil Company (New Jersey). Page 76 (top left)—Fred A. Schell. Page 76 (top right)—Drilling Magazine. Page 76 (bottom left)—Shell Oil Company. Page 76 (bottom right)—Mobil Oil Corporation.

Part 3: Pages 114, 115, 116, 117 and 118—Aramco Archives. Pages 120, 132, 141 (top), 142, 143, 161, 164, 165, 169, 170—Tor Eigeland. Pages 149, 151, 152—Khalil Abou El-Nasr.

Part 4: Pages 182, 192, 196-197—Tor Eigeland. Page 199—J. P. Mandaville, Jr. Page 201 (right), 212-213 (center), 219—Khalil Abou El-Nasr.

Part 5: Page 232—Black Star. Page 241—from *Persian Miniatures* by Maurice S. Dimand, published by Uffici Press, Milan. Pages 242, 243—from *A Handbook of Muhammadan Art* by Maurice S. Dimand, published by Metropolitan Museum of Art, 1958. Page 244—Metropolitan Museum of Art, Fletcher Fund. Page 250—Iraq Petroleum Company. Page 251 (bottom)—Arab Information Center. Page 252—Ewing Galloway. Page 255—New York Times.

Maps and Charts

NOTE ON BOUNDARIES

Some international boundaries in the Middle East are undefined or in dispute. Therefore some boundary indications in the Aramco Handbook are necessarily only approximate.

INTRODUCTION

The Aramco Handbook was originated to fill the void in comprehensive texts written in English about the Middle East. Employees of the Arabian American Oil Company coming to Saudi Arabia from abroad, principally Americans, needed reliable and fairly detailed knowledge of the kingdom. Nontechnical employees needed to be grounded in the fundamentals of the oil industry. Although recently a number of books on the area have been published, the handbook continues to be useful as a single source of information and background for Aramco employees.

In order to describe the Aramco venture in perspective, an unusual range of topics must be covered in the pages of this handbook: the history, culture, geography, religion and economic development of Saudi Arabia; the fundamentals of the oil industry; Aramco's early history and its present operations.

The handbook originally was distributed in five spiral-bound booklets in 1950, giving way two years later to a more convenient two-volume set. The previous edition appeared in 1960 in a one-volume version.

In the present edition some material which is readily available elsewhere has been omitted. Sections dealing with Aramco and modern Saudi Arabia have been recast to reflect some of the rapid changes of the past few years. Many of the photographs are new.

Arabic personal names and place names are spelled according to a system used by Aramco, which closely follows a generally accepted system of transliteration from Arabic to English. The system does not always represent the spelling or pronunciation of the Arabic original with complete accuracy, as Arabic contains letters and sounds for which no equivalents exist in English. Furthermore, pronunciation of Arabic varies from region to region.

An inverted apostrophy—standing for the Arabic letter 'ain—is used throughout the handbook. This distinctive consonant, which occurs often in Arabic place and personal names, has no counterpart in English.

The content of the book suggests the continued use of the name "Aramco Handbook," but with the subtitle, "Oil and the Middle East."

Dhahran, Saudi Arabia

Part 1

Background of Saudi Arabia and the Middle East

THE MIDDLE EAST
IN ANCIENT TIMES

With the march of civilization across Europe and the New World, the Middle East—the region between the eastern Mediterranean and India—for a time became somewhat isolated and eclipsed. Yet at one time that region was the center of the civilized world. Indeed, with neighboring Minoan Crete, it was the whole world then known to civilized man except for ancient China and the Indus Valley. It was in the Middle East that mankind's first steps were taken in the direction of organized social and community life. It was there that man first developed sciences, arts and skills for an intelligent solution of the problems of existence. These are the lands of the Bible, the birthplace of three great religions, all based on the worship of one God.

Americans are inclined to regard the discovery of the New World in 1492 as a long time ago, and the birth of Christ as occurring in ancient times. But in comparison with the less than 500 years of New World history, the Middle East measures its history in thousands of years. Christ was born into a civilization whose history was then at least twice as long as the period since His birth. When Abraham, who antedated Christ by about 2,000 years, was born, by tradition at Ur of the Chaldees, that city already had been a civilized community for thousands of years. When Moses lived in Egypt, the Pyramids already were monuments of antiquity.

In Mesopotamia, where civilization early reached a high level, there was from remote times an elaborate irrigation system which made the plains a prosperous region of farms and cities, and there was extensive trade with Arabian Gulf towns and with India. Despite changes of fortune through many periods of history, some of the ancient cities were occupied continuously until the Mongol invasion in 1258. In this disaster whole populations were slaughtered and the irrigation system upon which they depended was destroyed. Thus was eclipsed a civilization which had lasted for more than 5,000 years.

From that time until the modern era of industrial development, the Middle East lived largely in poverty without the productivity or strength to achieve an effective recovery. During the period when Western countries were making rapid progress in the settlement of new lands and in the arts, commerce and industry, the peoples of the Middle East had little to contribute either to their own prosperity or to world affairs. Their long history of civilization and culture, however, had left them with a tradition which manifested itself in gracious hospitality and social relations, in a deep sense of responsibility for their acts and for their relations with family and neighbors and an age-old wisdom of religion and custom.

n the beginning: A statue of a Sumerian scribe, perhaps dating to the twenty-fifth century B.C.

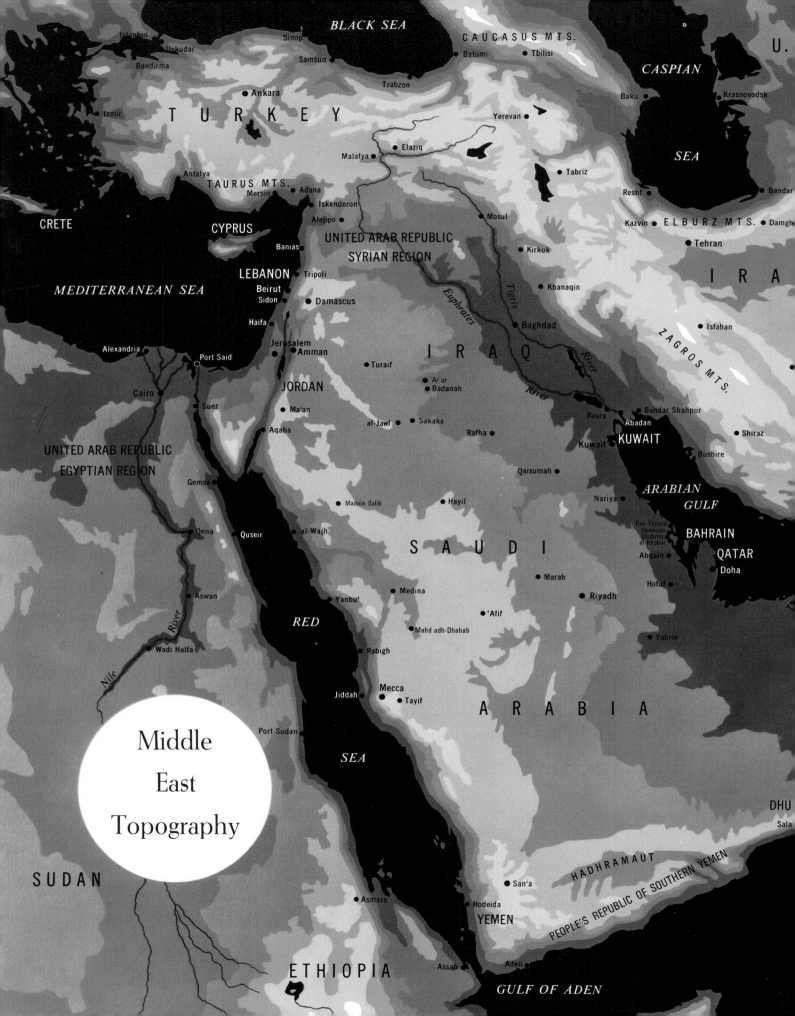

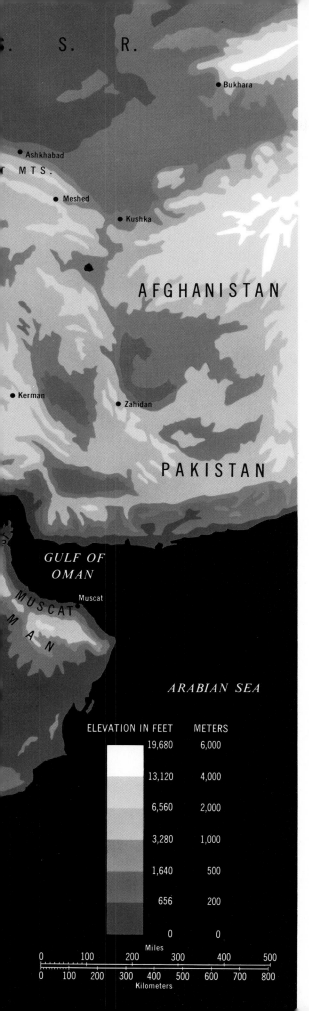

S. S. R.

• Bukhara

• Ashkhabad

MTS.

• Meshed

• Kushka

AFGHANISTAN

• Kerman

• Zahidan

PAKISTAN

GULF OF
OMAN

MUSCAT

Muscat •

OMAN

ARABIAN SEA

ELEVATION IN FEET   METERS

19,680	6,000
13,120	4,000
6,560	2,000
3,280	1,000
1,640	500
656	200
0	0

Miles
0   100   200   300   400   500

0   100   200   300   400   500   600   700   800
Kilometers

THE BEGINNINGS OF CIVILIZATION Tens of thousands of years ago our ancestors made their living by hunting game with the aid of crude stone and wooden implements. They lived in a period when most of Europe and parts of the Middle East were under a great sheet of ice. The lands to the south of the ice sheet, in Africa and Arabia, were covered with grass and had streams flowing in what today are dry wadis. As the climate gradually changed, the ice sheet retreated and grasslands became deserts. People had to make gradual but drastic adjustments in their way of life.

Some of the people in the Middle East were nomadic herdsmen living upon domestic animals and upon hunted game—and many follow that pattern of life to this day. Others turned to agriculture and began living together in communities. At some stage the store of accumulated skills and experience began to grow into what is known as civilization. Five thousand years or so ago writing was invented, and from that time onward civilized men passed on a record of what they learned and did.

Although much of the earlier story is still unclear, civilization probably began in the vicinity of the basins of the Tigris and the Euphrates Rivers in Mesopotamia, the Nile River in Egypt and the Indus Valley. From here it spread over the Middle East, while men in the rest of the world were still in a savage or primitive state. Some Asiatic and pre-Columbian American civilizations also are old, but in all of them writing and substantial developments in social organization came later than in the Middle East.

The recorded history of the Middle East is filled with drama. It is a panorama of the rise and fall of empires, of the growth and decline of great cities, of the ascendancy and eclipse of peoples, of wars, invasions and deportations, of kings and emperors who had their brief place in the sun, of treachery and intrigue, of great disasters. The story contains examples of rulers who were cruel and ruthless, but it also contains examples of others who were noble and humane. It is a record not

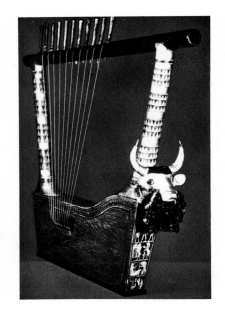

A reconstructed harp with bull's head of gold and lapis lazuli, found in "Royal Tombs" at Ur.

A plaque of shell inlaid in bitumen, which belonged to the sound box of a harp found at Ur.

A game board of shell, bone, limestone and lapis lazuli inlaid in bitumen, which was discovered in an Ur grave.

only of destructive warfare, but also of constructive achievements in written communication and literature, in practical and fine arts, in religion, and in science and law, which greatly contributed to the spread of civilization. There were long periods of comparative peace under stable governments. Some imperial dynasties lasted longer than the life of the British Empire or of the United States to date.

For the details of this long and complex story the reader must turn to the many available histories. He will find instances of lack of agreement among both historians and archaeologists, but he will see that more than a century of exploration and excavation and the resulting reinterpretation of history have added greatly to the previous knowledge of the ancient world. The whole story cannot be told here, but some of the highlights can be touched upon.

THE SUMERIANS One of the earliest civilizations in areas adjoining Arabia was that of the Sumerians. Non-Semites of unknown origin, they occupied by 3000 B.C. their new homeland of Sumer in the lower reaches of the Tigris and Euphrates at the head of the Arabian Gulf. The various city states which arose there were often at war with each other. The Sumerian city best known today was Ur; other principal ones were Erech, Lagash and Nippur. These were river towns, though changes in the courses of the rivers have left their sites, now marked only by mounds, out in the desert. Eridu was a thriving seaport, but because the silt deposits of the rivers pushed the waters of the gulf farther and farther southeastward, the site is now 130 miles inland.

The Sumerians reached an advanced state of civilization manifested by irrigation, extensive trade, the use of money and codes of laws. Their pictorial and syllabic writing, chiefly on clay tablets, developed into the cuneiform script widely used in the ancient Middle East. Their advanced knowledge of the stars, with Babylonian, Greek and Islamic developments, became the basis of our modern

This cuneiform tablet was dug up in 1934 at King Sargon II's palace at Khorsabad. It revealed the succession of 95 Assyrian kings from 2400 to 746 B.C.

science of astronomy. The Sumerian sexagesimal system of numbers is reflected today in the division of the hour into sixty minutes and of the circle into 360 degrees.

The Sumerians used wheeled vehicles and the architectural arch. The lack of building stone led them to the use of sun-dried bricks in construction, but they had many fine buildings, notably the beautiful and imposing tower temples known as ziggurats. A large portion of the one at Ur still remains. It may have been a familiar sight to Abraham before he received the command of the Lord: "Get thee out of thy country, and from thy kindred, and from thy father's house, unto a land that I will show thee."

Amazing technical skill was developed by Sumerian artists and craftsmen. Archaeologists have discovered many objects of rare beauty left in royal tombs and other graves. Furniture, utensils and sculpture were of excellent design and workmanship. Some examples have survived through the Sumerian practice of burying, with their kings, the men and women of all ranks who had been the deceased king's close servants, along with their possessions, in the belief that they and the material objects would serve their "divine" master in the realm of the gods.

SEMITES IN MESOPOTAMIA The peoples known as Semites, whose languages are closely related, traditionally came from Shem, the eldest son of Noah (Genesis 10:1). Whatever their geographical origin, the background of their known history lies in the Arabian Peninsula and the lands of the Fertile Crescent. North of Sumer there lived from early times groups of Semites who, as nomads from the Syrian and Arabian deserts, had filtered into both central and northern Mesopotamia. While occasionally raiding the more advanced Sumerians, the Semites gradually built up their own city states and local kingdoms such as Kish and Mari.

About 2360 B.C. a great leader, Sargon I, arose among the Semites in Mesopotamia. His conquests resulted in the establishment of the first empire of recorded history—that of Akkad, in the area later known as Babylonia. The realm reached from Elam, east of Sumer, to the Mediterranean Sea. Akkadian influence spread beyond Mesopotamia to Arabia. Destroyed after two centuries, this empire was succeeded by a dynasty in which the old city of Ur and its reinvigorated Sumerian culture had a prominent place.

BABYLONIA Although Akkadian Semites continued to be one of the main elements in the population, the ruling power passed to other Semitic invaders of Mesopotamia, the Amorites, who came from the west—the region of Syria.

The ancient city of Babylon became a center of empire in the eighteenth century B.C. under the Amorite King Hammurapi (until recently usually

10

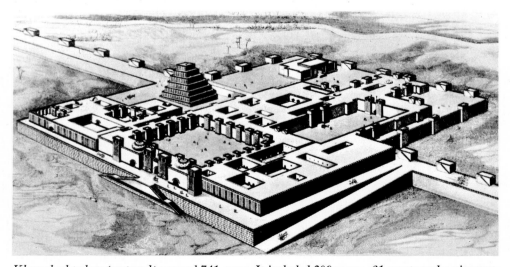

Khorsabad palace (restored) covered 741 acres. It included 209 rooms, 31 courts and a ziggurat.

spelled Hammurabi). In an extensive code, Hammurapi formalized the laws that had come into use through centuries of Sumerian and Semitic civilization. However, many other codifications of law existed in the ancient Middle East and Old Testament law and custom are more related to other systems than to that of Hammurapi. The great achievement of Hammurapi was the creation of a situation of security which made possible two centuries of remarkable activity in the fields of scholarship and science, particularly mathematics and astronomy.

The first Babylonian Empire was overwhelmed about 1600 B.C. by an invasion of the Hittites. This people of Asia Minor also added Syria to their empire and made historic international treaties with the Egyptians before they in turn were crushed in about 1200 B.C. by barbarian invaders from Europe. Babylonia continued for four centuries or so under the rule of the Kassite dynasty from western Iran and thereafter came to be ruled by Assyria.

ASSYRIA The Assyrians, of the same Amorite origin as the Babylonians, had settled in northern Mesopotamia. Their national god was Assur, whose name was also given to the capital of their first city state on the Tigris. Later the imperial capital was Nineveh, farther north on the same river. The Assyrians became an active commercial people. Cuneiform records disclose their extensive use of

stamped silver bars for money, their employment of letters of credit and their practice of lending money to neighboring people at twenty to thirty percent interest.

Although they borrowed their culture largely from Babylonia—as the Babylonians in turn had borrowed from the Sumerians—the Assyrians developed it in an elaborate and systematic way. They built great libraries for cuneiform documents and colossal palaces and temples, whose remnants may be seen in museums in Europe, America and the Middle East.

The Assyrians were a warlike people, employing iron weapons and combinations of archers, heavily armed infantry and cavalry. They became particularly powerful from the tenth to the seventh centuries B.C., with an empire extending over most of the Middle East, including Egypt. During this era they adopted the practice of the wholesale transplanting of conquered peoples, among whom were the "ten lost tribes" of Israel. At length, in 612 B.C., the Babylonians, Medes and Persians combined to overthrow the Assyrians. Nineveh was destroyed. It was only a memory until archaeologists excavated the site in 1852-54 and discovered the most important library of the ancient Middle East in the palace of Assurbanipal, the last great Assyrian king.

LATER BABYLONIA Babylon, on the other hand, continued to be a center of splendor and learning. Because of rebellion the city was destroyed by the

Ishtar Gate and great walls were the glory of the Neo-Babylonian Empire.

11

After the Sumerians and Akkadians were subjugated, Babylonia under Hammurapi became a powerful nation.

Babylonian Empire declined after being conquered by the Hittites and Kassites. Assyria rose to power in its stead.

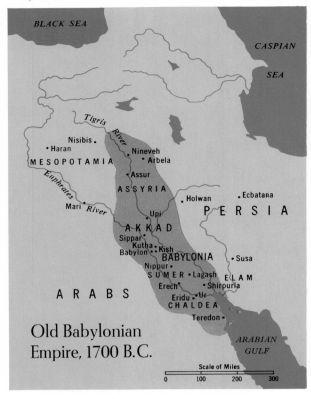

Old Babylonian
Empire, 1700 B.C.

Scale of Miles
0   100   200   300

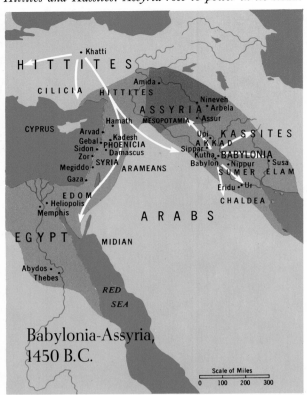

Babylonia-Assyria,
1450 B.C.

Scale of Miles
0   100   200   300

At its zenith the Assyrian Empire, from its capital at Nineveh on the Tigris River, controlled most of the Middle East, from the Nile to the Arabian Gulf. Its conquests included Babylonia, Syria, Phoenicia and Egypt.

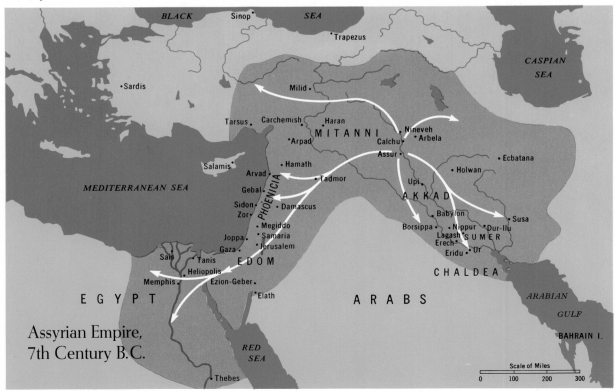

Assyrian Empire,
7th Century B.C.

Scale of Miles
0   100   200   300

After the overthrow of Assyria by the Medes, Persians and Babylonians, a new Babylonian Empire was built up by Chaldeans. Under King Nebuchadnezzar, Babylon became a magnificent capital, famous for its Hanging Gardens.

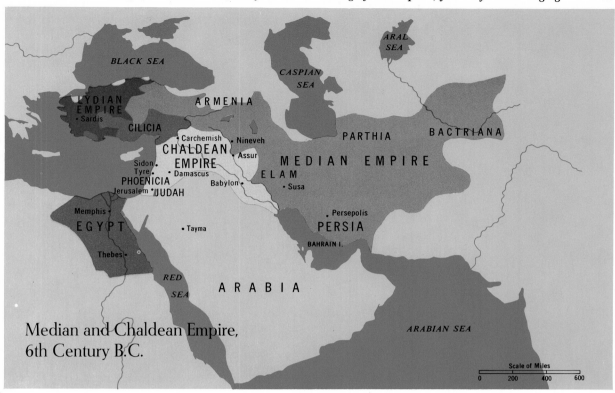

Median and Chaldean Empire,
6th Century B.C.

Under Cyrus the Great and his successors, the Persians built the largest empire the world had known. From their capitals at Susa and Persepolis, their rule spread from the Aegean to India, until they were conquered by the Greeks.

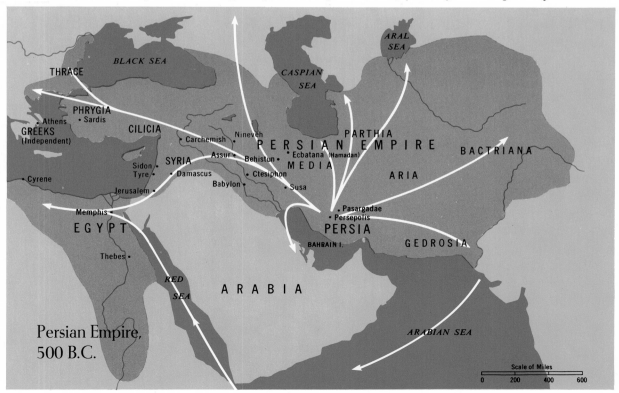

Persian Empire,
500 B.C.

At the Persian palace of Persepolis, near the present-day city of Shiraz, bas reliefs flanked the monumental stairways.

Assyrian conqueror Sennacherib, but it was rebuilt by his son and successor Esarhaddon. Then, under Nabopolassar, conqueror of Nineveh, Babylon again became the capital of an empire, known as Neo-Babylonia, which was built up by the Chaldeans, who included both Aramaeans and Arabians.

The history of Neo-Babylonia was brief but brilliant. The greatest of its kings was Nabopolassar's son, Nebuchadnezzar, who defeated a reviving Egypt, destroyed Jerusalem in 586 B.C. and rebuilt Babylon with greater grandeur. The later Babylonian scientists continued their work in astronomy for centuries after the empire was gone. Modern astronomy is still indebted to them.

Chaldean Babylon was famous for its great walls on which two chariots could be driven abreast, for its palaces and temples and for its Hanging Gardens, which were one of the seven wonders of the world. The Greek historian Herodotus, in the fifth century

B.C., pictured the city and its life in considerable detail. He mentioned round boats of the type still used in the area and described the amazing fertility of the irrigated plains, which he said no one could believe who had not been there. The ruins of Babylon were uncovered by the German archaeologist Robert Koldewey, who worked there from 1899 to 1914. Although the site does not offer well-preserved stone structures like those of Egypt or Baalbek in Lebanon, the Ishtar Gate is impressive.

Babylon was the scene of many dramatic events in the Bible. It was to Babylon that Nebuchadnezzar carried many of the people of Judah into exile. Babylon was also the scene of stirring episodes such as the trial of the three Hebrew youths Shadrach, Meshach and Abednego in the fiery furnace, the ordeal of Daniel in the lions' den, and the terror of King Belshazzar when he saw the handwriting on the wall. When Babylon fell to the Persian conqueror Cyrus in 539 B.C., many of the exiles took advantage of permission to return to their homes, but many others remained.

Cyrus took Babylon without a fight. The rule at the time apparently was held jointly or alternately

These majestic ruins survived at the palace of Persepolis in spite of the ravages of time—and of Alexander the Great.

14

The propylaea, built by Xerxes, formed the entrance at Persepolis.
Details show a double "bull" column and glazed tile mosaics.

by the king, Nabonidus, and his son Belshazzar, the crown prince. Nabonidus, who spent considerable time at the town of Tayma in northwestern Arabia, was a man whose eyes were turned to the past. He angered the priests of Marduk by favoring older cults. As one of the first ardent archaeologists, he studied and restored temples and other ruins in his realm which were practically as old then as the Ishtar Gate is now.

THE PERSIANS The Persians rose to power in the sixth century B.C. The taking of Babylon by Cyrus in 539 was only one step in the formation of the greatest empire the world had yet seen. Cyrus and his successors, Cambyses, Darius and Xerxes, conquered the region extending from India to Asia Minor and Egypt. The Persians twice threw their forces at southeastern Europe, and twice the Greeks threw them back. The Greeks defeated Darius I at Marathon in 490 B.C. and, after a Persian victory at Thermopylae and the sacking of Athens in 480 B.C., forced the armies and the fleet of Xerxes I to return to Asia. These Persian Wars are recounted by Herodotus in great detail.

Within their Middle Eastern empire the Persians established a stable and efficient administration with a system of fast communication by horse. Although speaking an Aryan language and having their own ethnic religion of Zoroastrianism, the Persian rulers used the Semitic language of Aramaic for correspondence between the capital and the provinces and employed Semitic Babylonian, as well as their own Aryan language written in cuneiform, for royal inscriptions. Just as the inscription of Ptolemaic times on the Rosetta stone in hieroglyphic, demotic Egyptian and Greek furnished the key for deciphering the hieroglyphs of the Nile Valley, so inscriptions of the Persian emperors in cuneiform Persian, Babylonian and Elamite at Persepolis and Behistun (Bisitun) gave the clue to deciphering the ancient languages of Mesopotamia.

After a little more than two centuries, the old Persian or Achemenid Empire was overwhelmed by the conquests of Alexander the Great in 334-323 B.C. It was in Babylon that Alexander died in 323 B.C., after wresting the ancient city from Persian rule and after completing his conquest of the whole civilized world from Macedonia to India. Greek culture, which already had been spreading over the Middle East, continued there in Hellenistic form through the succeeding era of the Seleucids in Syria and the Ptolemies in Egypt, as well as the later Roman and Byzantine empires, down to the age of Islam.

The vitality of Persia was shown in its revival in the Parthian Empire (250 B.C.—A.D. 226) and in the Sassanid Empire (A.D. 226-650). The Parthians kept the power of Rome from going east of the Euphrates. The frequent occurrence on Bahrain Island, as well as on the western shore of the Arabian Gulf, of certain types of Parthian pottery indicates a close relationship between Mesopotamia and the Arabian Gulf, at least during the second half of the Parthian Empire. The Sassanids were often more than a match for Byzantium in war and made significant achievements in architecture, art and textiles. The historic and fertile region of Mesopotamia attracted both the later Persian empires. Ctesiphon on the Tigris southeast of Baghdad was the Persian capital when the Sassanids were conquered by the Muslim Arab armies in 637-650.

OTHER ANCIENT PEOPLES OF THE MIDDLE EAST Certain other peoples played major parts in the story of the ancient times in the Middle East.

The Hebrews have left an indelible record of their troubled career in the Old Testament. They were never an important people politically, as compared with the more powerful of their neighbors, but they made a tremendous contribution in their religion and their literature. They did not come into existence as a nation until thousands of years after the rise of civilization in Mesopotamia and Egypt. Their earlier history in the Book of Genesis was probably adapted in a spiritualized and purified form from the ancient lore of Mesopotamia, where

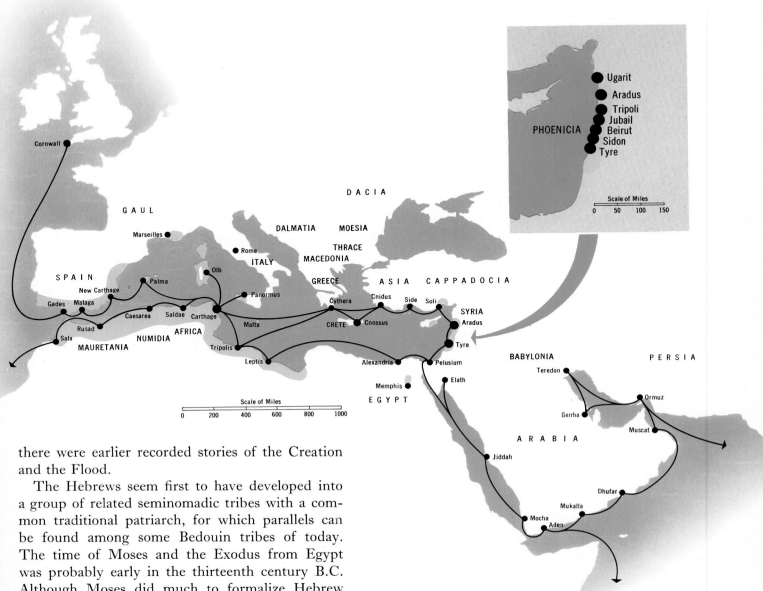

there were earlier recorded stories of the Creation and the Flood.

The Hebrews seem first to have developed into a group of related seminomadic tribes with a common traditional patriarch, for which parallels can be found among some Bedouin tribes of today. The time of Moses and the Exodus from Egypt was probably early in the thirteenth century B.C. Although Moses did much to formalize Hebrew religious and social institutions, many scholars believe that the first five books of the Old Testament did not achieve their final form until the period of the captivity or exile in Babylonia. The Hebrews were also influenced by the culture of the Canaanites of Palestine, part of whose land they filtered into and conquered, and by that of the Mediterranean Philistines, with whom they fought for control of the land and after whom Palestine was named.

Unable to stand against the great empires of Egypt, Mesopotamia, Persia, Greece and Rome

Phoenician Trade Routes

▭ PHOENICIA AND COLONIES

17

Phoenician warship (with ram) and merchantman of 750 B.C.

which successively ruled them, the Hebrews had independent control of their "promised land" for only comparatively brief periods between the time they entered it under Joshua in the thirteenth century B.C. and the time of their final disastrous rebellions against their Roman rulers in A.D. 66-70 and 132-135.

The Phoenicians, who were the more northerly Canaanites in a homeland covering what is now Lebanon and the coast of Syria, became active diffusers of culture and the greatest of all Semitic seafarers during a period of growth beginning with the twelfth century B.C. The old legend, mentioned by Herodotus, that they originated in the Arabian Gulf remains unproved.

The traditional view that the Phoenicians were the sole inventors and diffusers of the alphabet has been modified because of new knowledge about the long process by which this great improvement in human communication was achieved. However, outside the somewhat later South Arabian Kingdom, whose alphabetic writing is supposed to have spread by migration westward to Ethiopia, the main development of the alphabet took place in the Semitic territory of the Mediterranean coast between Sinai and Syria where the Phoenicians lived.

Here, during the second millennium B.C., the Phoenicians and other Canaanites had much to do with the devising of several forms of alphabetic script. One of these—the cuneiform script of Ras Shumrah or Ugarit, on the Syrian coast—was not perpetuated. Others, based upon pictographs of Egyptian type, gave rise to alphabets which in different forms continued to be used in the Middle East and also spread westward to Europe and eastward to India and Mongolia. Thus, numerous alphabets now in use throughout the world came originally from Semitic peoples in the Middle East. Among these peoples the Phoenicians—who used alphabetic writing in their colonies in North Africa and around the western Mediterranean—undoubtedly can be accorded much of the credit for giving the alphabet to the Western world.

The Phoenicians, who replaced the earlier Minoans of Crete as leaders in seafaring, obtained tin from western Europe (possibly including Cornwall or the nearby Scilly Isles), silver from Spain and murex shells for Tyrian purple from the Mediterranean and tropical seas. Their greatest center of colonial power was Carthage, near modern Tunis in North Africa. This city grew to be greater than the most important Phoenician homeland cities of Tyre, Sidon and Jubail (the Biblical Gebal and Greek Byblos—the Greek name meant papyrus and book and gave us the word Bible). In the three Punic (Phoenician) Wars of the third and second centuries B.C., Carthage almost defeated Rome in a long contest for control of the Mediterranean world. The Romans eventually won, however, and in 146 B.C. they destroyed Carthage.

The achievements of Phoenician sailors, in their

18

own commerce and in the service of the successive Egyptian, Mesopotamian, Persian, Greek and Roman empires, may have included the circumnavigation of Africa for Pharaoh Necho of Egypt (609-593 B.C.).

A Semitic people earlier known as Aramaeans and later called Syrians (the name Syria is an old one and, contrary to common conjecture, may not be derived from Assyria) had Damascus as their capital. Their kingdom, which was contemporary with those of the Hebrews, was at times in alliance with them and at times at war against them. Like the Phoenicians, the Aramaeans were great traders and penetrated other lands in pursuit of commerce. They adapted the Phoenician or Canaanite alphabet to their closely related language, Aramaic, which came to be used widely in the Middle East. Adopted by the Jews, it was used in parts of the Books of Daniel and Nehemiah and in other writings. Aramaic continued as the primary language of the people of Palestine for more than a thousand years —much longer than the lifetime of ancient Hebrew—until it was finally replaced by Arabic.

Thus Aramaic probably was the language of Christ, and it is most likely that at least Aramaic oral materials, if not written documents, predate the Greek of some books of the New Testament. Many Oriental Christians—in the Middle East, on the Malabar Coast of India and even in the United States—still have their Gospels and parts of their liturgies in a form of Aramaic called Syriac.

The civilization of ancient Egypt began about as early as the civilization of Mesopotamia. The main periods of Egyptian history were: the predynastic period, during which a calendar of 365 days came into use and the nomes or provinces were

The Carthaginians, descended from Phoenician colonists, contested the Romans bitterly for mastery of the Mediterranean before their capital was destroyed. Carthaginian effort was climaxed by Hannibal's use of elephants in the invasion of Europe.

during which Necho reportedly had the Phoenicians sail around Africa; and, finally, rule by the Persians, the Greek Ptolemies (one of whom was Cleopatra), the Romans and the Byzantines, until the Arab conquest shortly before the middle of the seventh century. The great monuments of the Egyptian historical pageant are more impressive than the remains of Mesopotamia because they were built of enduring stone.

In Egypt and other lands of the ancient Middle East, archaeology is making important contributions to the understanding of history. Modern discoveries have clearly shown that the people of the Middle East went a long way in developing the culture and the sciences which were to be the foundation of Western civilization.

united into the kingdoms of the north and the south; the old dynastic or archaic period, during which the country was consolidated as one kingdom and made conquests in Palestine and Syria; the Old Kingdom, including the Pyramid Age in the third millennium B.C.; the first period of disintegration, with invasions from Asia; the Middle Kingdom, with conquests in Nubia southward as well as in Palestine and Syria; the second period of disintegration, with occupation of the Delta area by the Hyksos from Asia; the Empire, extending from Nubia to the borders of the Babylonians, Assyrians and Hittites, and including the time of the Hebrew exodus from Egypt, probably in the thirteenth century B.C., and the temporary establishment of sun-god monotheism under Ikhnaton, the father-in-law of Tutankhamen; a period of rule by a Libyan and then a Nubian dynasty; the Lower Empire or an era of Egyptian renaissance,

The two Colossi of Memnon at Thebes, the only remains of a vast funerary temple near the banks of the Nile River.

20

A small part of the Temple of Amon at Karnak, the biggest columnar structure ever built. It took 2,000 years to construct.

Great Sphinx and pyramids of Gizeh, dating to the third millennium B.C.

21

THE EARLY ARABS

The better-watered and more arable lands bordering the north Arabian desert have been aptly called the Fertile Crescent. This area covers the valleys of the Tigris and Euphrates Rivers, the southern slopes of the Taurus Mountains and the eastern shores of the Mediterranean Sea. It was largely within these lands that the ancient civilizations of the Middle East flourished.

Throughout Middle Eastern history the people of the vast Arabian Peninsula also have played important roles. The distinctive contribution of the people of the great Arabian deserts, however, has been to supply their neighbors with new blood and with the stimulation of their less sophisticated but fresher energies.

The Arabian Peninsula has also had its own ancient centers of civilization. It has always had its oasis gardens and its towns, which still are centers of culture, trade and leadership. But the desert tracts have been peopled, as they are today, by the Bedouins.

From the time of the earliest civilizations, the desert nomads frequently made raids upon their more prosperous neighbors within the Fertile Crescent. On occasion, when organized by leaders who arose among them, they attacked and conquered some of the great centers of civilization, bringing with them the simplicity and virility of the desert and infusing new blood and vitality into the communities of which they became masters. They, in turn, absorbed the culture of the conquered.

In other instances Semitic peoples seem to have migrated en masse to new lands which had not been developed fully—probably gathering Bedouin allies as they went. The Akkadians, the Amorites, the Assyrians, the Chaldeans, the Hebrews and the Aramaeans were all Semites who may have come out of the Syrian and the Arabian deserts. Semites also made incursions into the land of the Nile. At one time, in the eighteenth century B.C., they probably took part in setting up a dynasty there, that of the Hyksos, which controlled Egypt for nearly 200 years. Later, fired by the new faith of Islam, the people of the Arabian Peninsula surged forth from their deserts to conquer much of the known world.

Another important role played by the peninsular Arabs in the old civilizations of the Nile and the Fertile Crescent was in trade and commerce. Southern Arabia was then a populous and thriving area, known to the Romans as Arabia Felix or Fertile Arabia. It was one of the principal sources of frankincense and myrrh, which were used extensively in unguents and perfumes, as incense for the many temples, and by the Romans in the cremation of royal and noble persons. Frankincense and myrrh are still produced in southern Arabia.

Southern Arabia was also a focal region for trade in spices, silks, ivory and other valuable goods destined for Egypt and other Mediterranean lands. The sources of these commodities—India, the Indies and East Africa—were apparently unknown to the consumer countries. Accordingly the Arabs had a practical monopoly of this highly profitable trade.

The Arabs are reported also to have supplied the more northern countries with gold, copper and precious stones. Some of the gold came from Arabia itself, where ancient mines existed. Copper may have come from the mountains of Oman. Western Arabia is still a source of semiprecious gems.

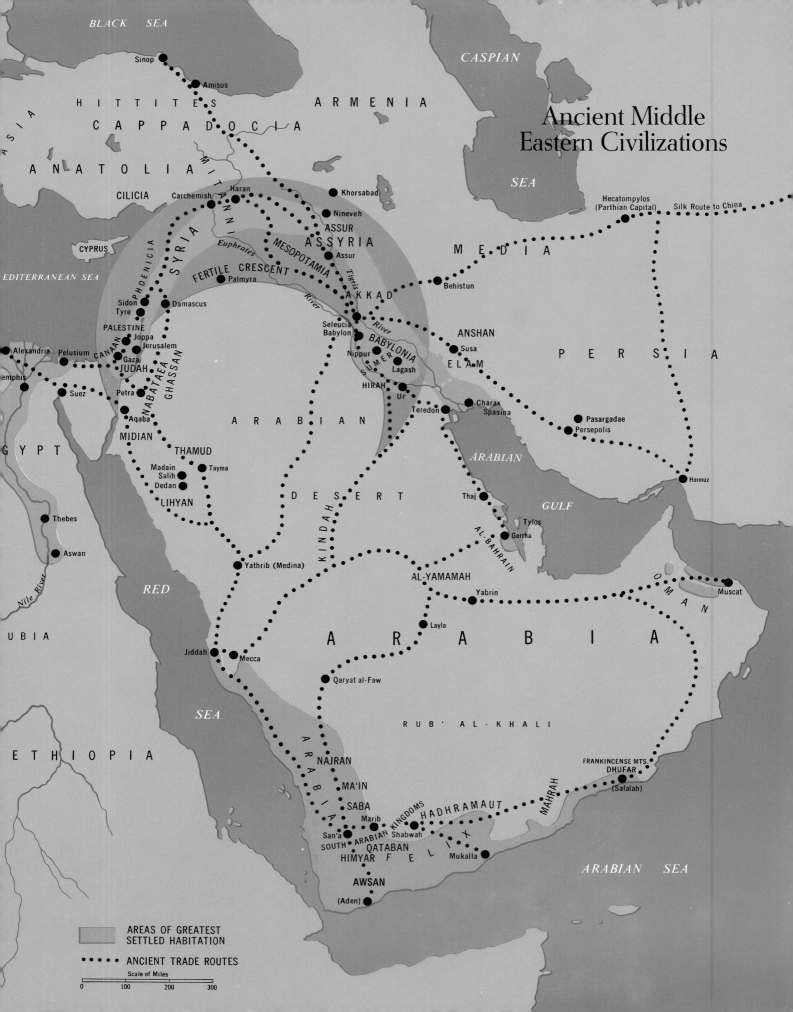

Ancient Middle Eastern Civilizations

BLACK SEA

CASPIAN

SEA

Sinop

Amisus

HITTITES

ARMENIA

CAPPADOCIA

ANATOLIA

ASIA

CILICIA

Carchemish

Haran

Khorsabad

Hecatompylos
(Parthian Capital)

Silk Route to China

Nineveh

ASSUR

ASSYRIA

MEDIA

MITANNI

CYPRUS

SYRIA

Euphrates

Assur

EDITERRANEAN SEA

PHOENICIA

FERTILE CRESCENT

MESOPOTAMIA

Behistun

Palmyra

AKKAD

Tigris River

Sidon

Damascus

PALESTINE

Seleucia
Babylon

SUMER

BABYLONIA

ANSHAN

Tyre

River

Susa

Joppa

Alexandria

Pelusium

Jerusalem

CANAAN

Nippur

ELAM

Lagash

PERSIA

emphis

Gaza

JUDAH

HIRAH

GHASSAN

Ur

Suez

Petra

NABATAEA

Teredon

Charax
Spasina

Pasargadae

Aqaba

ARABIAN

Persepolis

MIDIAN

THAMUD

Madain
Salih

Tayma

ARABIAN

Hormuz

Dedan

LIHYAN

DESERT

Thaj

GULF

Tylos

KINDAH

Gerrha

AL-BAHRAIN

Yathrib (Medina)

AL-YAMAMAH

OMAN

Muscat

Yabrin

RED

Layla

A R A B I A

Jiddah

Mecca

SEA

Qaryat al-Faw

RUB' AL-KHALI

UBIA

Thebes

Aswan

Nile River

ARABIA

FRANKINCENSE MTS.

DHUFAR

NAJRAN

MAHRAH

(Salalah)

ETHIOPIA

MA'IN

SABA

ARABIAN KINGDOMS

HADHRAMAUT

Marib

Shabwah

San'a

SOUTH

QATABAN

FELIX

Mukalla

HIMYAR

ARABIAN SEA

AWSAN

GYPT

(Aden)

AREAS OF GREATEST
SETTLED HABITATION

•••• ANCIENT TRADE ROUTES

Scale of Miles

0   100   200   300

Radiating from southwestern Arabia were great caravan routes. One of these ran along the western side of the peninsula through Mecca and Yathrib (now Medina) and thence to Palestine or Damascus or around the head of the Gulf of Aqaba to Egypt. Another one ran to the Arabian Gulf seaport of Gerrha, from which the goods from Arabia Felix were shipped to Babylonia and other areas. There were other important overland routes, and long trains of camels carrying rich and no doubt heavily guarded cargoes were a familiar part of the Arabian scene. The points at which they halted and the centers at which the goods were sold or redistributed by merchant middlemen became thriving communities.

Some of the ancient caravan routes still are in

Bronze statue unearthed in the ruins of the temple of 'Ilumquh.

use; others still are indicated by paths deeply worn by the tread of countless camels. Until replaced by airplanes and motor vehicles in recent years, camels carried pilgrims by the thousands to the Holy Cities of Mecca and Medina, using the old established trade routes.

ANCIENT ARABIAN CIVILIZATION Arabia in ancient times was not merely an adjunct to the civilized countries farther north. It had its own centers of civilization, although they developed later than those in Mesopotamia or Egypt.

At one time, no doubt during the Ice Ages, the whole of the Arabian Peninsula enjoyed a much more favorable climate than it does now. Evidence is found in the well-developed and well-entrenched water courses which hardly could have been formed under conditions existing today. Good examples of these water courses are al-Batin, which trends northeasterly from Najd past Kuwait, and as-Sahba, which runs easterly from the Tuwayq Escarpment south of the latitude of Riyadh. These at some time must have been the valleys of rivers.

Stone artifacts or implements found sporadically through the Arabian Peninsula provide traces of cultural levels of Middle Paleolithic aspect in northern Arabia, along the area now traversed by the trans-Arabian pipeline system, and of Late Paleolithic and Neolithic aspect in the western Rub' al-Khali. One hand ax from central Arabia and another from the western Rub' al-Khali can be classed as Early Paleolithic in type. At present none of these cultural levels, which should be of great antiquity, can be dated accurately in the peninsula.

The early traditions of the Arabs make a distinction between the Arabs of the north and the Arabs of the south. The distinction may have been made partly because many of those in the south lived in cities, while most of those in the north were nomads. As trade developed between the southern communities and the north, some mixing of the types of Arabs took place. Before the time of the Prophet Muhammad, many Arabs of southern origin already were living in northern Arabia. There

The ruins of the monumental temple of 'Ilumquh, dedicated to the moon god in the ancient kingdom of Saba in southern Arabia.

they figured in the tribal wars which inspired much of the pre-Islamic poetry belonging to the earliest period of Arabic literature. Many Arabs of both types also moved into the Fertile Crescent where they mingled with earlier settlers.

The mountains of the Yemen form a populous and relatively well-watered area which for many centuries has been somewhat isolated from the rest of the world. A wider region, comprising the southwestern and the central southern coast, was the scene of ancient kingdoms which engaged in international commerce.

The people of ancient southern Arabia built dams to impound and conserve the floods of the rainy periods, and their system of irrigation seems to have provided their basic means of support. The control they acquired over what was then the main highway for trade between the East and the West was an important element in their prosperity.

Among the earliest states in southwestern Arabia, which rose to prominence in the first millennium B.C., were Ma'in and Saba. The Queen of Sheba, who visited King Solomon in the tenth century B.C., may well have been an Arabian princess.

25

Marib dam today: Keystone of the irrigation system of ancient southern Arabia, it fell into disuse before the time of Muhammad.

However, she may have come from a Sabaean colony in the northern part of the peninsula rather than from the land of Saba in the south.

Other kingdoms in southern Arabia were Awsan in the southwestern corner nearest Aden; Qataban, northeast of Awsan, and Hadhramaut, east of Qataban. They fought many wars and experienced many changes in relative fortunes. This southern civilization in its later periods is often referred to as Himyaritic rather than Minaean or Sabaean, after the southwestern tribe of Himyar, which grew increasingly powerful.

With the exception of a few scholars such as al-Hamdani in the tenth century, the Arabs have largely neglected earlier Arabian history because of their preoccupation with Islamic civilization. Zealous believers, considering pre-Islamic culture to be of no consequence, destroyed many of its vestiges in their efforts to eradicate all traces of idolatry. Except for references in the writings of other ancient peoples and accounts by a few Arab authors, the Western world had no knowledge of the ancient cities of southwestern Arabia until the nineteenth century, when Western explorers visited the area. They found ruins of fine buildings, sculpture, canals, roads and well-planned cities, which revealed an advanced stage of culture.

Of particular importance was the great dam of Marib, constructed of finely hewn limestone and so well engineered that it compared favorably with the most ambitious structures in other ancient

26

*he ancient village of Khraibah is sheltered by the walls of the canyon
t deeply into the Hadhramaut plateau. Settlements cluster near
eam beds or, where the water flows underground, near wells.*

*he ancient fortress of Masna'ah, overlooking Wadi
au'an, in the Hadhramaut region of the Arabian Peninsula*

The carved cliff tombs of Madain Salih, 500 miles north of Jiddah in Saudi Arabia, reflect the same Hellenistic influence as the buildings at Petra. This area appears to have been the southernmost stronghold of the Nabataeans.

countries. This dam, which supplied an irrigation system adequate for a sizable population, fell into disuse between the time of Christ and the time of Muhammad.

Many inscriptions carved in stone in the Minaean and Sabaean script have been found in southwestern Arabia. Knowledge of the ancient history of this area is increasing rapidly with the collection and interpretation of these inscriptions.

The Arabs of the north developed more slowly. The first settled communities in their midst appear to have been outposts or colonies of the Minaeans and Sabaeans. Later a local people known as the Nabataeans assumed control of the northern portion of the rich trade route from the south and built a remarkably beautiful city at Petra, where large buildings were carved out of red sandstone cliffs. Lying in a remote spot in present-day Jordan, it had become lost to the knowledge of the West until rediscovered by the Swiss traveler John Lewis Burckhardt in the early nineteenth century.

Farther south, a Nabataean stronghold lay along the caravan route in present-day Saudi Arabia. The cliffs of Madain Salih, 500 miles north of Jiddah, contain ornately carved tombs of the same Hellenistic influence as at Petra. Remains of wells suggest a large population was accommodated there.

After the rise of Roman power, covetous eyes were turned upon the wealth and trade which Arabia Felix had so long enjoyed. An invasion based on Egypt was organized under the Roman general Aelius Gallus in 24 B.C. According to the Greek geographer Strabo, no difficulty was anticipated because "the Arabians, being engaged mostly in traffic and commerce, are not a warlike people." Strabo reported further that "the barbarians were entirely inexperienced in war and used their weapons unskillfully, which were bows, swords and slings; but the greater part of them used a double-edged ax."

The invasion is said to have been aided and guided by a Nabataean official. Najran was taken with ease. In a battle in the old Minaean district of al-Jawf in southwestern Arabia, 10,000 Arabs were said—most improbably—to have been killed with the loss of only two Romans. Running short of water, the Romans were forced to retire without having reached the incense country of Hadhramaut. By the time Aelius Gallus returned to Egypt, most of his army had perished from disease, starvation and thirst. Thus the first Western invasion of the Arabian Peninsula ended in failure.

The military threat, however, was not the only menace to the trade monopoly enjoyed by the Arabs. The Greeks and Romans acquired the Arabs' skill of navigating to India with the aid of the monsoon winds. Thereafter the economic decline of Arabia was only a question of time. The Arabs, for their part, attributed this decline to the breaking of the Marib dam and the consequent ill effects on the agricultural economy.

A northward migration resulted from the southern decline. The kingdoms of al-Hirah in lower Iraq and Ghassan in what is now Jordan were formed by the southern Arabs. Others, of the tribe of Kindah, formed a kingdom in northern Najd, but it was short-lived.

The Abyssinians or Ethiopians fought with the Sassanid Persians for control of southwestern Arabia. The former were largely Semitic in language as a result of earlier migrations from Arabia. The Abyssinians invaded and conquered areas of southwestern Arabia in the fourth century and again in the sixth century. After the latter invasion the Abyssinian ruler, Abraha, made an unsuccessful expedition against Mecca in or about 570. His forces included at least one elephant, an animal singularly unsuited for desert warfare. The Prophet Muhammad was born in Mecca during the same year in which the Holy City was saved from danger.

During the rise of Islam in the seventh century, Sassanid Persia again held the Yemen. The Sassanids, who earlier had controlled a part of northeastern Arabia, looked with disdain upon the tribes of Arabia Deserta. These same tribes, under the banner of Islam, soon conquered the Sassanid Empire.

The Treasury of Pharaoh at Petra, standing at the end of the narrow gorge known as the Siq. This and neighboring structures, carved out of the red sandstone cliffs, show the Hellenistic (later Greek) architectural influence.

29

Excavations at Ras al-Qal‘ah on Bahrain Island by a Danish archaeological expedition have uncovered what is believed to be the location of Dilmun, fabled center of an ancient culture whose people traded with the city state of Sumer and the Indus Valley.

EARLY TIMES
IN THE
ARABIAN GULF

The lands on the western side of the Arabian Gulf have held a place in history for thousands of years, going back almost to the beginning of civilization. They offer an interesting field for archaeological exploration—a field, however, which remains virtually untouched except for brief surface surveys, the excavation of a burial mound at Jawan in Saudi Arabia, and the work done in recent years on Bahrain Island and various other shaykhdoms of the Arabian Gulf by a Danish archaeological expedition. The finds have been enlightening, but most present-day knowledge about the early peoples of this region comes from ancient historians of other countries.

There is little doubt that civilized man lived here at least as far back as the development of the art of seafaring, which was known in the Arabian Gulf by the dawn of recorded history about 4,000 B.C.

It is likely that the ancient Sumerians of Mesopotamia carried on an active trade with the peoples of the Arabian Gulf. Ancient cuneiform inscriptions refer to a land called Dilmun in Babylonian and Assyrian and named Niduk-ki in Sumerian. This land may have been the Bahrain Islands and a part of the Eastern Province of Saudi Arabia. Possibly the Sumerians at one time set up colonies in this area.

A Danish archaeological expedition from the University of Aarhus, with the support of the Bahrain Government and Danish philanthropic organizations, has been working in the Arabian Gulf, but most particularly on Bahrain, for a number of years. The principal sites which have been excavated on Bahrain are that of a temple near the village of Barbar and the townsite in the immediate vicinity of the old Portuguese fort at Ras al-Qal'ah. A number of interesting finds indicate without much doubt that these sites were occupied during Parthian and even Neo-Babylonian times. A series of other remains, among which perhaps the most interesting is a group of seals, are likely to be of earlier date and have led members of the Danish expedition to the conclusion that the remains on Bahrain are of extreme antiquity and that the

earlier levels are to be identified with the culture of Dilmun, known from Babylonian inscriptions. The Danish expedition has also dug at several sites in Qatar, the Trucial Shaykhdoms and Oman, and has excavated an interesting Hellenistic temple at the island of Faylakah, in the gulf off Kuwait.

One of the most interesting features of Bahrain and parts of the Eastern Province is the presence of many large mounds or tumuli and tens of thousands of small ones, which were the tombs or sepulchers of the dead of an ancient people. Some of these may be seen today in the Dhahran area. The mound-building tradition in Arabia and Bahrain probably covered a considerable time span. It is certain that burial mounds were being built in this region down to the second century of the Christian era, but a date for the beginning of this tradition has not yet been established.

Mounds of this type have been found also in other parts of Arabia, particularly at al-Kharj and Yabrin and, by H. St. John B. Philby, in the ancient home of the Sabaeans in southwestern Arabia. The ancient Phoenicians followed a similar practice. A tomb complex at Jawan, near the road from Dhahran to Ras Tanura, has been excavated by an Aramco archaeologist with the agreement of the Saudi

One of the many Himyaritic inscriptions left by the South Arabians.

A traditional Arab fortress, now demolished, in the Qatif Oasis, with characteristic battlements and adjacent buildings.

Arabian Government. Objects found in the tomb belong to the middle of the first century of the Christian era.

Greek and Roman geographers tell of the city of Gerrha, or perhaps its seaport, which may have been located near the present port of al-'Uqayr. Gerrha was reported by Greek geographer Strabo to have been a Chaldean colony; that is, a colony of Babylon. Strabo says:

> The merchants of Gerrha generally carry the Arabian merchandise and aromatics by land; but Aristobulus says, on the contrary, that they frequently travel into Babylonia on rafts and thence sail up the Euphrates with their cargoes, but afterwards carry them by land to all parts of the country.

Gerrha was apparently an important center of trade with Babylonia in products not only from southwestern Arabia but also from Oman and India. Speaking of Gerrha's wealth, Strabo says, quoting earlier writers:

> By the trade both the Sabaeans and Gerrhaei have become the richest of all tribes, and possess a great quantity of wrought articles in gold and silver, as couches, tripods, basins, drinking vessels, to which we must add the costly magnificence of their houses, for the doors, walls and roofs are variegated with inlaid ivory, gold, silver and precious stones.

Both Strabo and Pliny stated that the houses of Gerrha were built of blocks of salt. It is more likely that they were constructed of bricks made out of salty mud from the *sabkhahs* (salt flats).

Tomb complex at Jawan, near Ras Tanura, as excavated by an Aramco archaeologist.

Dhows with lateen sails are still seen on the Arabian Gulf.

Pliny described the location of Gerrha as being opposite Tylos (presumably Bahrain), which even then was "famous for the vast number of its pearls." He also referred to the region of Attene, fifty miles inland, which doubtless was on or near the site of present-day Hofuf. The date gardens along the coast were probably much more extensive in Pliny's time than they are now, as sand dunes through the years have encroached upon them.

In the first few centuries of the Christian era, many inhabitants of eastern Arabia became Christians. Darin, on Tarut Island, was a bishopric of the Nestorian Church. A number of gravestones found in the Qatif area, inscribed in the Sabaean or Himyaritic alphabet, are thought to commemorate some long-forgotten Christians. Oriental Christian sources mention bishoprics here from the third Christian century. The region did not accept Muslim domination without a struggle. Following the death of the Prophet there was a rebellion which was put down only with the taking of Darin by Muslim troops who waded from the mainland to Tarut Island.

A few centuries later, at the end of the ninth century, much of the present Eastern Province and Bahrain were taken over by, and became the headquarters of, a violent Muslim sect known as the Carmathians. The Carmathians gained control over a large part of Arabia. They even took Mecca in 930 and carried off the sacred Black Stone of the Ka'bah to their capital in eastern Arabia, near what is now Hofuf. The stone was soon restored to Mecca.

In the sixteenth century the Portuguese were active in the Arabian Gulf. On Bahrain Island they built a large fort, which is still standing. Bahrain also was under limited and temporary rule by the Persians on several occasions. The present ruling family of Al Khalifah took the Bahrain Islands from the Persians in 1783. Meanwhile the British, after forming the East India Company in 1600, had won control of the gulf, first from the Portuguese and then from the Dutch.

Until the rise of the House of Sa'ud, eastern Arabia was at times under local leaders, such as the chiefs of the tribe of Bani Khalid, and at other times under Turkish provincial governors. Occasionally Arabian Gulf pirates used coastal points as bases for their operations. A now-demolished fort at Dammam was the lair of a notorious pirate during the early nineteenth century.

33

THE RISE OF ISLAM
AND THE
ARAB EMPIRE

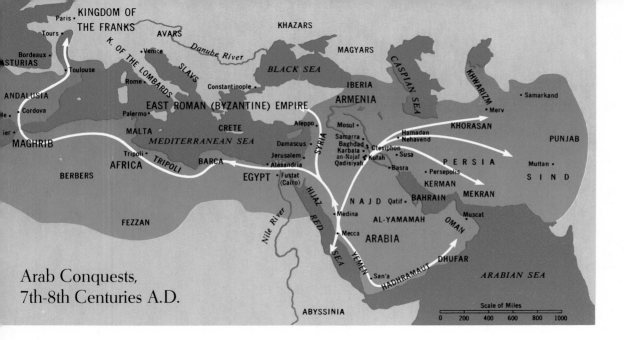

Arab Conquests, 7th-8th Centuries A.D.

One of the most amazing episodes in the experience of mankind was the birth of a new faith, Islam. From humble beginnings, it first enkindled the town and desert peoples of the Arabian Peninsula and then swept over most of the civilized world. It remains today the vital faith of some 500,000,000 people.

At the time of the birth of Muhammad at Mecca, about 570, the Western world was in a state of decadence and unrest. The Roman Empire, which had controlled the world in the first few centuries of the Christian era, had succumbed long since to the onslaught of European barbarians. Its successor, the Christian Byzantine Empire centered at Constantinople, had been engaged with the Sassanid Empire of Persia in wars which had exhausted both. It was a disorganized world into which Muhammad was born. His teachings spread because they were propagated with zeal and offered a refreshing new outlook to many misgoverned and disheartened people.

Arabia had been in a state of anarchy, with constant tribal feuds and fights and occasional religious persecutions, such as that of the Christians by the

The House of God in Mecca: The Ka'bah in the great courtyard of the Sacred Mosque of the Holy City of Islam. All over the world Muslims at prayer face toward this cubical stone building, which is shrouded in black silk and contains in one corner the sacred Black Stone. The Muslims believe that the patriarch Abraham and his son Ishmael built the Ka'bah.

Jews in the southwestern part of the country. The majority of the Arabs still worshipped pagan gods. Even before the rise of Islam, Mecca was a sacred city, the site of a temple, the Ka'bah. Large pilgrimages were made to this shrine, and at that time, as today, the pilgrimage was one of the sources of revenue for the residents of Mecca.

The Prophet Muhammad was born, according to tradition, in the Year of the Elephant, so named because it was the year when Mecca was being threatened by the Abyssinian army accompanied by an elephant. Muhammad belonged to the clan of Hashim in the tribe of Quraysh, whose members were custodians of the Ka'bah. Even before Muhammad's birth there had been a rift between his clan and another Qurayshite clan known as the Umayyads. This rift foreshadowed a great schism in the ranks of Islam after Muhammad's death.

Muhammad was the son of 'Abd Allah ibn 'Abd al-Muttalib of Mecca. His mother, Aminah, was a daughter of the tribe of Quraysh. Little is known of the first forty years of his life except that he became an orphan at an early age, was reared by his grandfather and by an uncle and at the age of twenty-five married a rich widow, Khadijah, fifteen years his senior, whose caravans he successfully managed. He spent a portion of his boyhood among the Bedouins and from them learned the simplicity of life and the purity of speech of the desert.

35

At the age of about forty Muhammad began to have revelations. He became convinced that God had chosen him to perfect the religion earlier revealed to Abraham, the prophets of Israel, and Jesus. Among his initial converts were his wife, his first cousin 'Ali (later also his son-in-law) and another kinsman Abu Bakr (later also one of his fathers-in-law), a leader among the Quraysh. Other leaders of Quraysh were jealous and suspicious of Muhammad's teachings, which threatened their vested interest in the pilgrim trade.

Muhammad continued to make converts, mostly among poor people and slaves. The hostility against him twice grew to a point where he advised his followers to take refuge in Christian Abyssinia. At length his enemies plotted to murder him, but he was forewarned, and 'Ali, his cousin, heroically lay in Muhammad's bed feigning sleep when the would-be murderers arrived. Meanwhile Muhammad, accompanied by Abu Bakr, fled to a nearby mountain cave and after two nights continued on to Medina, then known as Yathrib. The way had been prepared in the previous year by a compact between the Prophet and leaders of Medina.

The Dome of the Rock ("Mosque of 'Umar") in Jerusalem.

The year of this transfer to Medina, the *hijrah* (the origin of the English word hegira), was later taken as Anno Hegirae or A.H. 1 of the Muslim calendar (A.D. 622). At that time Muhammad was fifty-one.

Muhammad's teachings were widely accepted in his new home except by Judaized Arabs. The new faith began to spread to other parts of Arabia. The people of Mecca, however, remained hostile and a number of battles were fought before they came to terms. In 630 Muhammad returned to Mecca as its master. By the time he died in 632 large numbers of people in all parts of Arabia had embraced the faith of Islam.

Late in life Muhammad began thinking of extending his work beyond the borders of Arabia, and his followers proceeded to put this idea into effect. After quelling some rebellious elements in the country, including eastern Arabia, they started forth with an army of 3,000 to 4,000 men on campaigns that were to lead to extensive conquests. As the movement gathered momentum, the numbers were swelled from newly converted populations outside Arabia.

Abu Bakr, the devoted companion of Muhammad, succeeded to the leadership of Islam and became the first caliph (*khalifah* or successor). Khalid ibn al-Walid was one of his most brilliant generals and ranks among the foremost military men of history. Under Khalid's leadership the Muslim armies struck east toward Sassanid Persia and north towards the Eastern Roman or Byzantine province of Syria. Wherever the armies encountered resistance they offered three alternatives: embrace the religion of the true God, surrender and pay tribute, or war. Often they were welcomed and they converted large numbers of the conquered.

The Byzantine army was dealt a decisive defeat in 636 near the Yarmuk River, east of the Sea of Galilee, and was forced subsequently to retreat north of the Taurus Mountains.

The Sassanid Persian Emperor was given good cause to regret his scornful and insulting treatment of the first emissaries of Islam. The Muslims won all of Iraq and Persia between 637 and 650. Their greatest victories over the Persians were decisive

The Great Mosque of Medina, one of th[e] holiest shrines of the Islamic world, where th[e] tomb of the Prophet Muhammad is locate[d.]

battles at Qadisiyah, Jalula and Nehavend. The Arab victory at Qadisiyah forced the Persians to abandon Ctesiphon, the Sassanid winter capital, to the Arabs.

After Abu Bakr died in 634, 'Umar, another of the Prophet's fathers-in-law, became the second caliph. He continued the conquests, and one country after another fell or surrendered. Jerusalem, the third holiest city in Islam, was taken in 638 and was visited by the pious caliph himself. The Christians were permitted to retain their faith and their shrines. Egypt was won from the Byzantines in 640 and 641, and the city of Alexandria was retaken in 646 after a Byzantine counterattack. Fustat (later Cairo) in Egypt and Basra and Kufah in Iraq were founded as military encampments and afterwards became great cities.

The conquests continued for more than one hundred years. By 750 the Muslims had swept over North Africa and Spain and over central Asia toward China, but they had failed to conquer Constantinople or France.

Like the Prophet Muhammad, the earlier caliphs were humble and democratic leaders inspired by a great faith. Thereafter, rivalries for the caliphate developed which resulted in the principal division of the Muslim world into the Shi'ah (or Shi'ites) and the people of the Sunnah (or Sunnites).

The third caliph, 'Uthman, was an old man by the time his rule began. He was from the Umayyad clan of the tribe of Quraysh of Mecca. This clan had been rivals of the Hashimite clan even before the birth of the Prophet. 'Uthman aroused the displeasure of many by showing special favors to members of his own group. He was murdered in his house at the age of eighty.

'Ali, the cousin and son-in-law of Muhammad, became the fourth caliph. Another Umayyad, Mu'awiyah, the able Muslim governor of Syria, charged 'Ali with implication in the murder of 'Uthman and challenged his leadership. In a battle, the forces of 'Ali were nearly victorious, but the followers of Mu'awiyah turned the tide by mounting copies of the Quran on their spears to signify that the issue should be decided by the holy word. 'Ali was impressed and agreed to arbitrate. The arbitration went against him, but since it was regarded as unfairly conducted, he did not accept the decision.

'Ali continued as nominal caliph. He was opposed, however, by the followers of Mu'awiyah and he lost many of his own supporters, who turned against him because he had agreed to arbitration. He put down a rebellion, but then was assassinated. Mu'awiyah thus gained the caliphate.

Ever since that time Islam has been divided between the Shi'ites, who believe that the caliphate should have descended to the heirs of Muhammad's daughter Fatimah and her husband 'Ali, and the Sunnites, who believe it was properly an elective office. A few years after the death of 'Ali, the Shi'ites attempted to place Husayn, the son of 'Ali, in the caliphate. He and his followers were overcome and massacred at Karbala in Iraq in the Arabic month of Muharram, A. H. 61 (October, 680). This tragic event is still mourned and commemorated by the Shi'ites during Muharram each year. Karbala and an-Najaf, where 'Ali was buried, are important Shi'ite shrines.

Medina had been the original Islamic capital, but even before the death of 'Ali the control of the new empire had passed from Arabia, which was left in the status of a province dignified chiefly by possession of the two Holy Cities. Mu'awiyah set up his caliphate in Damascus. The Umayyad dynasty which he founded lasted until 750. It was then violently overthrown by descendants of al-'Abbas, an uncle of Muhammad. Thus began the Abbasid dynasty, which retained the caliphate until overwhelmed by the Mongols in 1258.

Such are the highlights of the Muslim caliphate down to the fall of the great Arab Empire. Thereafter, the caliphate was merely an appendage of Mameluke rule in Egypt and later of the Ottoman Empire. The last caliph was deposed by the Republic of Turkey in 1922 and the office was abolished in 1924.

THE GOLDEN AGE

After seizing the caliphate in 750, the Abbasids moved their capital to Baghdad, the scene of the golden age of the Arabs. This age brought together the art, skill, philosophy, learning, science and culture developed by many great civilizations.

On the material side, Baghdad became a fabulous city of mosques, palaces and mansions. Gold and silver, pearls, ivory, jewels, silks, works of art, spices, and all types of luxurious foods and handicrafts poured into Baghdad from many parts of the world. Baghdad was not the only city to prosper. Cairo, Alexandria, Damascus, Aleppo and Basra also became centers of wealth and luxury.

The accumulation of learning encouraged the Arabs to carry on energetic research in various fields. They welcomed, sponsored and stimulated learned men, scientists, artists, musicians and poets from many places. They established schools in which the knowledge and wisdom of great scholars and philosophers could be studied. The works of such men—Greek, Roman, Syrian, Persian and Indian—were translated into Arabic and thus were preserved for future civilizations. The Arabs also made new contributions of their own to medicine and other sciences and to literature, especially to poetry. They invented algebra and chemistry, the names of which are derived from Arabic words. They greatly advanced the knowledge of astronomy.

While the evidence seems to be that Arabic numerals were brought to Baghdad from India, it was in the great days of Baghdad that the cipher was invented. This concept revolutionized and simplified numerical calculations by leading to the development of the decimal and place system—that is, the use of only ten numerals in an indefinite number of places (units, tens, hundreds, thousands, etc.).

The Arabs had an important role in advancing the manufacture and use of paper, originally devised in China. They introduced this more practical substitute for earlier writing materials, such as clay tablets, papyrus and parchment, through Spain into Europe in time to facilitate the rapid development of printing with movable type.

The tales of *The Arabian Nights* provide an insight into the life and culture of the brilliant age of the Caliph Harun ar-Rashid. These tales are widely known in the Western world even though the real significance of those days has been largely forgotten: that the Arabs brought to fruition the accumulated knowledge of world experience and also kept the torch of knowledge burning during the so-called Dark Ages in Europe.

Harun ar-Rashid died in 809. While the glories of his age continued with diminishing brightness long after his time, the empire of the Arabs weakened and decayed. Many areas became independent under separate dynasties. In Iraq several caliphs fell under the power of Turkish mercenaries, and the capital was moved temporarily from Baghdad northward to Samarra. A militant revival occurred in the period 1055-1194 with the westward sweep of the Seljuk Turks, new converts to Islam, who wrested power from the Muslim Arabs and all others who stood in their path. It was during the Seljuk dominance that the Crusades occurred.

The Crusades, although highly dramatized in the West, did not have much effect upon the general course of events in the Middle East. They did not even stir up any great religious animosity among Muslims, whose usual tolerance for other religions has been a commendable trait. One important result of the Crusades was to bring Europeans into contact with Middle Eastern civilization and culture, which contributed greatly to the Renaissance in Europe.

In 1258 the Arab Empire was invaded by the Mongols or Tartars under Hulagu Khan, grandson of Genghis Khan, who had ravaged Asia and terrorized Europe. The Mongols were ruthless warriors. Their guiding creed was expressed by Genghis Khan in these words:

The greatest joy is to conquer one's enemies, to pursue them, to seize their property, to see their families in tears, to ride their horses, to possess their daughters and wives.

The shrine of the sister of the Imam Riza, Fatimeh Ma'sumeh ("Fatimah the Chaste"), at Qum, south of Tehran in Iran.

When Hulagu Khan and his hordes swept down upon Baghdad, the powerless Abbasid caliph surrendered after a weak defense. To show his scorn, Hulagu had him put in a sack and trampled to death. Although suffering less than some other cities, Baghdad was plundered, priceless libraries and works of art were destroyed and many of the inhabitants were massacred. The Mongols continued their destruction elsewhere in Mesopotamia and Syria. What remained of the great system of irrigation, which had made this region fertile and prosperous for thousands of years, was ruined. The area is only now recovering from that devastating blow.

The Mongols were defeated near Nazareth by the Egyptian Mamelukes and withdrew for a period of rule in Persia. The Mamelukes took over Palestine and Syria, ejected the last of the Crusaders in 1291 and joined these lands with Egypt until they themselves were conquered by the Ottoman Turks in 1517. The Middle East suffered another destructive invasion by the Mongols under Tamerlane (Timur the Lame) between 1393 and 1402.

Meanwhile, the Ottoman Turks had come into Asia Minor in the wake of the Seljuks. Recovering from the blows by Tamerlane, they ended the Byzantine Empire with the capture of Constantinople in 1453. Ottoman military power was feared throughout Europe for about two centuries thereafter. However, after the failure of the second Ottoman attempt to take Vienna in 1683, the empire declined—and with it the Middle Eastern lands under its inefficient rule.

About the time that Columbus discovered the New World, Portuguese seafarers and merchants were establishing footholds on the coasts of India and the Arabian Gulf. After them came the British and, temporarily, the Dutch. The British not only displaced the Portuguese but challenged the hold of the Turks at strategic points. These developments, however, had little effect upon the slumbering lands of the Middle East.

The lavishly decorated Alcazar, Seville, from Spain's Moorish e

Art in Arabic science: Egyptian astrolabe, with signs of the Zodiac.

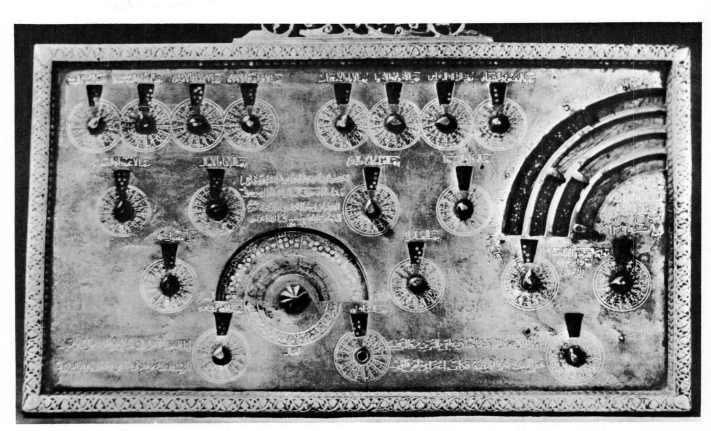

Astronomical table from Mosul in Mesopotamia, an outstanding example of inlaid metalwork with gold and silver inscriptions.

42

The Court of Lions in the Alhambra at Granada, Spain, the most famous Moorish structure, noted for its arabesque decorations.

The labyrinth of many-colored columns in the Great Mosque at Cordova in Spain.

43

The Taj Mahal at Agra, the crowning glory of Muslim architecture in India. This royal mausoleum dates to A.D. 1630-53.

The Mosque of Sultan Ahmed I, the "Blue Mosque," in Istanbul, dating to Ottoman times in the early seventeenth century.

THE RELIGIOUS REVIVAL—
THE RISE OF
THE HOUSE OF SA'UD

The era of Baghdad's glory was indeed a golden age. It was Islam, conceived and cradled in Arabia, that provided the stimulus for the material and intellectual achievements of that age. In the subsequent political and economic decay of the Arab Empire—which continued to decay despite periods of missionary expansion, intellectual activity and internal reform—the Muslims lost vigor in upholding the faith of their fathers. Popular practices obscured the simplicity of the religion originally preached by Muhammad. In some quarters the faith was nearly smothered by the addition, from century to century, of legalistic detail; in other quarters the old piety was nearly lost in a fog of exotic mysticism.

In the early part of the eighteenth century, Arabia was awakened to revival and reform by the preaching of a religious leader, Shaykh Muhammad ibn 'Abd al-Wahhab. Shaykh Muhammad was born in Najd, not far from Riyadh, in 1703 or 1704. He came from a family of religious judges and was steeped in religious teachings as a boy. By the age of ten he had memorized the Quran. He continued his studies in Mecca, Medina, Basra and al-Hasa. He was a follower of the Hanbalite school of Islamic law and was much influenced by the reforming zeal of a Hanbalite scholar of the fourteenth century, Ibn Taymiyah. The terms *Wahhabi* and *Wahhabism* are often applied to followers of

Shaykh Muhammad ibn 'Abd al-Wahhab and the movement he started. Shaykh Muhammad and his followers, however, called themselves *Muwahhidun* (Unitarians).

Shaykh Muhammad preached a return to the strict and simple message of the Quran and the teachings of the Prophet Muhammad. His movement provided the moral basis for the unification of most of the Arabian Peninsula under the House of Sa'ud and strengthened other reform movements within the wider community of Islam.

When Shaykh Muhammad began preaching, Arabia had long been divided into a multitude of small principalities. These were controlled by lords of the walled towns or by Bedouin chiefs, who constantly struggled for survival or mastery.

Like many inspired teachers, Shaykh Muhammad had his difficulties and his opponents. He was driven out of his home town of al-'Uyaynah because the strictness of his teachings irked the community leaders. He was welcomed, however, in the nearby town of ad-Dir'iyah. Muhammad ibn Sa'ud, whose family had governed ad-Dir'iyah for several generations, had a reputation for courtesy, justice and honor. He became the strong ally and supporter of Shaykh Muhammad, little dreaming that the movement which he supported would ultimately make the grandson of his great-grandson the ruler of a kingdom named after his family, Saudi Arabia. The

46

House of Sa'ud has remained the temporal champion of the Shaykh's movement. It also has preserved the family relationship; the mother of King Faysal was a descendant of Shaykh Muhammad ibn 'Abd al-Wahhab.

The new religious revival was carried forward with the same conviction as that which had governed the Prophet Muhammad and his followers: all converts were to be welcomed, but those who offered opposition were to be subdued. Shaykh Muhammad was a sincere and eloquent teacher and adherents were gained in mounting numbers and in widening areas. Even the people who had driven him from his home were won over.

Not all of the chiefs of Najd, however, were complacent about the rising power of the movement. The independent town of Riyadh led the fight against it. Muhammad ibn Sa'ud died in 1765 before Riyadh had been defeated, but his able son and successor, 'Abd al-'Aziz, carried the movement forward. Riyadh was taken in 1773. Thereafter the Saudi state spread rapidly. Within

fifteen years it embraced all of Najd. In the winter of 1789-90 the ruling Bedouin tribe in al-Hasa, Bani Khalid, was defeated in battle at the hill of Ghuraymil south of Abqaiq.

Shaykh Muhammad died in 1792, but the progress of his movement continued under the leadership of the House of Sa'ud. In 1802 its forces took the Shi'ite pilgrimage center of Karbala in Iraq. Before much of the nineteenth century had gone by, the Saudi state had spread its domain over most of the Arabian Peninsula, including Oman and the Hijaz and parts of the Yemen. The Holy Cities of Mecca and Medina came under Saudi control. Raids were made far into Syria, and in 1811 a campaign was planned against Baghdad.

The movement became such a threat to the Ottoman Empire that the Sultan decided to take drastic action. He appointed the governor of Egypt, Muhammad 'Ali, to organize a punitive expedition. A force under Tusun, a son of Muhammad 'Ali, invaded Arabia but was badly defeated, though it managed to gain control of Mecca. Muhammad

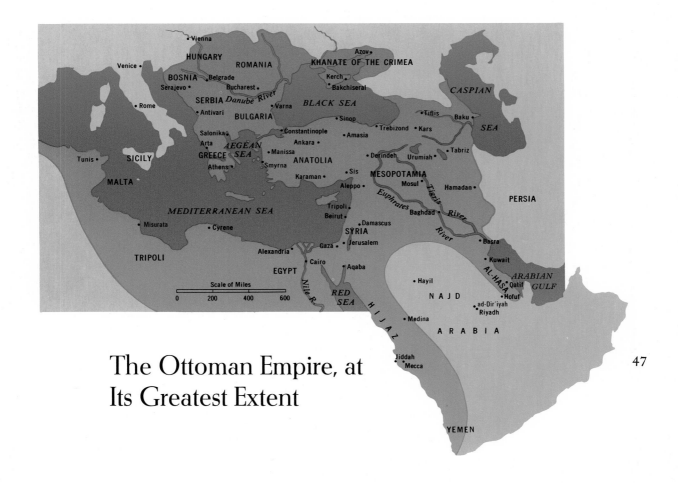

The Ottoman Empire, at Its Greatest Extent

47

'Ali thereupon went to Arabia and took personal charge for a time. Then he sent a formidable army under another son, Ibrahim. The Saudis put up a stout defense, but they were badly shaken by the death in 1814 of their leader, Sa'ud, the successor to 'Abd al-'Aziz. Ibrahim took ad-Dir'iyah in 1818 after a long siege. The city was destroyed. The Saudi chief was taken to Constantinople and beheaded.

Although militarily defeated, the House of Sa'ud soon regained political control of central Arabia and the reform movement continued. In 1824, Turki, the great-great-grandfather of the present King, established himself in Riyadh, thenceforth the capital of the House of Sa'ud. He proceeded to reconquer Najd and what is now called the Eastern Province, but was assassinated in 1834. His successor was his son, Faysal, who suffered early defeats at the hands of the Egyptians, but later reestablished Saudi rule over Najd and eastern Arabia. Faysal did so with the help of 'Abd Allah ibn Rashid of Jabal Shammar in northern Arabia, but the House of Rashid later became a bitter

enemy of the House of Sa'ud. Faysal also received strong support from his brother Jiluwi. The son of Jiluwi was the right-hand man of the present King's father during his early battles.

The history of the House of Sa'ud immediately after the death of Faysal in 1865 is complicated and obscure. It is a story of rivalry between two of Faysal's sons, 'Abd Allah and Sa'ud, which developed into a civil war that lasted for some years and provided an opportunity for the occupation of the eastern coast by the Turks in 1871. Turkish rule there continued until the liberation of the region by the father of the present King in 1913. Saudi weakness at this time also paved the way for the rise to power of the House of Rashid.

With the death of the rival brothers, a third brother, 'Abd ar-Rahman, the present King's grandfather, became head of the family. He and his allies challenged the new rule of the House of Rashid, but at length they were badly defeated. In 1891 the House of Rashid placed a governor and a garrison in Riyadh and 'Abd ar-Rahman was forced to take his family into exile.

Genealogical Table of the House of Sa'ud (Simplified)
With the Order and Duration of Rule

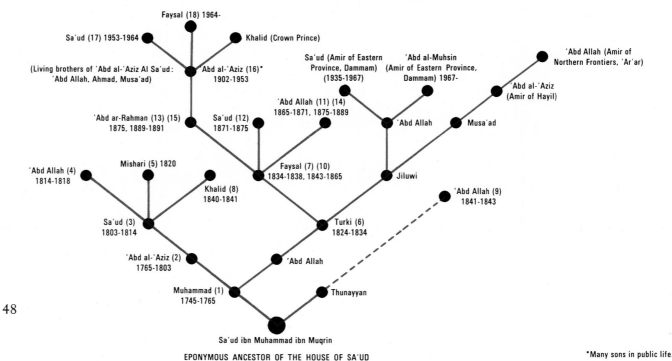

48

EPONYMOUS ANCESTOR OF THE HOUSE OF SA'UD

*Many sons in public life.

THE CAREER OF
'ABD AL-'AZIZ AL SA'UD

It was during the troubled times in the latter part of the nineteenth century that the present King's father was born in Riyadh. He was 'Abd al-'Aziz ibn 'Abd ar-Rahman Al Faysal Al Sa'ud, commonly known during his lifetime as Ibn Sa'ud.[1] The exact date of his birth is uncertain, but it was probably in November or December, 1880.

The father of 'Abd al-'Aziz was a strict adherent of Islam as expounded by Shaykh Muhammad ibn 'Abd al-Wahhab. The life of the family was austere and conservative and set moral standards which 'Abd al-'Aziz followed without deviation throughout his life. In early boyhood he was tutored in reading and writing and the doctrine and laws of Islam by a religious teacher from al-Kharj. He also spent a great deal of his time out of doors and, in the martial spirit of his time, learned to ride well and to play at the arts of war. Moreover, he witnessed warfare which was not play during a hard-fought campaign organized by his father.

'Abd al-'Aziz was about eleven years old when his family took flight from Riyadh. For a time they lived with Bedouins on the edge of the Rub' al-Khali. Later they moved to Qatar, then to Bahrain Island. Finally they took refuge in Kuwait, where they spent the better part of a decade. The life of 'Abd al-'Aziz during this period left him with an understanding of the Bedouins which was no

small element in his later success as an Arab ruler. In Kuwait he also learned a great deal about political facts in the Arabian Gulf, particularly the powerful position of the British and their rivalry with the Germans, the Russians and the Turks for control of that important channel of commerce. Those were the days of the proposed Berlin-to-Baghdad railroad, which the Turks and Germans hoped to terminate in Kuwait. At the same time, the Russians were intriguing for influence in Persia and for possible outlets on the Arabian Gulf.

'Abd al-'Aziz became a protégé of Mubarak Al Sabah, who had seized control of Kuwait by killing his two half brothers. Mubarak was an able ruler and, for a while, a strong ally of 'Abd al-'Aziz.

CAPTURE OF RIYADH About the time that the powerful and agile 'Abd al-'Aziz reached his twentieth year, Mubarak was faced with a serious threat. The formidable Muhammad ibn Rashid, who held the towns of Najd, had died. His rash nephew, 'Abd al-'Aziz ibn Rashid, set out to take Kuwait in order to extend his realm to the sea. He was instigated and supported in this effort by the Turks, who had little liking for Mubarak and his friendship with the British. Under this threat Mubarak entered in 1899 into close treaty relations with the British.

At first the warfare consisted of skirmishes in which 'Abd ar-Rahman, father of 'Abd al-'Aziz Al Sa'ud, took part. In the latter part of 1900,

---

[1] *Although the father of King Faysal was almost universally known as Ibn Sa'ud, it is becoming increasingly common to refer to him as 'Abd al-'Aziz Al Sa'ud or simply 'Abd al-'Aziz.*

'Abd al-'Aziz ibn 'Abd ar-Rahman Al Faysal Al Sa'ud, King of Saudi Arabia until his death on November 9, 1953.

however, Mubarak took the field with a force of about 10,000 men. 'Abd al-'Aziz, at his own request, was allowed to make a diversionary sortie against Riyadh with a small band. He gathered supporters as he went, but Mubarak was defeated, and this first attempt on Riyadh had to be abandoned.

Ibn Rashid now planned another offensive against Kuwait, but was deterred from pressing it too far by British power, manifested in the presence of a warship in Kuwait harbor. He failed to get effective help from the Turks for the same reason.

Kuwait was still threatened by Ibn Rashid, however, when 'Abd al-'Aziz Al Sa'ud conceived another attempt on Riyadh which proved to be a turning point in the history of Arabia. Mubarak humored his young friend by supplying camels, arms and food for the party, numbering about forty close comrades, relatives and servants. Accompanying 'Abd al-'Aziz, among others, were his brother, Muhammad, and his cousins, 'Abd Allah ibn Jiluwi and 'Abd al-'Aziz ibn Musa'ad. They set forth from Kuwait, and Ibn Rashid, camped at Hafar al-Batin and intent upon his contest with Mubarak, scorned to take serious notice of this feeble threat.

Some months were spent on the fringes of the Rub' al-Khali near Yabrin and in the vicinity of Haradh. 'Abd al-'Aziz hoped to get reinforcements from the tribes, but he had little success. He ignored pleas from his father and Mubarak to return to Kuwait. Instead, he started out for Riyadh with only about twenty more followers than he had when he left Kuwait.

At a distance of one and a half hours' march from Riyadh, he left twenty of his sixty-odd men with the camels, with instructions to return to Kuwait if no message was forthcoming within twenty-four hours. With the rest of the party he advanced on foot to the date gardens on the outskirts of Riyadh. Here he left his brother, Muhammad, with thirty-three men.

Ibn Rashid's men had built a fort, called al-Masmak, within the city. It was the custom of the governor, 'Ajlan, to spend his nights there, but 'Abd al-'Aziz Al Sa'ud did not know this. In fact, he seems to have had no special plan in mind when he and six companions crept in the darkness into Riyadh. To quote his own account, "We thought to ourselves, 'What shall we do?' "

What they did was to enter a house near the home of the governor in which a cattle seller lived. This man's daughters, who recognized 'Abd al-'Aziz, were silenced and locked up. Their father fled. 'Abd al-'Aziz and his men had hoped to be able to jump from this house to the house of the governor but they discovered that they could not do so. They leaped to an adjoining house. Finding a man and his wife asleep there, they tied them up in their bedclothes and threatened them with death if they should speak.

Word was sent back to Muhammad to bring his men quietly into the city. After they had arrived without raising an alarm, 'Abd al-'Aziz and his little group stealthily climbed into the governor's house by standing on one another's shoulders. As they entered, they seized the sleepy servants and locked them up. They hoped to surprise the governor in bed, but instead found only his wife sleeping with her sister. From them they learned that the governor was in the fortress and would not come out until sunrise.

They spent the last few hours of darkness in the governor's house, opposite the fortress gate, drinking coffee and eating dates. As 'Abd al-'Aziz later recalled, they "slept a little while ... prayed the morning prayer and sat thinking about what we should do."

They planned to ambush the governor in his own house and dressed one of their men in the clothes of the woman who usually opened the door for him. After the gate of the fort was opened, however, they saw the governor coming out with ten men. 'Abd al-'Aziz and some of his followers made a rush for 'Ajlan, leaving four men in the house to support them with rifles.

The governor's men fled back into the fortress,

The old al-Murabba' Palace in Riyadh, built of sun-dried mud bricks and long occupied by 'Abd al-'Aziz.

leaving him standing alone, with only a sword for defense. Ibn Jiluwi threw a spear at the governor, but missed. The point remains embedded in the gate of the fort to this day.

"He made at me with his sword," said 'Abd al-'Aziz, "but its edge was not good. I covered my face and shot at him with my gun. I heard the crash of the sword upon the ground and knew that the shot had hit 'Ajlan, but had not killed him. He started to go through the postern gate, but I caught hold of his legs. The men inside caught hold of his arms while I still held his legs. His company were shooting their firearms at us and throwing stones upon us. 'Ajlan gave me a powerful kick in the side so that I was about to faint. I let go his legs and he got inside.

"I wished to enter, but my men would not let me. Then 'Abd Allah ibn Jiluwi entered with the bullets falling about him. After him ten others entered. We flung the gate wide open, and our company ran up to reinforce us. We were forty, and there before us were eighty. We slaughtered half of them. Then four fell from the wall and were crushed. The rest were trapped in a tower; we granted safe-conduct to them, and they descended. As for 'Ajlan, Ibn Jiluwi slew him."

Such is the epic story, as related by the late King 'Abd al-'Aziz, of how Riyadh was retaken on January 16, 1902, as the sun was casting its first red rays across the desert and the city was just coming to life. The fight was over in less time than it takes to tell the story. 'Abd al-'Aziz was proclaimed the new ruler and welcomed joyfully by his people, who had suffered under the harsh rule of the House of Rashid.

From that day on, the path of 'Abd al-'Aziz was forward. Being a man of wisdom as well as strength, he knew when to bide his time if conditions did not favor an advance, but he never lost his momentum nor suffered a serious reverse.

CONQUEST OF NAJD The taking of Riyadh was a master stroke, but it was only a small engagement in what was to prove a long, arduous and battle-filled campaign. Riyadh was, after all, only one town on the edge of a large region which had been conquered by Muhammad ibn Rashid. The rest of the region was still strongly held by his successor.

As yet, 'Abd al-'Aziz seemed no great threat to this domain. He was a young man. His following was small and his resources few. He had little to offer the townspeople and tribesmen of Najd other than the hope of throwing off the rule of the House of Rashid. These men of Najd, whose hard struggle for existence has taught them to depend first upon God and then upon themselves, do not readily accept a leadership which does not offer visible advantages. If the capture of Riyadh was to be anything but a short-lived, inconsequential stroke of luck, 'Abd al-'Aziz had to meet a severe test requiring much talent and courage.

The qualities he needed were manifest even at this early stage of his career: enormous strength, boldness and vitality; magnetic personality; sound judgment; thorough integrity; the ability to forgive his enemies or to be harsh and even ruthless as the occasion demanded, and above all, a solid faith in his religion, the precepts of which were his guide and inspiration.

The apparent unimportance and weakness of 'Abd al-'Aziz in the beginning were beneficial to him. Ibn Rashid still was camped at Hafar al-Batin intent upon his campaign against Kuwait. The small detail of punishing the Saudi upstart for his insolent raid on Riyadh and the murder of the governor could await Ibn Rashid's convenience. This delay gave 'Abd al-'Aziz precious time to strengthen his position.

With frantic haste the defenses of Riyadh were repaired, and the town was put in condition to withstand assault or siege. The father of 'Abd al-'Aziz was brought back from Kuwait and placed in control of the city while his son took the field. This relationship between father and son, which lasted until the death of 'Abd ar-Rahman nearly thirty years later, has few parallels in the annals of ruling families. It was a relationship of mutual respect, of profitable consultation on all important questions, of a willingness on the part of the father

The door of al-Masmak fort in Riyadh, scene of the brief skirmish in which 'Abd al-'Aziz captured the city in 1902.

The rooftops of old Riyadh in 1950, with their crenelated parapets looking toward the date gardens in the background.

Tribal Map of the
Arabian Peninsula

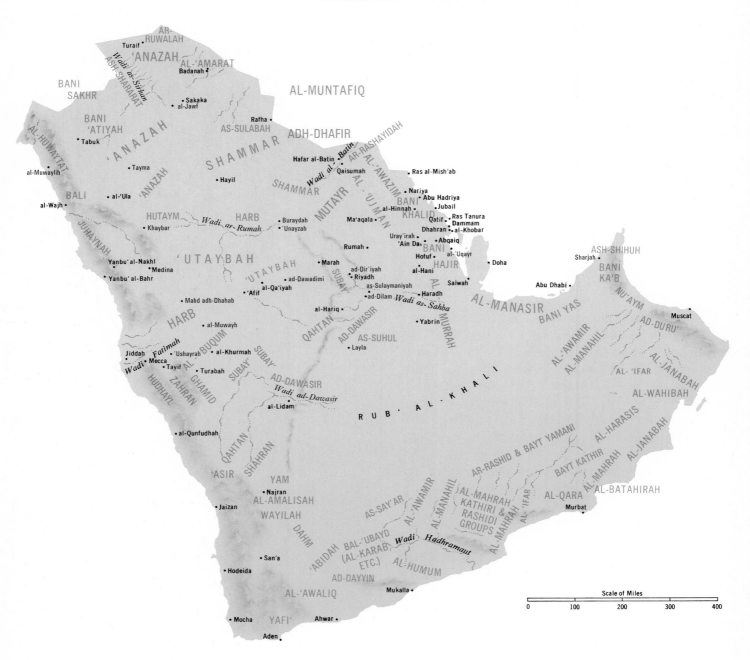

AR-RUWALAH
Turaif •
'ANAZAH
AL-'AMARAT
Badanah •
BANI SAKHR
ASH-SHARARAT
AL-MUNTAFIQ
BANI 'ATIYAH
• Sakaka
• al-Jawf
• Tabuk
AS-SULABAH
ADH-DHAFIR
Rafha •
al-Muwaylih •
'ANAZAH
SHAMMAR
AR-RASHAYIDAH
AL-'AWAZIM
Hafar al-Batin •
Qaisumah •
Ras al-Mish'ab •
• Tayma
Wadi al-Batin
AR-'UJMAN
Nariya •
BALI
• Hayil
SHAMMAR
MUTAYR
• Abu Hadriya
al-Wajh •
BANI KHALID
• al-Hinnah
Jubail •
HUTAYM
HARB
Ma'aqala •
Qatif •
Ras Tanura
JUHAYNAH
Wadi ar-Rumah
• Buraydah
Dhahran • Dammam
al-Khobar
• Khaybar
• 'Unayzah
Uray'irah •
Abqaiq •
Yanbu' al-Nakhl •
'AIN Da •
BANI HAJIR
Yanbu' al-Bahr •
• Medina
'UTAYBAH
Rumah •
Hofuf • al-'Uqayr
• Doha
ASH-SHIHUH
Sharjah •
BANI KA'B
'UTAYBAH
ad-Dir'iyah •
al-Hani •
• Marah
as-Sulaymaniyah •
Salwah •
• Mahd adh-Dhahab
• ad-Dawadimi
• Riyadh
SUBAY'
Abu Dhabi •
AL-MANASIR
NU'AYM
• Afif
• al-Qa'iyah
ad-Dilam •
Haradh •
Wadi as-Sahba
BANI YAS
AD-DURU'
AL-'AWAMIR
• Muscat
HARB
al-Hariq •
QAHTAN
MURRAH
AL-MANAHIL
AL-'IFAR
AL-JANABAH
Jiddah •
Fatimah •
AD-DAWASIR
• Yabrin
AL-WAHIBAH
Wadi • Mecca
'Ushayrah •
• al-Khurmah
AS-SUHUL
• Tayif
• Turabah
AL-BUQUM
SUBAY'
• Layla
R U B '   A L - K H A L I
AL-HARASIS
GHAMID
SUBAY'
HUDHAYL
ZAHRAN
AD-DAWASIR
Wadi ad-Dawasir
AL-JANABAH
• al-Lidam
AR-RASHID & BAYT YAMANI
AL-MAHRAH
• al-Qunfudhah
QAHTAN
BAYT KATHIR
AL-MAHRAH
AL-BATAHIRAH
SHAHRAN
AL-'IFAR
'ASIR
YAM
AL-'AWAMIR
AL-QARA
AL-AMALISAH
AL-MANAHIL
• Murbat
WAYILAH
• Najran
AL-MAHRAH
KATHIRI & RASHIDI GROUPS
AS-SAY'AR
AL-'AWAMIR
AL-MANAHIL
• Jaizan
DAHM
'ABIDAH
BAL-'UBAYD (AL-KARAB) ETC.)
Wadi Hadhramaut
AL-HUMUM
AD-DAYYIN
• San'a
AL-'AWALIQ
Mukalla •
• Hodeida
• Mocha
YAFI'
Ahwar •
Aden •

Scale of Miles

0   100   200   300   400

54

to acknowledge the leadership of his son and on the part of the son to place his father in the position of highest honor on every public occasion.

With the aid of his loyal brother, Sa'd, and the appeal of his own enthusiasm and charm, 'Abd al-'Aziz next set about, with reasonable success, winning the support of the people in the southern Najd. Here, in the districts of al-Kharj, al-Aflaj and Wadi ad-Dawasir, the House of Rashid never had been fully in control.

After most of 1902 had slipped by, Ibn Rashid headed south in the fall. By-passing the refortified city of Riyadh, he made a quick stab at al-Kharj, hoping to recapture this district before 'Abd al-'Aziz could prepare for its defense. 'Abd al-'Aziz was alert. He and his troops made a forced night march and were waiting in ambush when Ibn Rashid's army advanced upon the date groves at ad-Dilam. After a fierce, day-long battle, Ibn Rashid retreated to his capital city of Hayil. 'Abd al-'Aziz was not able to follow, being nearly out of ammunition, although Ibn Rashid was not aware of this circumstance.

This victory gave a great lift to the prestige of the young 'Abd al-'Aziz. As matters now stood, he could count on the support of the people of southern Najd, from Riyadh southward. In the next few years, 'Abd al-'Aziz and Ibn Rashid struggled almost constantly for mastery of the intervening portion of Najd, a region of walled towns and tough Bedouin tribes divided in their loyalties and whose leaders were ready to seize any advantage for themselves.

Ibn Rashid was a soldier of considerable ability, but in the field of human relations and government he was no match for his young opponent. 'Abd al-'Aziz successively won over to his side the people of the districts of al-Washm, Sudayr and al-Qasim. By the spring of 1904 he was master of central Najd up to the borders of Jabal Shammar.

Ibn Rashid retired into Shammar country to collect more troops. He also appealed to his Turkish allies for help. By this time the Turks had reason for anxiety over the success of 'Abd al-'Aziz, who

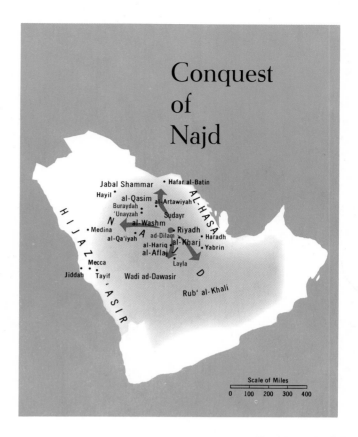

Conquest of Najd

was known to be a friend of Mubarak of Kuwait, who was in turn a friend of the British. Accordingly, when Ibn Rashid came back to resume the contest at the end of May, 1904, he was accompanied by eight battalions of Turkish troops equipped with artillery. This force presented a new problem of warfare to 'Abd al-'Aziz. His army was highly mobile, but its weapons were comparatively primitive, consisting of single-shot muskets, lances, daggers and swords.

'Abd al-'Aziz went out from the town of Buraydah in al-Qasim to meet the advancing force. The battle was running in his favor until he was wounded by shrapnel and had to retire. But if well-trained and well-equipped troops presented a new problem to 'Abd al-'Aziz, the fierce heat and other desert conditions presented a difficult problem to the Turks. Following a summer of comparative inactivity, in which the Turks in their heavy uniforms

The ruins of ad-Dir'iyah, ancestral capital of the House of Sa'ud, which was destroyed in 1819.

suffered greatly from the heat, 'Abd al-'Aziz resumed the battle. Seeing some of his men begin to waver, 'Abd al-'Aziz personally led a furious attack into the enemy's central position, held by the Turks and their artillery. The Turks gave ground and the Shammar forces of Ibn Rashid broke and fled. The retreat became a rout. Stores of equipment and even a large sum of Turkish gold fell into the hands of 'Abd al-'Aziz.

The Turkish Government had little stomach for further fighting in Arabia. It attempted to reach an agreement with 'Abd al-'Aziz under which al-Qasim would become a Turkish-controlled buffer between his domain and that of Ibn Rashid. The negotiations came to nothing.

Not long after the defeat of Ibn Rashid and the Turkish detachments, a feud arose between the two leading families of Buraydah, one of which was friendly to 'Abd al-'Aziz and the other to the Turks.

To the surprise of the local people, 'Abd al-'Aziz refused to interfere. He took the position that the people should decide for themselves whether they preferred to be ruled by him or the Turks. He went off to Qatar to assist the local ruler in putting down a revolt engineered by the ruler's brother.

While 'Abd al-'Aziz was gone, Ibn Rashid again seized control of al-Qasim and reestablished his high-handed rule. As 'Abd al-'Aziz hoped, the people of al-Qasim sent delegations to Riyadh pleading with him to return. After a few months of skirmishing he caught his old enemy by surprise. While Ibn Rashid was trying to rally his troops, he was shot down in his own camp at Rawdat Al Muhanna near Buraydah in April, 1906. So ended the contest between the old warrier, 'Abd al-'Aziz of the House of Rashid, and the young campaigner, 'Abd al-'Aziz of the House of Sa'ud—four years and three months after the seizure of Riyadh.

56

NEW TROUBLES — FROM WITHIN AND WITHOUT

The decisive defeat of 'Abd al-'Aziz ibn Rashid did not end the difficulties of 'Abd al-'Aziz Al Sa'ud. During the ensuing years he was beset with so many troubles that he scarcely settled one before another was upon him. A lesser man would have been unable to overcome them.

The tribe of Mutayr, living between Najd and Kuwait, rose in a revolt instigated by the Turks and by Mubarak of Kuwait, who had become jealous of the success of 'Abd al-'Aziz. While 'Abd al-'Aziz was dealing with the tribe, the House of Rashid continued to harass him. In the final battle of this campaign he broke his collarbone when his horse fell, but his forces defeated the men of Mutayr and destroyed their camp. The governors of Buraydah continued to be troublesome until he placed his powerful and loyal cousin, 'Abd Allah ibn Jiluwi, in charge of the entire district of al-Qasim. There was no further trouble.

No sooner had reasonable order been established in the north than a new threat took form in the south—a threat arising within the House of Sa'ud. The father of 'Abd al-'Aziz was the youngest of three brothers who had ruled in Arabia. The grandsons of one of the older brothers, Sa'ud, were held by Ibn Rashid after his victory in 1891. During the conquest of al-Qasim in 1904 by 'Abd al-'Aziz, they had escaped into the arms of their kin. This branch of the family has been known since then as 'Araif, a Bedouin word for camels which have been taken as booty and then retaken by their rightful owner.

These individuals, however, were not given positions in which they could acquire power or create trouble. They began living with the strong 'Ujman tribe of eastern Arabia, to whom they were related by marriage. Regarding 'Abd al-'Aziz as a usurper, they awaited an opportunity to assert themselves.

The 'Araif got support not only from the 'Ujman but also in the district of al-Aflaj and in the town of al-Hariq south of Riyadh. In 1909, the Hazzanis, an important family of al-Hariq, stirred up trouble which 'Abd al-'Aziz put down by besieging their town and threatening to set off a mine under the main fort. The Hazzanis were forgiven, but later again allied themselves with the 'Araif and paid for their disloyalty.

The year 1910 was marked by a severe drought in which thousands of camels and other livestock died. The 'Ujman raided Kuwait in disregard of the complaints of Mubarak and the orders of 'Abd al-'Aziz. The tribe of Mutayr raided Najd and, along with the House of Rashid, incited the 'Ujman. 'Abd al-'Aziz was unable to deal decisively with this situation, since his resources and his mobility were seriously affected by the drought. While he was nearly stalemated, the 'Araif fomented a new revolt in the south. At the same time a new threat, which would continue until the Saudi conquest of the Hijaz, arose in the west.

The Hijaz had long been under the control of the Ottoman Empire. With its Holy Cities and its position on the Red Sea, it was a most important province. A railroad was built from Damascus to Medina between 1904 and 1908, ostensibly to facilitate the movement of pilgrims to the Holy Cities, but also as a strategic measure. Discord and disorder had characterized the regime in the Hijaz for some time. In the hope of improving this situation, Husayn ibn 'Ali was installed by the Turks as Sharif of Mecca in 1908. A descendant of the Prophet Muhammad's own family, the Hashimites, Husayn had been born in Mecca. However, he had spent most of his life in Constantinople court circles and was nearly sixty years old when he was appointed to the sharifate. Husayn was a man of great charm, culture and integrity, but he was also stubborn and overwhelmingly ambitious. He and the residents of the more cosmopolitan cities of the Hijaz underrated the capacities of 'Abd al-'Aziz and the people of Najd.

One of the great tribes of western Najd was the 'Utaybah. 'Abd al-'Aziz regarded its members, and they regarded themselves, as being under his jurisdiction. Husayn contended that they owed allegiance to him. He persisted in this view until it proved to be his undoing.

In June, 1912, 'Abd al-'Aziz, needing more troops to put down the rebellion of the 'Araif, sent his favorite brother, Sa'd, among the 'Utaybah to collect reinforcements. At the same time, without the knowledge of Sa'd, Husayn embarked upon an expedition into this territory. Sa'd, with his small entourage, fell into Husayn's hands.

Husayn now proposed to release Sa'd on condition that 'Abd al-'Aziz acknowledge Turkish suzerainty over the district of al-Qasim and pay a small annual tribute. The alternative was that Sa'd would remain a prisoner in the Hijaz. With his beloved brother captured, 'Abd al-'Aziz had no choice but to accept these humiliating terms.

'Abd al-'Aziz proceeded to put down the rebellion of the 'Araif. He dealt with the leaders sternly, in contrast to his usual practice of treating his conquered enemies with charity and generosity. After rounding up the rebels who had assisted his cousins, he had eighteen members of the Hazzani family publicly executed at Layla, the capital of al-Aflaj. They had been forgiven once, but now they had forfeited the right to further mercy. Sa'ud ibn 'Abd al-'Aziz (Sa'ud al-Kabir), the oldest member of the 'Araif, was given a chance to go into exile, but chose instead to become a loyal subject of the ruler. As the husband of the King's favorite sister, Nurah, he outlived his brother-in-law. Other members of the 'Araif escaped to the Hijaz or to eastern Arabia.

'Abd al-'Aziz now had a breathing spell in which to give thought to the necessity for unity and stability in the land. The achievements of his predecessors of the House of Sa'ud were ever present in his mind. He took steps to supplant the tribal loyalties of the Bedouins with a broader loyalty. After consulting his father and other elders, 'Abd al-'Aziz founded agricultural communities peopled by Bedouin recruits. In some cases, new communities were built from the ground up; in others, Bedouins were assigned to existing villages. Here they were to cultivate the soil and study and practice their faith. 'Abd al-'Aziz provided for them generously, giving money, seed and agricultural implements. Religious teachers were appointed and money was given to build mosques. Furthermore, the settlers were furnished arms for defense. These Bedouins were to offer allegiance to the Reform Movement and to the House of Sa'ud and to remain devoted to each other. They were called the *Ikhwan*—the Brethren.

The first such colony was started with tribesmen of Mutayr at the wells of al-Artawiyah in northern Najd in 1912. The mosque and houses were built by the new colonists themselves. Other *Ikhwan* colonies were gradually established. They not only rooted tribesmen to the soil and provided them with more stable means of livelihood, but also supplied the state with thousands of first-class fighting men in case of need. The *Ikhwan* were uncompromising in their religious temperament and fearless fighters whose chief fault was overzealousness.

Well over a hundred of these *Ikhwan* colonies were eventually established as missionaries systematically drew recruits for them from the tribes. Missionaries were regularly assigned to newly subdued tribes, where they were much more effective than force in confirming loyalties. They usually founded new *Ikhwan* colonies among these tribes.

CONQUEST OF EASTERN ARABIA Eastern Arabia was almost constantly under the control of the House of Sa'ud from 1790 to 1871. While members of the House of Sa'ud were engaged in civil war, the Turks seized the region in 1871. They remained in occupation until 1913. Hofuf, the principal town of the oasis of al-Hasa, was the headquarters of Turkish administration. The Turks had a garrison there and smaller forces at Qatif and al-'Uqayr on the Arabian Gulf coast. They also had a garrison in the capital of Qatar and repeatedly threatened to occupy Kuwait.

58

Not only was 'Abd al-'Aziz cut off by the Turks from the Arabian Gulf, but he also was hemmed in on the west and north by other fringes of the Ottoman Empire. Along the Red Sea were the Ottoman provinces of the Yemen, 'Asir and the Hijaz. To the north were the domains of the House of Rashid.

The Turks were the historic enemies of the House of Sa'ud. Either directly or through vassals in Egypt, the Hijaz and Jabal Shammar, they had been almost constantly at war with 'Abd al-'Aziz and his ancestors. But now the Turks were having troubles with the Italians and in the Balkans, and they were soon to lose most of their empire in World War I.

The time was propitious and 'Abd al-'Aziz struck. On a moonless night in April, 1913, he

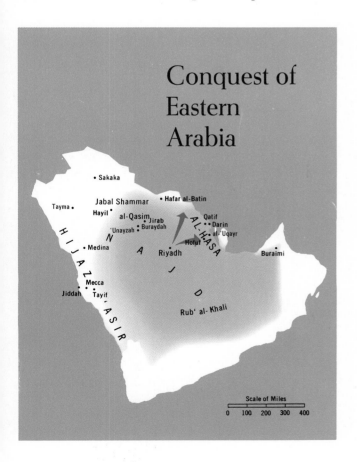

Conquest of Eastern Arabia

approached the fortifications of Hofuf with 600 men. They stealthily scaled the wall with the aid of ropes and palm tree trunks. Before the sleeping Turkish troops could rouse themselves, 'Abd al-'Aziz was in control of the *Kut*, the inner fortress area. Many of the Turkish troops and their families took refuge in the mosque of Ibrahim, but under the threat of being destroyed by a mine, the governor promptly surrendered. Quick thrusts to al-'Uqayr and Qatif overcame the Turkish troops stationed there. All the Turks were allowed to depart with their weapons. 'Abd Allah ibn Jiluwi was transferred from al-Qasim to Hofuf, where he remained as governor until his death a quarter of a century later.

After the conquest of Hofuf, 'Abd al-'Aziz negotiated with the Turks for the purpose of regularizing the new situation in the Arabian Gulf region. At the same time the Turks made an agreement with Sa'ud ibn Rashid, the new head of the House of Rashid, under which he was to receive rifles for an attack on Najd. Recognizing the duplicity of the Turks, 'Abd al-'Aziz laid the groundwork for an understanding with the British. He had several meetings with British officials. In the winter of 1913, Captain W. H. I. Shakespear, the British Political Agent at Kuwait, visited him in Riyadh, and the first steps were taken which led to the Anglo-Saudi treaty of 1915.

ARABIA DURING THE FIRST WORLD WAR Long before the discovery of large quantities of oil in the area, the Middle East was important as the geographical link between East and West, the crossroads of commerce between Europe and the Orient. The Middle East always has been of vital strategic importance. International rivalry for mastery of the entire area was among the causes of World War I.

When the powers of Europe went to war in 1914, the Ottoman Empire extended over parts of the Arabian Peninsula and all the Arab lands to the north. The Russians had dreams of expansion into the Middle East. The Germans had started to implement their "Drive to the East," which included

plans for completion of a Berlin-to-Baghdad railway, with an outlet on the Arabian Gulf.

At the same time, British military forces controlled Egypt and the Suez Canal. Britain had an important harbor and coaling station in Aden and outposts in and along the Arabian Gulf. These outposts made the British practically masters of the Arabian Gulf, though their position was not undisputed. The British considered the Arabian Gulf area within their sphere of influence and had announced in 1903 that establishment of a naval base or fortified port in the Arabian Gulf by any other power would be regarded as "a very grave menace to British interests" and one which Britain would "certainly resist with all the means" at its disposal.

British control of the gulf extended even to Kuwait, nominally a part of the Ottoman Empire. The Shaykh of Kuwait, Mubarak, had signed a treaty in 1899 with the British under which he bound himself to grant no concessions to any foreign interest without British consent. This treaty had thwarted German plans to use Kuwait as a railroad terminus.

Soon after the outbreak of war, Britain began a campaign to wrest control of Mesopotamia from the Turks. The British realized that 'Abd al-'Aziz could be a valuable ally and sent Captain Shakespear to Riyadh to propose action against Sa'ud ibn Rashid. Actually, Ibn Rashid took the initiative and advanced into the domains of 'Abd al-'Aziz. A fierce battle took place at Jirab in al-Qasim. While the issue was still in doubt, members from the tribe of the 'Ujman—who had resented the capture of their lands in eastern Arabia by 'Abd al-'Aziz and were to give him much trouble later on—suddenly deserted the Saudi ranks. Captain Shakespear, who was directing the fire of the Saudi guns, was killed

The Kut area of Hofuf, showing the fortress and mosque of Qasr Ibrahim (left) and the fortress of Qasr al-'Abid (right).

An old fort at Dammam, now demolished, which was the lair of a notorious Arabian Gulf pirate in the early nineteenth century.

in a charge of Ibn Rashid's cavalry. Both sides retired, each claiming victory.

This inconclusive battle, and particularly the death of Shakespear, cooled for a time the enthusiasm of the British for further participation with 'Abd al-'Aziz in Arabian campaigns. However, Sir Percy Cox, the British Political Resident in the Arabian Gulf, met 'Abd al-'Aziz at Darin on Tarut Island in December, 1915. There they concluded a treaty under which 'Abd al-'Aziz accepted a formula, similar to the one used in other British treaties in the Arabian Gulf area, giving the British control over his relations with other powers.

Another British mission was sent to Riyadh in the fall of 1917, with the two-fold purpose of inducing an attack on Ibn Rashid and of reconciling 'Abd al-'Aziz and the Sharif Husayn of Mecca. A prominent member of this mission was H. St. John B. Philby, who thus began his explorations and studies of the country. His keen observations and painstaking researches have been recorded in many articles and books.

The British mission was partially successful in that 'Abd al-'Aziz launched another attack against Ibn Rashid in 1918. Aside from this attack, which failed to capture Hayil, 'Abd al-'Aziz took no active part in the world conflict. He had troubles enough in other quarters. He carried on a long campaign against the rebellious 'Ujman tribe—a campaign which cost 'Abd al-'Aziz the life of his favorite brother, Sa'd, and in which he himself was twice severely wounded. The tribes to the north, allies of the Turks, were a constant threat. To make matters worse, Husayn of Mecca, now an ally of the British, made several attacks on the tribe of 'Utaybah in western Najd. Though these attacks were beaten back by the men of 'Utaybah themselves, they added to the difficulties of the situation.

The war years were trying for 'Abd al-'Aziz. He cooperated with the British when he was not distracted by internal troubles, but the rewards he received were small. He won no new territory. At the end of the war he found himself threatened by an ambitious antagonist, the Sharif Husayn, who had been armed and supported by the British.

The branch of the British Government which dealt with 'Abd al-'Aziz was the Government of India, under the jurisdiction of the India Office in London. Another branch, the Arab Bureau of Cairo, which reported to the military authorities, tended to concentrate its attention on the Hijaz and the Sharif Husayn. The British in Cairo conducted secret negotiations with Husayn which resulted in an agreement for an Arab revolt against the Turks. The British accepted certain conditions, among which was recognition of the independence of extensive Arab territories should the Allies be successful. Later other British authorities made commitments to the French, Russians and Zionists which were in conflict with the promises made to Husayn and which created serious complications after the war.

When Husayn raised the flag of revolt in June, 1916, the initial reaction of 'Abd al-'Aziz was favorable, since he approved of any move against the Turks. Husayn was assisted by a small military mission. Among its members was T. E. Lawrence, who described the campaigns in his *Revolt in the Desert* and his longer classic, *Seven Pillars of Wisdom.*

CONQUEST OF HAYIL AND THE HIJAZ The postwar settlements gave the Arabs much less independent territory than they had been led to expect. Husayn was recognized by the British and other Allies as King of the Hijaz, although he had assumed the title of King of the Arabs. His son Faysal was proclaimed king of an independent Syria on March 8, 1920, by a national congress in Damascus, but France, which had been granted a mandate over Syria by the San Remo Conference, was opposed to the emergence of an independent monarchy. When Faysal rejected an ultimatum demanding recognition of the mandate, French forces occupied the country and drove the new king into exile.

Subsequently, Faysal was elected king of British-mandated Iraq by an almost unanimous plebiscite. Britain continued to maintain mandate control after the plebiscite, but Faysal was allowed to rule as titular head of state. 'Abd Allah, another son of Husayn, was made amir of the British mandate of Transjordan, now Jordan.

On three occasions in 1918 Husayn had made attacks upon al-Khurmah, an oasis on the western fringe of the lands of the tribe of 'Utaybah. Each time the local inhabitants repulsed the attacks. After the third one they received a promise from 'Abd al-'Aziz that he would come to their aid in case of further aggression.

The British Government was thus faced with a policy decision in the event that war should break out between its two Arabian allies. In early 1919,

Conquest
of Hayil
and the Hijaz

British military experts were emphatic in stating that the forces of 'Abd al-'Aziz would be hopelessly outclassed by the seasoned, well-trained and well-equipped troops of King Husayn. The only dissenting voice was that of Philby. As he did not qualify as a military expert, Philby was ignored. The British decided, for expediency, to back Husayn's claim to al-Khurmah and 'Abd al-'Aziz was warned not to contest it.

Encouraged by this manifestation of British support, Husayn sent an army of 4,000 men to take the disputed oasis. The force, headed by his son 'Abd Allah, was well-supplied with artillery, machine guns and other military stores. In May, 1919, the confident army moved to the town of Turabah and encamped there before attacking al-Khurmah itself. In the middle of a dark night the Saudi *Ikhwan* struck the army from all sides. Before the troops of 'Abd Allah could organize a defense they were cut down. Only 'Abd Allah and about 100 out of the entire force escaped by taking flight at the first alarm. Husayn's army was virtually annihilated.

The attack had been made by the men of al-Khurmah and the tribe of 'Utaybah before 'Abd al-'Aziz and his forces reached the scene. With the road to Mecca open to 'Abd al-'Aziz, the British made frantic political moves to forestall him from inflicting further indignities upon the kingdom they had fostered. However, their fears were groundless, at least for the time being. 'Abd al-'Aziz simply annexed al-Khurmah to his territories and retired to Riyadh.

In 1921 Jabal Shammar with its capital, Hayil, was finally conquered. Although the House of Rashid had been weakened by internal strife, the Saudis still had to campaign for most of the year before Hayil fell. 'Abd al-'Aziz, as usual, had laid his plans with great care. Surviving members of the House of Rashid, foes of the House of Sa'ud for generations, were brought to Riyadh, where they remained as honored guests of the royal family. In the same year the highlands of 'Asir were added to the territories of 'Abd al-'Aziz as the result of an expedition headed by his son, Faysal, who later became King.

In the following year the domains of 'Abd al-'Aziz were extended still farther to include the oases of Khaybar and Tayma west of the Great Nafud, and Wadi as-Sirhan and al-Jawf to the north. This campaign was aided by many local people who had become converts to the Reform Movement. A column of the *Ikhwan* almost reached Amman in Transjordan, killing the inhabitants of a village on the way, before it was overwhelmed by British armored cars and airplanes.

The boundaries of the Saudi state in the direction of Iraq and Kuwait were agreed upon in a general way by 'Abd al-'Aziz and Sir Percy Cox in a meeting at al-'Uqayr late in 1922. 'Abd al-'Aziz at first objected to attempts to curb, by imaginary lines across the open desert, the movement of tribes accustomed to roaming widely in their search for pasture and water. This objection was eventually overcome by the establishment of neutral zones in two places, one between Iraq and Saudi Arabia and the other between Kuwait and Saudi Arabia. It was also agreed that the borders should not be fortified by any of the governments concerned.

Despite the measure of success which 'Abd al-'Aziz achieved at al-'Uqayr, the *Ikhwan* continued to clamor for war against "the unrighteous," and the rivalry between the House of Sa'ud and King Husayn and his sons continued along its bitter course. The British arranged a conference in Kuwait in an effort to settle the differences between their Arabian friends, but both sides were uncompromising. No practical basis for agreement could be found. The anger of the Saudis was further inflamed when, in March, 1924, the Turkish Republic abolished the caliphate and Husayn promptly had himself declared caliph. The Saudis were not willing to concede Husayn even theoretical authority over all Muslims, especially since they believed he condoned conditions and practices in the Hijaz which were out of keeping with the character of the Holy Cities.

Hostilities started when an advance detachment of Saudis appeared before the mountain city of Tayif early in September, 1924. The force probably had no intention of attacking the town, for the detachment's commander, Sultan ibn Bijad, one of the leaders of the tribe of 'Utaybah and chief of the *Ikhwan* colony of Ghatghat, was a few hours' march in the rear. Husayn's eldest son, 'Ali, happened to be in Tayif at the time. Although he had sufficient troops at his disposal, the mere sight of the dread *Ikhwan* apparently created a panic. 'Ali quickly withdrew his forces toward Mecca.

The townsmen, left defenseless, agreed to surrender the town peaceably. When the gates were swung open, however, the *Ikhwan* were fired upon,

The ancient Mecca Gate in Jiddah, now demolished, through which countless Muslim pilgrims passed on the way to Mecca.

possibly by people uninformed of the agreement. Whatever the reason, the *Ikhwan* thought they had been betrayed and went on a rampage of killing and looting before Sultan ibn Bijad arrived and assumed control. The number killed was about 300. Exaggerated reports of what had happened terrified the people of the Hijaz. This was the only time during the Hijaz campaign when the Saudi forces were not under strict control.

Following the occupation of Tayif a number of the influential citizens of the Hijaz brought pressure to bear on Husayn to abdicate. The old man held out against this step as long as he could, but in the end he had to yield. He boarded a ship at Jiddah in October, 1924, and moved to Jordan. After a time the British transferred him to Cyprus, where he spent his last years.

'Ali was proclaimed King of the Hijaz. One of his first acts was the evacuation of Mecca, which was considered indefensible once Tayif had fallen. He concentrated his forces in Jiddah. Mecca surrendered to 'Abd al-'Aziz without resistance. The troops of Sultan ibn Bijad immediately set about destroying various ornamental tombs and monuments which the Saudis regarded as sacrilegious. 'Abd al-'Aziz entered Mecca for the first time on October 13, 1924, in the humble garb of a pilgrim.

The walled town of Jiddah was put under siege by the Saudis. There was no attempt at an attack, except for a desultory bombardment. King 'Ali attempted without success to obtain armed support from the British. Having captured ports both north and south of Jiddah, 'Abd al-'Aziz reopened the country to pilgrims. Although few Muslims made the 1925 pilgrimage, it was conducted in an orderly manner which created a favorable impression in the rest of the Muslim world. In keeping with an age-old custom, 'Abd al-'Aziz suspended the siege of Jiddah during the pilgrimage season.

In the first days of December, 1925, the town of Medina surrendered to a force under Muhammad, the third son of 'Abd al-'Aziz, with a guarantee that the *Ikhwan* would not be allowed to enter

The old city of Jiddah, which was captured by the forces of 'Abd al-'Aziz in 1925, completing the Saudi conquest of the Hijaz. The fortified wall was pulled down in the late Nineteen Forties to give the city more growing room.

the city. Jiddah capitulated two weeks later, and 'Ali boarded a ship for Iraq, where his brother, Faysal, reigned.

On January 8, 1926, the leading citizens of Mecca offered allegiance to 'Abd al-'Aziz as successor to the title 'Ali had once held, King of the Hijaz. The ceremonies, which took place in the Great Mosque in Mecca, were devoid of any pomp. The new King swore that he would rule in accordance with the laws of Islam.

Rule over the Hijaz brought with it new responsibilities. 'Abd al-'Aziz recognized a common religious interest in the Holy Places on the part of Muslims throughout the world. As protector of the Holy Places he assembled an Islamic congress in Mecca to give all Muslims an opportunity to suggest appropriate measures in the best interests of the pilgrimage and other matters. He made it clear to all that the political administration of the

Hijaz would remain under his exclusive control.

'Abd al-'Aziz remained in the Hijaz nearly two years. He was engaged in the prodigious task of setting up a new administration and a system of control over the Bedouins. This system, although simple, had worked well in other parts of his territory. The chief of each tribe was made responsible for the prompt punishment of any crime committed by his people. In the event of failure of any chief to do his duty, the chief of the neighboring tribe was responsible for taking action; if he failed, the King's army was prepared to move in.

While curbing lawlessness with determination, 'Abd al-'Aziz assisted the tribes through periods of drought and distress. Thereby he removed a basic incentive for raids upon neighboring tribes. As a result of his reforms, Saudi Arabia enjoyed a high degree of security and a lower crime rate than that of many other countries in the world.

65

THE NEW KINGDOM

After 'Abd al-'Aziz returned to Riyadh he was requested to take the title of King of Najd so that his position in his homeland would not be inferior to that in the Hijaz. In January, 1927, 'Abd al-'Aziz was proclaimed King of the Hijaz and Najd and Its Dependencies. He had been known since 1921 as Sultan of Najd and Its Dependencies.

'Abd al-'Aziz established his court at Riyadh, although his ministers made their headquarters at Mecca. Britain, in the Treaty of Jiddah in May, 1927, recognized the kingdom as a sovereign state. On September 22, 1932, the country was renamed the Kingdom of Saudi Arabia.

While 'Abd al-'Aziz was organizing the administration of his kingdom, he was forced to take the field against two *Ikhwan* leaders who had aided him in the conquest of the Hijaz—Faysal ad-Dawish of the tribe of Mutayr and Sultan ibn Bijad of the tribe of 'Utaybah. These *Ikhwan* leaders, in defiance of 'Abd al-'Aziz, embarked in 1928 upon retaliatory measures after Iraq began building a fort near the Najd border in violation of the 1922 Agreement of al-'Uqayr. 'Abd al-'Aziz was too weak to fight Iraq and the British, but he could not tolerate *Ikhwan* insubordination, which threatened the existence of his young state. The two rebel leaders and their followers were defeated after a bitter struggle, ending in a battle in the spring of 1929 near the first and greatest *Ikhwan* colony of al-Artawiyah.

In 1933 Saudi Arabia opened the eastern part of the kingdom to oil development, but it was five years before commercial production of petroleum began. During the early years of World War II, from 1939 on, oil development came to a virtual standstill. The number of pilgrims from abroad to the Holy Cities of Mecca and Medina dwindled, weakening the government's finances by the loss of this important source of foreign currency. Below normal rainfall added to the difficulties, and Bedouins lost large numbers of sheep and camels.

At first 'Abd al-'Aziz met his essential expenditures by obtaining substantial advances against future oil royalties. Later Britain assumed responsibility for aid to Saudi Arabia. In early 1943 the United States made Saudi Arabia eligible for lend-lease and other assistance, which lasted through 1945.

From 1939 until March, 1945, when Saudi Arabia entered the war on the Allied side, the King maintained a position of benevolent neutrality toward Britain and the United States. His open sympathy for the Allied cause had its effect upon Muslims in the Arabian Peninsula and elsewhere.

Diplomatic ties between the United States and Saudi Arabia were strengthened. An American Legation was opened in Jiddah in 1942 and a Saudi Arabian Legation in Washington in 1944. Both missions were raised to embassies in 1949. A historic meeting between President Franklin D. Roosevelt and King 'Abd al-'Aziz took place on an American cruiser anchored in Great Bitter Lake in the Suez Canal in February, 1945.

A number of the King's sons, including Faysal, Khalid and Saʿud, visited the United States. Faysal first went to the United States in 1943 and returned on several occasions as head of the Saudi Arabian Delegation to the United Nations, of which Saudi Arabia is a charter member. In 1962, as Crown Prince, Faysal met with President John F. Kennedy in Washington and in 1966, on a state visit as King, held talks with President Lyndon B. Johnson.

After World War II, Saudi Arabia resumed its evolution from a tribal and regional society into a

King ʿAbd al-ʿAziz confers with President Franklin D. Roosevelt on an American cruiser in the Suez Canal in 1945.

King Faysal and President Lyndon B. Johnson review the Honor Guard on the White House lawn during a state visit in 1966.

modern state. This transition is continuing with increasing momentum. The growing oil industry has provided a substantial flow of revenues for the country's continuing development.

King 'Abd al-'Aziz established the basis of the country's present administration. A month before his death the King sanctioned formation of a Council of Ministers to act as a cabinet under the presidency of his eldest son, Crown Prince Sa'ud.

'Abd al-'Aziz died November 9, 1953, Sa'ud became King and Faysal was named Crown Prince. For much of King Sa'ud's reign, Faysal was President of the Council of Ministers and assisted his brother in extending the administrative structure of the state. New ministries and autonomous agencies were established to guide the nation's economic and social development. Most elements of the personal and direct rule which had characterized the reign of 'Abd al-'Aziz were eliminated or modified.

Pushing forward rapidly on a development program, the nation's spending outran its increasing oil revenues. King Sa'ud called upon the Crown Prince to take over the government in March,

1958. Faysal instituted tight fiscal controls. Faysal's austerity program was successful and the financial crisis was halted. King Sa'ud again took control of the government, and in December, 1960, Faysal withdrew from public life. Sa'ud's health, however, began to deteriorate. In November, 1961, the King made the first of several trips abroad for medical treatment, and again Faysal was asked to take over the direction of the government. Sa'ud was out of the kingdom for extended periods, and in November, 1964, Faysal was persuaded by the Royal Family, the Ulema and other dignitaries to replace his elder brother as King. The Royal Family, supported by the Ulema, the Council of Ministers and the Consultative Council, constitute what is called in Islamic law *ahl al-'aqd wal-hall*, "the people who bind and loose," and who, by historical precedents and the acknowledgment of Muslim jurists, are competent to replace and elect the head of state. Khalid ibn 'Abd al-'Aziz became Crown Prince and was named Vice President of the Council of Ministers. Fahd ibn 'Abd al-'Aziz later was appointed second Vice President of the Council.

A cement factory near Hofuf.

The Ministry of Information office in Jiddah.

The streets of the Holy City of Mecca are thronged during the pilgrimage.

Modern apartment and office buildings in Riyadh, the capital of Saudi Arabia.

The Ministry of Petroleum and Mineral Resources in Riyadh.

Al-Thagir Model School in Jiddah.

Part 2

The Oil Industry and Its Growth in the Middle East

THE DEVELOPMENT
OF THE
PETROLEUM INDUSTRY

The history of petroleum goes back many centuries before Christ. The Old Testament contains a number of references to large oil and gas seepages and to uses of petroleum in the Middle East. Noah smeared his ark with pitch, or bitumen, "within and without." Herodotus and other ancient historians wrote about petroleum; ancient kings and businessmen recorded its use on cuneiform tablets, and modern archaeologists have confirmed these records through their excavations. Ancient peoples used petroleum as mortar, for waterproofing, as medicine and in some cases as fuel for lamps.

The development of machines and factories during the nineteenth century created a large demand for lubricants and lighting oils. Mutton and beef tallow, lard and castor oil served as lubricants. The demand for lubricants and lamp oil gave rise to a whaling industry so successful that whales were almost exterminated and sperm oil became scarce and expensive.

In 1850 a Scot named James Young patented a process for extracting lamp oil from coal. The process was adapted to obtain kerosene from petroleum and kerosene still is often called coal oil. Petroleum was fairly well known in America at the time of Young's invention and some efforts had been made to find commercial uses for it. The Indians had collected it from natural springs for centuries and prized it highly for medicinal purposes. Other men followed their example and

petroleum became a familiar item on the shelves of drugstores. It was also used to a small extent in lamps and for lubrication and it had been refined experimentally. Petroleum was found occasionally in wells drilled to obtain salt water for the salt industry in West Virginia and elsewhere. Many good salt-water wells were considered ruined in this way.

In 1859 a well was drilled for the specific purpose of finding oil near seepages along Oil Creek, Venango County, Pennsylvania. The well was financed by a small, adventurous group in New Haven, Connecticut, who believed that petroleum had a future. The drilling was supervised by a former railroad conductor, "Colonel" Edwin L. Drake. After many trials and tribulations, the Drake well struck oil at a depth of sixty-nine and a half feet. It was not a large well, but it launched an industry which is now among the world's largest.

The discovery was followed by a mad scramble to drill wells and build primitive refineries. In its early days the industry was disorderly and haphazard. Wells were drilled largely on hunches and by chance. The quality of the refined products was uncontrolled and unpredictable. Prices fluctuated wildly as gluts of oil from new fields alternated with shortages when gushers ran dry. Intense competition among thousands of oil producers and between producers and marketers led to bitter conflicts and to much waste of gas and oil which would not be tolerated today. Gradually, however, the foundation for a more orderly and scientific industry was laid. The petroleum industry grew steadily. Petroleum has brought wealth to many countries with unfavorable natural environments which otherwise might have remained impoverished, and it has aided in the continued development of industrial nations.

Within a decade following Drake's discovery, oil was being produced in Russia, Rumania, Canada and Italy. By 1900 oil had been discovered in Poland, Japan, Germany, India, Peru and the Dutch East Indies (now Indonesia) and by 1908 had been found in Mexico, Argentina, Trinidad and Iran.

During the nineteenth century and the early twentieth century, kerosene for lamps and stoves was the principal petroleum product; lubricants

Drake (right) founded an industry with his well.

and some fuel oil were also used. The highly volatile gasoline and lighter fractions had no commercial uses and normally were dumped or burned.

The development of the internal combustion engine and subsequent growth of the automotive industry created a market for gasoline, expanded the market for other petroleum products and transformed oil refining from a relatively crude process into a highly sophisticated operation. World War I greatly accelerated engine development, particularly for heavy transport equipment, tanks and airplanes. The navies of the world were converted to oil, followed gradually by world merchant fleets. By 1915 gasoline accounted for eighteen percent of the United States' oil consumption and fuel oil, forty-nine percent. Kerosene, which constituted fifty-eight percent of U. S. oil consumption in 1900, had dropped to twenty-four percent.

After World War I, the Russian revolution removed temporarily from the world markets a country which in 1900 accounted for the production and export of more than half the world's oil. Oil from Venezuela and Iran soon replaced it.

Mexico briefly attained the position of the world's second largest oil producer and exporter in 1920. Mexico was soon displaced in importance by Venezuela. Oil production was developed on a large scale in Iran during World War I and Iran became a major European supplier during the interwar period. Iraq became an important oil source during the late Nineteen Thirties, and major oil discoveries were made in other Middle Eastern countries. Burma and the Dutch East Indies held a modest share of the world's oil production during the interwar period.

World consumption outside the Soviet Union rose from one million barrels daily in 1915 to more than five million barrels daily in 1940, with the United States accounting for about seventy percent of world consumption.

The task of supplying the vast amounts of energy needed by the Allies in World War II was a tre-

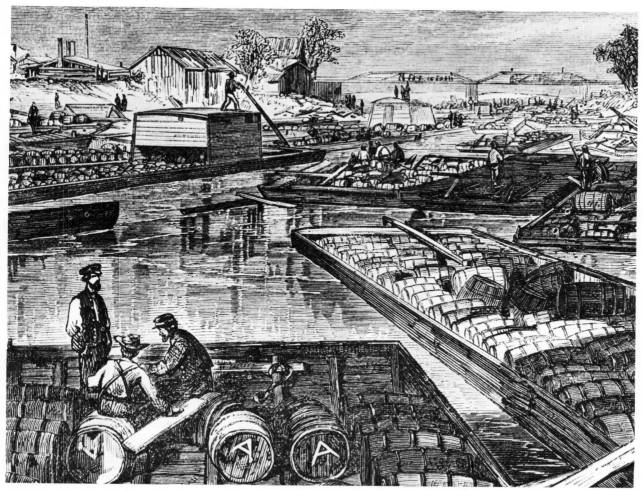

Barrels of oil were transported by barge down Oil Creek in Pennsylvania in the first years after Drake's discovery.

An early tank truck of the old Standard Oil Company.

mendous challenge to the petroleum industry. Most of the oil fields and refineries in Europe and the Far East were controlled by the Axis powers, great destruction was inflicted on the world's shipping fleets, and the use of Middle East oil was hampered by transportation problems and a partial Axis blockage of the Eastern Mediterranean. Oil from the Western Hemisphere, mainly from the United States and Venezuela, supplied most of the needs of the Allies. By the end of the war international oil companies again turned their attention to the Middle East, where earlier exploration had uncovered vast crude oil reserves. Considerable work to expand petroleum production in this area was under way by the end of the war in 1945.

A forest of drilling derricks at Spindletop, Texas, in 1901.

Muscle-power method of laying oil pipelines in the 1890's.

Tank car for moving oil from Titusville, Pa., in the 1860's.

Sailing vessels carried petroleum products during the 1900's.

THE CHANGES
IN SUPPLY AND DEMAND

The tremendous expansion and rebuilding of industry after World War II created an unprecedented demand for petroleum, particularly in the Eastern Hemisphere. Many areas of the world, which had lagged behind the United States in using petroleum as an energy source, turned to this liquid fuel for power to produce more food, more goods and more services.

The United States still retains its place as the world's largest producer and user of petroleum, but the demand for petroleum in the rest of the world has been increasing at a greater rate than in the United States. Between 1946 and 1968, petroleum demand in the United States increased two and one-half times. But in the remainder of the world, petroleum usage jumped more than eightfold in those twenty-two years. The increase for the world as a whole was almost fivefold.

The outstanding feature of this postwar growth of the world oil industry was the pronounced regional shift in the pattern of oil consumption and supply. These shifts in supply and demand reflected the changed political and economic climate. European reconstruction was followed by social pressures for a better life. There were similar pressures in Japan. In many countries in the Eastern Hemisphere, the motor scooter replaced the bicycle, the small automobile replaced the scooter and cars became bigger and more numerous. Demands grew for more electric power, more heat, more

light. In areas with a firm industrial base and technically trained workers, progress was rapid.

Russia has emerged once again as an exporter of petroleum and the second largest producer and consumer. In volume, the Soviet Union produces about half as much oil as the United States and consumes about one-third as much. In addition to being the largest producer and consumer of petroleum, the United States has become the largest importer of crude oil and products. Most of these imports are supplied by the Venezuelan-Caribbean area and Canada.

The most startling rate of growth in petroleum use has been in Japan, where the annual average increase for 1961-66 was twenty-one percent. For this same period Western Europe's annual consumption increased thirteen percent.

Although the rate of oil consumption in parts of the world other than Western Europe and Japan rose much more rapidly than that of the United States, the relative proportion of world oil production which they absorbed did not change materially. Most countries in the Middle East, Latin America, Asia and Africa entered the postwar era with little industry, few and inadequate roads, few motor vehicles and populations living at or near the subsistence level. Some have made impressive progress, but in many, advances have been slow.

The most rapid rise in world crude production was during the immediate postwar years. New

Growth in World Oil Production

Millions of Barrels Per Day

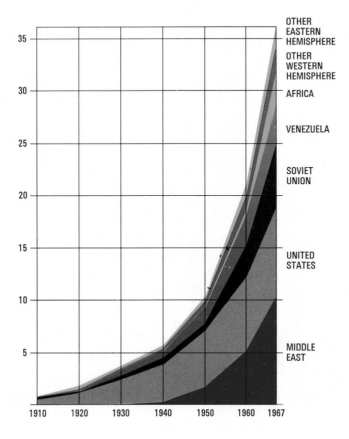

Middle East fields discovered shortly before the war were brought into production to meet increasing demands for oil. Between 1946 and 1950 Middle East production rose from about 700,000 to 1,750,000 barrels daily, about twenty-six percent yearly, while the increase for the rest of the world was less than seven percent. The Middle East steadily increased in importance and emerged as the world's largest crude oil producing area by 1965, when combined production reached 8,340,000 barrels daily, exceeding that of the United States. Middle East fields in 1967 supplied almost all of the crude oil needed by Japan and about half that used in Western Europe. As oil fields in Algeria, Libya and Nigeria were developed, Africa became one of the major producing areas. These countries are still in an era of rapid expansion, with Libya the leading African producer. Their oil goes mainly to the nearby markets of Western Europe. The shares of other oil producing areas in world production have undergone only minor changes.

The leading producing nations in 1967, ranked in order, were the United States, the Soviet Union, Venezuela, Saudi Arabia, Iran and Kuwait, while the top consuming nations were the United States, the Soviet Union, Japan, Germany, the United Kingdom and France.

It has been estimated that by 1977 world demand for petroleum will reach fifty-eight million barrels daily, of which the Middle East is expected to supply more than twenty million.

OIL TRANSPORTATION By 1948 increasing amounts of oil were moving out of the Arabian Gulf to Europe and the U. S. east coast. The Suez Canal became an important artery in world oil flow. Oil tonnage moving from south to north through the canal increased from eight million tons in 1938 to 194 million by 1966. Indonesia and the United States west coast could no longer supply the bulk of the increasing needs of Japan, Australia and Southeast Asia, and these areas too began to take increasing quantities of oil from the new Middle East oil producing countries.

Larger movements of oil and the heavy shift to the Middle East greatly increased the requirements for tankships. The wartime need for more tankers had been filled in part by hiking the size of the vessels to 16,500 deadweight tons. These larger tankships resulted in cheaper transport costs and began a trend toward bigger and faster ships. Postwar tankers grew in size to 26,000 deadweight tons, and by the time 35,000 tons had been exceeded, a revolution in tankship size and design was under way. While in 1948 a 26,000-ton tanker was considered a giant, ships of 100,000 to 200,000 tons are rapidly replacing smaller tankers. Tankers of 300,000 tons are under construction, and designs are being made for ships of up to one million tons.

The increasing size of tankships with their greater draft soon taxed the depth of the Suez Canal and it became necessary to introduce a long-term program of increasing the depth from thirty-five feet in 1953 to thirty-eight feet in 1966 and finally to forty-eight feet by 1971. Presumably, if this depth is attained, laden vessels in the 180,000-deadweight-ton class will be able to transit the canal. Until that time, however, larger tankers carrying oil westward from the Arabian Gulf must take the longer route around Africa's Cape of Good Hope, but can return empty through the canal.

Large-diameter oil pipelines built in the United States during the war to avoid the dangerous sea routes proved that pipelines laid in a direct route overland could economically replace circuitous

A giant tanker loads oil at sea island off Ras Tanura.

Number of Large Tankers in World Tanker Fleet 1957-1967

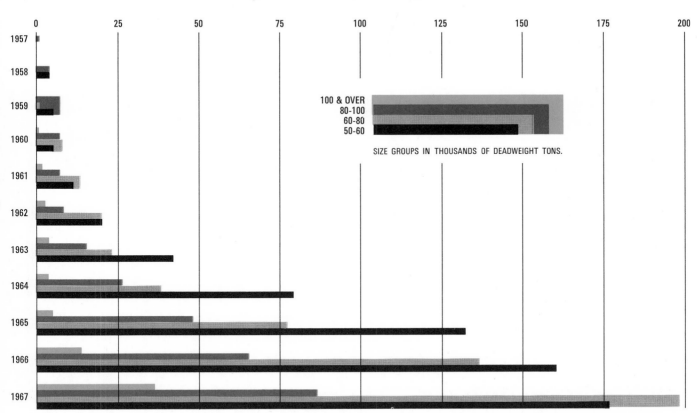

79

World Oil Movements by Tanker
1967

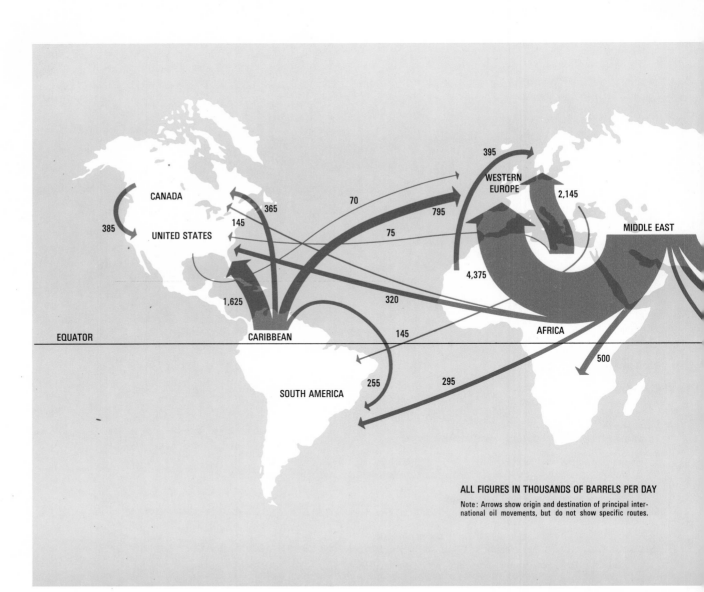

CANADA

385

UNITED STATES

CARIBBEAN

1,625

365

145

EQUATOR

SOUTH AMERICA

255

70

795

75

395

WESTERN
EUROPE

2,145

MIDDLE EAST

4,375

320

145

295

AFRICA

500

ALL FIGURES IN THOUSANDS OF BARRELS PER DAY

Note: Arrows show origin and destination of principal international oil movements, but do not show specific routes.

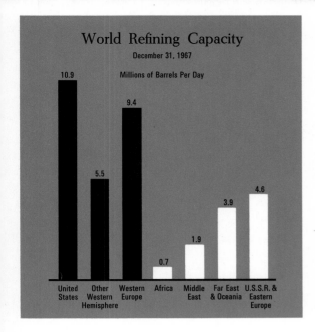

World Refining Capacity
December 31, 1967

Millions of Barrels Per Day

United States	Other Western Hemisphere	Western Europe	Africa	Middle East	Far East & Oceania	U.S.S.R. & Eastern Europe
10.9	5.5	9.4	0.7	1.9	3.9	4.6

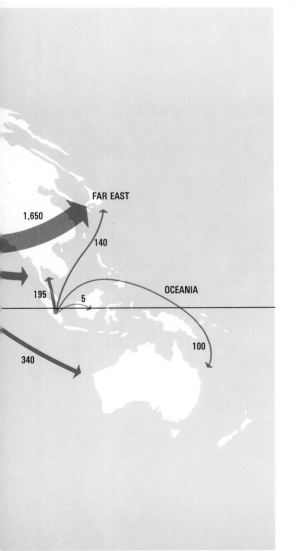

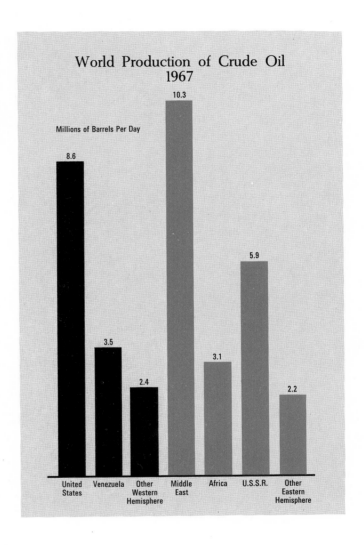

World Production of Crude Oil
1967

Millions of Barrels Per Day

United States	Venezuela	Other Western Hemisphere	Middle East	Africa	U.S.S.R.	Other Eastern Hemisphere
8.6	3.5	2.4	10.3	3.1	5.9	2.2

81

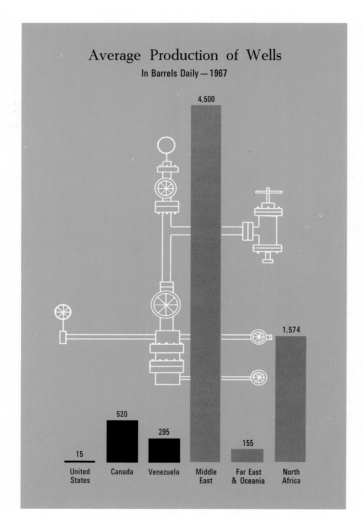

Average Production of Wells

In Barrels Daily — 1967

15	520	295	4,500	155	1,574
United States	Canada	Venezuela	Middle East	Far East & Oceania	North Africa

tanker sea routes. The first big-diameter lines in the Middle East, a pipeline system stretching from the Aramco producing area to the eastern Mediterranean shore near Sidon, replaced the equivalent of seventy-two tankers of 16,500 tons traveling 3,300 miles around the Arabian Peninsula and through the canal. The development of giant tankers routed around Africa to Europe, with consequent savings in cost, threatens elimination of the competitive value of the line.

As European oil use grew, pipelines were laid to carry crude oil from the ports of Rotterdam and Hamburg to replace higher cost barge and overland movements. New lines from southern Mediterranean ports such as Marseilles, Genoa and Trieste to new refineries in central European areas have reduced the cost of crude oil and products delivered into the inland areas of Western Europe.

SHIFT IN REFINERY LOCATION For a number of reasons the newer, modern refineries mostly are constructed near the market for their products. Before the war the tendency was to locate the refinery near the crude oil source and to ship the products to market. But these factors have resulted in a shift in location of new refineries:

It is cheaper to transport crude oil than refined products by tanker.

Nations can buy more crude oil than refined products with their foreign exchange.

Manufacturers in industrial centers now obtain feedstocks, formerly considered worthless, from nearby refineries and use them in making petrochemicals.

Consuming nations obtain the economic benefits of refinery construction and operation.

Crude oil, however, continues to be refined at the source to supply local and nearby markets, to provide bunker fuel for vessels in international trade and to supplement the output of consumer-located refineries during periods of peak demand.

82

Petroleum Demand vs. Production in the World
1967

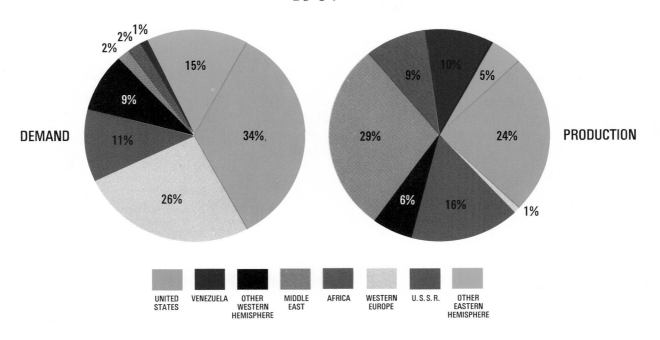

DEMAND

2% 2% 1%
15%
9%
11%
34%
26%

PRODUCTION

10% 5%
9%
29% 24%
6% 16%
1%

UNITED STATES | VENEZUELA | OTHER WESTERN HEMISPHERE | MIDDLE EAST | AFRICA | WESTERN EUROPE | U.S.S.R. | OTHER EASTERN HEMISPHERE

Crude Oil Reserves of the World*
In Billions of Barrels

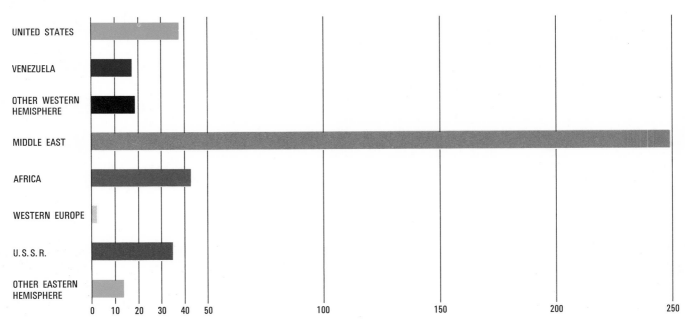

* Source: Oil and Gas Journal, December 25, 1967

COMPETITION

Petroleum is found throughout the world in marine sedimentary basins which were overlain by ancient seas millions of years ago. These basins now lie beneath the surface of the earth and they can be located only by extensive exploration work and finally by actual drilling. It is believed that less than one-third of the world's oil has been located so far. Much more oil remains to be discovered in these sedimentary basins which underlie vast offshore areas of the continental shelves as well as land areas.

Oilmen will continue searching for new areas where commercial oil deposits may exist. Every year sees newly found oil seeking its place in world oil markets. Libya, which produced as much as two million barrels daily during peak periods in 1967, had no oil production only six years earlier. Nigeria began exporting petroleum in 1958 and in the following decade became an important source of world supply. The amount of oil found in recent years has far exceeded the increased demand for petroleum. The result has been a highly competitive situation with more and more sellers vying for the same customers. Increasing competition basically has expressed itself in lower prices for petroleum. These lower prices have stimulated the growth in the uses of petroleum and have given oil a decided competitive advantage over all other forms of energy. Coal, for instance, has steadily lost markets to oil.

An important characteristic of the highly prolific oil fields in the Middle East has been their lower producing costs. This, combined with the lower transportation costs of giant tankers and large-diameter pipelines, has made it possible to meet price competition from other oil producing areas and other energy sources.

OTHER HYDROCARBONS Petroleum is a mixture of liquid hydrocarbons, compounds which mainly contain hydrogen and carbon in varying combinations with small amounts of other elements. If the day comes when petroleum cannot be produced in quantities sufficient to meet world demands, there are other forms of hydrocarbons which can be used. These other hydrocarbons occur in tar sands, shale oil and coal. In the province of Alberta, Canada, there are some 700 billion barrels of liquid hydrocarbons locked in the Athabasca tar sands. In the Rocky Mountains of the United States, there are more than 300 billion barrels of liquid hydrocarbons trapped in the Green River shale formations. In 1967 a plant began processing 40,000 barrels daily of liquid hydrocarbons from the Athabasca tar sands, but producing costs are high. There are also huge deposits of coal throughout the world from which liquid hydrocarbon products could be produced if prices rise greatly or technical developments make their costs competitive. These other sources of liquid hydrocarbons loom always as potential competitors to natural deposits of petroleum and may some day possibly serve as supplemental sources of hydrocarbon energy.

NUCLEAR POWER Of more immediate concern to the oil industry is the development of nuclear power plants. Huge new nuclear plants have been developed to operate as cheaply in areas of high electricity consumption as plants fired by fuel oil or coal. It is estimated that by 1980 more than fifteen percent of the electric power supply of the United States will be generated by nuclear plants. A similar trend is evident in the United Kingdom and other parts of Europe. Fuel oil, with which nuclear energy competes, is the lowest-value product extracted from crude oil. Outside of the United States it is the major product of refining, accounting for nearly fifty percent of output. The loss of the market for a barrel of fuel oil displaced by nuclear energy might represent the loss of the sale of nearly two barrels of crude oil.

NATURAL GAS The greatest competitor of crude oil, however, is a related product often produced in association with it. Natural gas is a hydrocarbon in gaseous form. It is a form of energy that competes with both industrial fuels and home heating oils. In the United States gas has competed with oil and coal for years and is a growing competitor of both in Europe. Large fields of natural gas have been discovered in Holland. These gas fields now serve a large network of gas transmission lines throughout northwestern Europe. The gas discoveries in Holland led to the belief that deposits of gas might be found in the North Sea off the coast of England. Exploration drilling during 1966–67 found several large deposits and the first pipeline was built to carry gas to consumers in England.

For years high transportation costs impeded sales of natural gas from fields far from mass markets.

Large pipelines were used to bridge distances overland, but it was only recently that the problem of sea transport was overcome. A process was developed for liquefying natural gas at minus 267°F. and transporting it in liquid form in refrigerated tankers. The first commercial application of this system is the fifty-million-dollar plant in Arzew, Algeria, which liquefies gas from the Hassi R'Mel gas field, 500 miles inland from the Mediterranean coast. The liquefied gas is shipped to gas concerns in France and England. A similar plant is situated in Libya. Liquefied natural gas, or LNG, operations require higher capital investment and return less profit than crude oil production and transportation, but LNG could become a major competitor.

The petroleum industry has invested more than 150 billion dollars to produce, transport, refine and market the petroleum resources of the world.

To maintain these operations and to supply the increasing needs of consumers, the oil industry must invest approximately twelve and a half billion dollars every year. Most of these funds must be generated from profits and from the reinvestment of depreciation reserves.

Probability of Crude Oil Occurrence

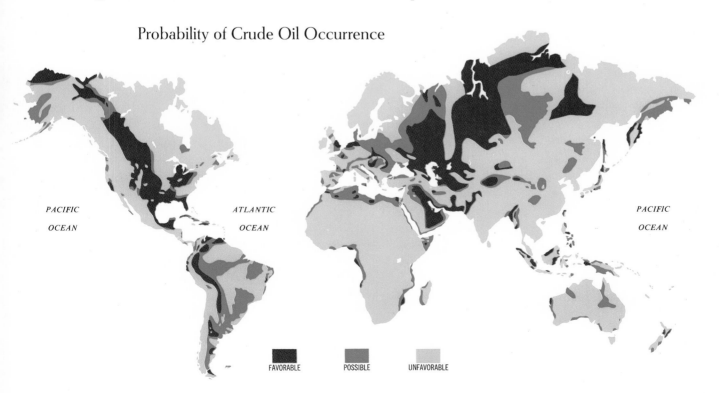

PACIFIC OCEAN   ATLANTIC OCEAN   PACIFIC OCEAN

FAVORABLE   POSSIBLE   UNFAVORABLE

THE OIL INDUSTRY
IN THE MIDDLE EAST

The world's largest petroleum reserves lie in a sedimentary basin bounded by the Taurus Mountains of Turkey in the north, the mountains of Lebanon and Syria and the highlands of Saudi Arabia on the west and the mountain ranges of Iran and Muscat and Oman on the east. The valleys of the Tigris and Euphrates Rivers and the Arabian Gulf are in this basin. In terms of regional geology, the area is a structural as well as a topographic basin. Oil fields are found most commonly in structural basins and this one was particularly suited to the generation and accumulation of petroleum.

Oil was discovered in Iran before World War I, but greatest development of the area's petroleum resources came after the end of World War II. In 1944 the world's proved crude oil reserves were more than fifty billion barrels with fifteen and a half billion barrels, or some thirty percent, in the Middle East. At the beginning of 1967 the proved reserves for the world were 398 billion barrels, with 244 billion barrels, or sixty-one percent, in the Middle East. Most of these reserves are in countries around the Arabian Gulf and in the gulf itself. Proved reserves are the volumes of known deposits of crude oil which can be recovered by existing production methods.

Production costs in the Middle East are the lowest in the world. Average daily production of a Middle East oil well is about 4,500 barrels compared to an average of less than 300 for Venezuelan wells and only fifteen for wells in the United States. Most Middle Eastern wells also are free flowing

while the oil must be pumped out of American wells and a high percentage of those in other major producing areas, such as Venezuela. Additionally, much of the Middle East oil is produced from fields close to the Arabian Gulf near marine shipping points. These savings more than offset the high costs of plant and equipment and other operating expenses.

The huge reserves and low production costs inevitably have attracted more and more oil companies to seek concessions in the gulf area. Middle Eastern governments, too, have sought a wider role in the development of their oil resources. For most of these nations, petroleum accounts for a large part of their income and foreign exchange earnings.

Several Middle Eastern governments have set up national oil companies or other special agencies to participate in the industry. National oil companies sometimes prefer to enter into agreements with foreign firms for joint exploration, production, refining and marketing of oil. Such agreements may stipulate substantial initial capital investments, either as a bonus payment or in the form of exploration outlays by the foreign enterprises, but provide for recovery of all or part of these initial expenses if commercial production is realized. After oil production begins, ownership, capital investment and management are shared.

In some Middle Eastern countries, national concerns do some refining and market most oil products sold within their areas.

Another form of government participation is

development of a broad spectrum of industries ancillary to oil, including natural gas and petrochemicals. National oil companies or government agencies in Iran, Kuwait and Saudi Arabia are either negotiating with or have entered into agreements with foreign firms for the joint production of one or more of a wide range of petrochemicals, including ammonia, urea and plastics. The objective is to reduce the country's dependence on a narrow range of petroleum products. Government enterprises of this sort generally have as their ultimate objective the integration of petroleum production and petrochemicals into an overall national economic development plan.

Many Middle Eastern governments, including those of Saudi Arabia, Kuwait, Iran and Iraq, now hold seats on the boards of directors of foreign-owned companies. Kuwait and Saudi Arabia also hold minority shares in one foreign producer, the Arabian Oil Company.

IRAN The first oil found in commercial quantities in the Middle East was produced in 1908 in southern Iran at the Masjid-i-Sulaiman field by a British company shortly afterward reorganized as the Anglo-Persian Oil Company. Oil exploration had been started in 1901 and was almost abandoned just prior to the discovery. The first oil shipment was made in 1912 from Abadan, where a refinery was completed the same year.

Iranian production received a great impetus from the conversion of British naval vessels from coal to oil just before World War I. When the war began in 1914 the British Government acquired a majority interest in the Anglo-Persian Oil Company, enabling the British Navy to control a large source of fuel oil and the company to treble production and refining capacity during the war. The company's name was later changed to Anglo-Iranian Oil Company.

Production continued to grow steadily after the war and by 1938 reached 215,000 barrels a day. It declined because of transportation difficulties early in World War II, but in 1942 both producing and refinery facilities were augmented as a war measure with American lend-lease help. Daily oil production passed 700,000 barrels early in 1951.

After the war the Iranian Government pressed Anglo-Iranian for more favorable concession terms and a Supplemental Agreement, dated July 17, 1949, was reached. This agreement, however, was rejected in December, 1950, by the Iranian Parliament (Majlis) led by Premier Mohammad Mossaddeq. A resolution passed by the Majlis on March 15, 1951, nationalized "the oil industry throughout all parts of the country ... that is to say, all operations of exploration, extraction and exploitation shall be carried out by the government."

The National Iranian Oil Company (NIOC) assumed control of oil operations in Iran. By August, 1951, Iranian oil operations, which had been the largest in the Middle East, were virtually suspended.

Efforts to solve the dispute were unsuccessful until the replacement of the Mossaddeq regime in August, 1953. By October, 1954, new arrangements providing for a resumption of operations in southwest Iran by a consortium of oil companies were ratified by the Iranian Parliament. The consortium includes British, Dutch, French and American companies. Anglo-Iranian (now called British Petroleum Company) has a forty percent interest. Royal Dutch/Shell has fourteen percent, the Compagnie Française des Pétroles (CFP) has six percent and five large American companies—Gulf Oil Corporation, Mobil Oil Corporation, Standard Oil Company of California, Standard Oil Company (New Jersey) and Texaco Inc.—each hold seven percent. The remaining five percent is held by a group of seven American independent oil producers.

In 1958 Iran granted oil concessions in areas outside of consortium operations to Italian, American and Canadian companies. AGIP Mineraria, S.p.A., a subsidiary of the Italian Government oil company Ente Nazionale Idrocarburi, entered into equal partnership with NIOC to form Société

Middle East Oil Concessions

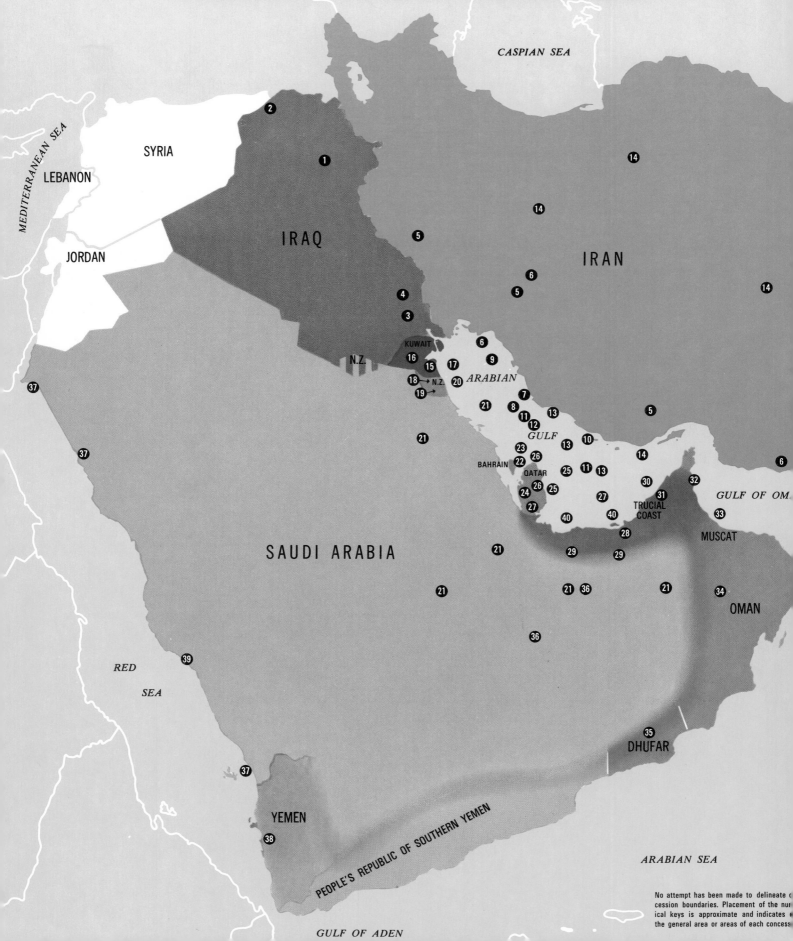

No attempt has been made to delineate c
cession boundaries. Placement of the nur
ical keys is approximate and indicates e
the general area or areas of each concess

1 IRAQ PETROLEUM CO. LTD.

CONCESSION: 75 years from 1925.

AREA: The former concession area, covering about 35,000 square miles, was unilaterally reduced by Iraqi Law 80 of 1961 to the areas of the producing fields (289 square miles in the Kirkuk, Bai Hassan and Jambur fields).

OWNERSHIP:
British Petroleum Co. Ltd.	23.75%
Royal Dutch/Shell Group	23.75%
Compagnie Française des Pétroles	23.75%
Near East Development Corp.	23.75%
Standard Oil Co. (N. J.) 50%	
Mobil Oil Corp. 50%	
Participations and Explorations Corp.	5.00%
(C. S. Gulbenkian Estate)	

2 MOSUL PETROLEUM CO. LTD.

CONCESSION: 75 years from 1932.

AREA: The former concession area, covering about 41,000 square miles, was unilaterally reduced by Iraqi Law 80 of 1961 to the areas of the producing fields (24 square miles in the Ain Zalah and Butmah fields).

OWNERSHIP: Same as Iraq Petroleum Co. Ltd.

3 BASRAH PETROLEUM CO. LTD.

CONCESSION: 75 years from 1938.

AREA: The former concession area, covering about 87,000 square miles, was unilaterally reduced by Iraqi Law 80 of 1961 to the areas of the producing fields (436 square miles in the Rumaila and Zubair fields).

OWNERSHIP: Same as Iraq Petroleum Co. Ltd.

4 ENTREPRISE DE RECHERCHES ET D'ACTIVITES PETROLIERES (ERAP)

AGREEMENT: ERAP acts as a general contractor for Iraq National Oil Co. Term is 6 years from 1967 for exploration and 20 years for exploitation.

AREA: 4,170 square miles in the central and southern parts of Iraq of which 695 square miles are in Iraq's territorial waters in the Arabian Gulf.

5 IRANIAN OIL PARTICIPANTS LTD.

(Under Agreement with Government of Iran and National Iranian Oil Co.)

(Iranian Oil Exploration and Producing Co. – Operator)

AGREEMENT: 25 years from 1954, plus 15 years optional.

AREA: Approximately 75,000 square miles.

OWNERSHIP:
British Petroleum Co. Ltd.	40%
Royal Dutch/Shell Group	14%
Gulf Oil Corp.	7%
Mobil Oil Corp.	7%
Standard Oil Co. of California	7%
Standard Oil Co. (N.J.)	7%
Texaco Inc.	7%
Compagnie Française des Pétroles	6%
Iricon Agency Ltd.	5%
Atlantic Richfield Co.	1.667%
Signal Oil and Gas Co.	0.833%
American Independent Oil Co.	0.833%
Getty Oil Co.	0.417%
San Jacinto Petroleum Corp.	0.417%
Standard Oil Co. (Ohio)	0.417%
Tidewater Oil Co.	0.417%

6 SOCIETE IRANO-ITALIENNE DES PETROLES (SIRIP)

CONCESSION: From 1957 until 25 years from start of petroleum sales, with three 5-year extensions.

AREA: Approximately 6,483 square miles in the Iranian offshore area of the Arabian Gulf, on eastern slope of central Zagros Mountains and on coast of Gulf of Oman.

OWNERSHIP:
AGIP Mineraria, S.p.A.	50%
(Ente Nazionale Idrocarburi— Italian state corporation)	
National Iranian Oil Co.	50%

7 DASHTESTAN OFFSHORE PETROLEUM CO. (DOPCO)

CONCESSION: 12-year exploration period from 1965 and a 25-year exploitation period from time 630,000 barrels of petroleum are exported; 3 optional 5-year extension periods.

AREA: Approximately 2,332 square miles in the Iranian offshore area of the Arabian Gulf.

OWNERSHIP:
Royal Dutch/Shell Group	50%
National Iranian Oil Co.	50%

8 FARSI PETROLEUM CO. (FPC)

CONCESSION: 12-year exploration period from 1965 and a 25-year exploitation period from time 630,000 barrels of petroleum are exported; 3 optional 5-year extension periods.

AREA: Approximately 2,224 square miles in the Iranian offshore area of the Arabian Gulf.

OWNERSHIP:
Société Française des Pétroles d'Iran (SOFIRAN)	50%
Entreprise de Recherches et d'Activités Pétrolières (ERAP).. 80%	
Société Nationale des Pétroles d'Aquitaine 20%	
National Iranian Oil Co.	50%

9 IRAN PAN AMERICAN OIL CO. (IPAC)

CONCESSION: From 1958 until 25 years from date when the first 629,000 barrels of oil have been produced, sold and delivered, with three 5-year extensions.

AREA: Approximately 3,282 square miles in the Iranian offshore area of the Arabian Gulf.

OWNERSHIP:
American International Oil Co.	50%
(Standard Oil Co. (Indiana))	
National Iranian Oil Co.	50%

10 PERSIAN GULF PETROLEUM CO. (PEGUPCO)

CONCESSION: 12-year exploration period from 1965 and a 25-year exploitation period from time 630,000 barrels of petroleum are exported; 3 optional 5-year extension periods.

AREA: Approximately 1,988 square miles in the Iranian offshore area of the Arabian Gulf.

OWNERSHIP:
Deutsche Erdöl A.G.	10%
Gelsenkirchener Bergwerks A.G.	10%
Wintershall A.G.	10%
Preussag	6%
Scholven-Chemie A.G.	6%
Gewerkschaft Elwerath	5%
Deutsche Schachtbau-und-Tiefbohr G.m.b.H.	3%
National Iranian Oil Co.	50%

⑪ IRANIAN MARINE INTERNATIONAL OIL CO. (IMINOCO)

CONCESSION: 12-year exploration period from 1965 and a 25-year exploitation period from time 630,000 barrels of petroleum are exported; 3 optional 5-year extension periods.

AREA: Four separate blocks totaling approximately 3,073 square miles in the Iranian offshore area of the Arabian Gulf.

OWNERSHIP:
AGIP Mineraria, S.p.A.	16-2/3%
Phillips Petroleum Co.	16-2/3%
Hydro-Carbon (India) Ltd.	16-2/3%
National Iranian Oil Co.	50%

⑫ IRANIAN OFFSHORE PETROLEUM CO. (IROPCO)

CONCESSION: 12-year exploration period from 1965 and a 25-year exploitation period from time 630,000 barrels of petroleum are exported; 3 optional 5-year extension periods.

AREA: Approximately 869 square miles in the Iranian offshore area of the Arabian Gulf.

OWNERSHIP:
Tidewater Oil Co., Superior Oil Co., Sunray DX Oil Co., Cities Service Co., Inc., Kerr-McGee Corp., Atlantic Richfield Co., Skelly Oil Co.	45%
Compañía Española de Petróleos S.A.	5%
National Iranian Oil Co.	50%

⑬ LAVAN PETROLEUM CO. (LAPCO)

CONCESSION: 12-year exploration period from 1964 and a 25-year exploitation period from time 630,000 barrels of petroleum are exported; 3 optional 5-year extension periods.

AREA: Three blocks totaling approximately 3,089 square miles in the Iranian offshore area of the Arabian Gulf.

OWNERSHIP:
Atlantic Richfield Co.	12-1/2%
Murphy Oil Corp.	12-1/2%
Sun Oil Co.	12-1/2%
Union Oil Co. of California	12-1/2%
National Iranian Oil Co.	50%

⑭ SOCIETE FRANÇAISE DES PETROLES D'IRAN (SOFIRAN)

AGREEMENT: SOFIRAN acts as a general contractor for National Iranian Oil Co. The exploration period is for 6 years from 1966 and the exploitation period is for 25 years beginning when 630,000 barrels have been produced and sold on a regular export schedule.

AREA: Acreage in Iran onshore blocks 6, 8, 11, 12, 14 and 18 totaling 102,702 square miles, and offshore District 2 in the Arabian Gulf totaling 7,722 square miles.

OWNERSHIP:
Entreprise de Recherches et d'Activités Pétrolières (ERAP)	80%
Société Nationale de Pétrole d'Aquitaine	20%

⑮ KUWAIT OIL CO. LTD. (KOC)

CONCESSION: From 1934, expires 2026.

AREA: Most of onshore eastern Kuwait, and two small blocks in the northwest. Total area is 2,584 square miles.

OWNERSHIP:
British Petroleum Co. Ltd.	50%
Gulf Oil Corp.	50%

⑯ KUWAIT-SPANISH PETROLEUM CO.

CONCESSION: 35 years from 1967, with provision for five-year extension.

AREA: Three onshore blocks, totaling 3,575 square miles, the largest covering most of western Kuwait; and two smaller areas, one in the northeast corner and one in the southeast corner of Kuwait.

OWNERSHIP:
Kuwait National Petroleum Co.		51%
Kuwait Government	60%	
Private Kuwaiti interests	40%	
Hispanoil		49%
Instituto Nacional de Industria, a Spanish Government agency.	40%	
Cia. Española de Petróleos S.A.	20%	
Petroliber	20%	
Financiera Fierro	10%	
Cia. Ibérica de Petróleos	10%	

⑰ KUWAIT SHELL PETROLEUM DEVELOPMENT CO. LTD.

CONCESSION: 45 years from 1961.

AREA: All of offshore Kuwait.

OWNERSHIP: Royal Dutch/Shell Group 100%

⑱ AMERICAN INDEPENDENT OIL CO. (AMINOIL)

CONCESSION: 60 years from 1948.

AREA: All of Kuwait's undivided half-interest in Saudi Arabia-Kuwait Neutral Zone, including territorial waters. In 1949 a wholly owned subsidiary, American Independent Oil Co. of California, was granted a new concession for the islands of Kubr, Qarawah (Qaru) and Umm al-Maradim (off the Neutral Zone) and their territorial waters.

OWNERSHIP:
Phillips Petroleum Co.	37.34%
Signal Oil and Gas Co.	33.58%
Ashland Oil and Refining Co.	14.13%
J. S. Abercrombie Mineral Co.	7.07%
Globe Oil and Refining	3.53%
Sunray DX Oil Co.	2.94%
Pauley Petroleum Inc.	1.41%

❾ GETTY OIL CO.

CONCESSION: 60 years from 1949.

AREA: All of Saudi Arabia's undivided half-interest in Saudi Arabia-Kuwait Neutral Zone, including territorial waters.

OWNERSHIP: J. Paul Getty and others 100%

❿ ARABIAN OIL CO. LTD.

CONCESSION: From Saudi Arabia, 2-year exploration license from 1958 with 2-year renewal option and 40-year lease from date of discovery of commercial production. From Kuwait, $44\frac{1}{2}$ years from 1958.

AREA: Offshore area of the Saudi Arabia-Kuwait Neutral Zone, extending beyond territorial waters.

OWNERSHIP: Japan Petroleum Trading Co., Ltd. ... 80%
Saudi Arabian Government 10%
Kuwait Government 10%

㉑ ARABIAN AMERICAN OIL CO. (ARAMCO)

CONCESSION: From 1933, expires 1999.

AREA: About 125,000 squares miles of Saudi Arabia, including offshore areas.

OWNERSHIP: Standard Oil Co. of California 30%
Texaco Inc. 30%
Standard Oil Co. (New Jersey) 30%
Mobil Oil Corp. 10%

㉒ BAHRAIN PETROLEUM CO. LTD. (BAPCO)

CONCESSION: From 1934, expires 2024.

AREA: All of Bahrain, including islands, waters and submerged lands over which the ruler has or may acquire dominion, except for an offshore block northeast of the reef Fasht al-Jarim and an offshore block southeast of Bahrain which includes the Huwar Islands.

OWNERSHIP: Standard Oil Co. of California 50%
Texaco Inc. 50%

㉓ CONTINENTAL OIL CO. OF BAHRAIN

CONCESSION: 45 years from September 1965.

AREA: An offshore block of approximately 1,350 square miles located northeast of the reef Fasht al-Jarim and a smaller block of 150 square miles located southeast of Bahrain and including the Huwar Islands.

OWNERSHIP: Continental Oil Co. 50%
Pure Oil Middle East Inc. 50%
(Union Oil Co. of California)

㉔ QATAR PETROLEUM CO. LTD. (QPC)

CONCESSION: 75 years from 1935.

AREA: The Dukhan oilfield in Qatar and a narrow surrounding area.

OWNERSHIP: Same as Iraq Petroleum Co. Ltd.

㉕ SHELL CO. OF QATAR LTD.

CONCESSION: 75 years from 1952.

AREA: A large offshore block northeast of Qatar and a small offshore block east of the peninsula, totaling 3,266 square miles.

OWNERSHIP: Royal Dutch/Shell Group 100%

㉖ CONTINENTAL OIL CO. OF QATAR

CONCESSION: Granted in 1963 for an undisclosed term.

AREA: All the land and offshore area of Qatar not held by QPC or by Shell Company of Qatar (except for 1,104 square miles near Doha) comprising approximately 9,500 square miles.

OWNERSHIP: Continental Oil Co. 50%
Pure Oil Middle East Inc. 50%
(Union Oil Co. of California)

㉗ ABU DHABI MARINE AREAS LTD. (ADMA)

CONCESSION: 65 years from 1953.

AREA: Area totaling 10,618 square miles offshore from Abu Dhabi beyond the 3-mile limit, except for two small released blocks along the coastline, one in the southeast and one in the central coastal area.

OWNERSHIP: British Petroleum Co. Ltd. 66-2/3%
Compagnie Française des Pétroles .. 33-1/3%

㉘ ABU DHABI PETROLEUM CO. LTD. (ADPC)

CONCESSION: 75 years from 1939.

AREA: Most of the Abu Dhabi onshore area and the territorial waters to the 3-mile limit, totaling 11,197 square miles.

OWNERSHIP: Same as Iraq Petroleum Co. Ltd.

㉙ PHILLIPS - AGIP - AMINOIL

CONCESSION: 11-year exploration period with progressive relinquishments, then long-term exploitation rights.

AREA: Four onshore blocks, totaling 4,997 square miles: one in the southwest corner of Abu Dhabi, one in the south central portion, one in the northeastern corner, and Abu Dhabi island.

OWNERSHIP: Phillips Petroleum Co. 33-1/3%
AGIP Mineraria, S. p. A. 33-1/3%
American Independent Oil Co. 33-1/3%

㉚ DUBAI MARINE AREAS LTD. (DUMA)

CONCESSION: 60 years from 1952.

AREA: Dubai offshore area beyond the 3-mile limit, totaling about 2,035 square miles.

OWNERSHIP: Continental Oil Co. 35%
British Petroleum Co. Ltd. 33-1/3%
Compagnie Française des Pétroles .. 16-2/3%
Deutsche Erdöl A.G. 10%
Sun Oil Co. 5%

㉛ DUBAI PETROLEUM CO. (DPC)

CONCESSION: 45 years from 1963.

AREA: All of the land area of the Shaykdom of Dubai, totaling about 1,429 square miles.

OWNERSHIP: Continental Oil Co. 55%
            Deutsche Erdöl A.G. 22-1/2%
            Sun Oil Co. 22-1/2%

32 BOMIN BOCHUMER

CONCESSION: 50 years from 1966.

AREA: All the land and offshore area of the Shaykdom of Fujairah.

OWNERSHIP: Bochumer Mineralöl G.m.b.H. 100%

33 WINTERSHALL

CONCESSION: From 1965 for an undisclosed term.

AREA: A strip of Muscat's offshore area from the 3-mile limit seaward to a water depth of 1,000 feet, extending 300 miles northwestward from Ras al-Hadd.

OWNERSHIP: Wintershall A.G. 65%
            Deutsche Erdöl A.G. 12.5%
            Gelsenberg A.G. 12.5%
            Deutsche Schachtbau-und-
            Tiefbohr G.m.b.H. 10%

34 PETROLEUM DEVELOPMENT (OMAN) LTD. (PDO)

CONCESSION: 75 years from 1937.

AREA: All of the land area of Muscat and Oman.

OWNERSHIP: Royal Dutch/Shell Group 85%
            Compagnie Française des Pétroles 10%
            Participations and Explorations Corp. ... 5%
            (C. S. Gulbenkian Estate)

35 MECOM - PURE - CONOCO

CONCESSION: Granted in 1953 for 25 years from date of achieving commercial production with an option to renew for another 25 years.

AREA: All of land and the territorial waters of Dhufar totaling about 30,000 square miles.

OWNERSHIP: John W. Mecom 33-1/3%
            Pure Oil Co. 33-1/3%
            (Union Oil Co. of California)
            Continental Oil Co. 33-1/3%

36 PETROMIN - AGIP

CONCESSION: Contract type agreement from 1967 with 3-year exploration period, renewable for additional 3 years; 30-year exploitation period if oil is found, renewable for additional 10 years.

AREA: About 30,000 square miles, relinquished by Aramco, in the Rub' al-Khali area of Saudi Arabia.

OWNERSHIP: The Saudi Arabian Government agency the General Petroleum and Mineral Organization (Petromin) retains legal title to the concession but has assigned its rights and obligations to AGIP Mineraria, S.p.A., a subsidiary of the Ente Nazionale Idrocarburi, an Italian state corporation. If commercial oil production is found, an operating company will be set up in which Petromin may own 30 to 50 percent, depending upon the level of production.

37 SOCIETE AUXILIAIRE DE L'ENTREPRISE DE RECHERCHES ET D'ACTIVITES PETROLIERES (AUXERAP)

CONCESSION: 2-year exploration period from 1965, renewable for an additional three years, and a 30-year exploitation period.

AREA: Three blocks containing onshore and offshore acreage along the Red Sea coast: one in the south including the Farasan islands, and two in the north near the Gulf of Aqaba. Total area is about 10,348 square miles.

OWNERSHIP: Entreprise de Recherches et d'Activités Pétrolières (ERAP) 100%
            (During the exploitation phase, a joint company, Saudi Arabian Government 40%, and AUXERAP 60%, will operate the concession.)

38 MECOM - PURE

CONCESSION: 5 years from 1961 with provision for extensions. Original term believed to be still in effect because of force majeure.

AREA: About 10,000 square miles along the Yemen coastline both onshore and offshore.

OWNERSHIP: John W. Mecom 50%
            Pure Oil Middle East Inc. 50%
            (Union Oil Co. of California)

39 SINCLAIR ARABIAN OIL CO.

CONCESSION: Contract type agreement from 1967 with 3-year exploration period, renewable for additional 3 years; 30-year exploitation period if oil is found, renewable for additional 10 years.

AREA: Half of the area along the Red Sea coast of Saudi Arabia not held by AUXERAP.

OWNERSHIP: Legal title to the concession resides with the Saudi Arabian Government agency the General Petroleum and Mineral Organization (Petromin) which has assigned its rights and obligations to the Sinclair-Natomas-Pakistan group. Sinclair Arabian is the operator. If commercial oil production is found, Petromin may participate 50 percent in its development.

40 ABU DHABI PETROLEUM DEVELOPMENT CO.

CONCESSION: 45 years from 1967.

AREA: Two Abu Dhabi offshore blocks totaling 1,705 square miles previously relinquished by ADMA.

OWNERSHIP: Maruzen Oil Co. 33-1/3%
            Daikyo Oil Co. 33-1/3%
            Nippon Mining Co. 33-1/3%
            (The Abu Dhabi Government has the option to take 50% interest if oil in commercial quantities is discovered.)

Irano-Italienne des Pétroles (SIRIP). Two years later, SIRIP discovered the offshore Bahrgan Sar oil field. A second field was found at Norouz, thirty-four miles southwest of Bahrgan Sar, in late 1966. American International Oil Company, a subsidiary of Standard Oil Company of Indiana, formed a similar partnership with NIOC called Iran Pan American Oil Company (IPAC). IPAC has found four oil fields—Darius, Cyrus, Esfandiar and Fereidoon—in its offshore concession. The concession of the Canadian company Sapphire Petroleum Ltd. lapsed through failure to start exploration within the agreed time.

In 1964 Iran opened additional offshore areas for bids but stipulated that the companies must enter into equal partnership with NIOC to get a concession. Six agreements were concluded in 1964 and 1965, yielding Iran more than 185 million dollars in initial bonuses, plus guaranteed exploration expenditures in excess of 115 million dollars within twelve years. Each agreement provides that if oil is discovered in commercial quantities prior expenditures can be amortized. NIOC will share all subsequent expenditures equally with its foreign partners. Profits will be taxed in accordance with Iranian income tax laws, which in 1967 set the rate at fifty percent.

Of the six companies which acquired offshore areas, two have made oil discoveries. Lavan Petroleum Company (LAPCO) discovered the major Sassan field and a field tentatively called W-field. Iranian Marine International Oil Company (IMINOCO) found oil in a field tentatively called R-field, and has a shut-in gas well in T-field.

In 1966 NIOC and the French state-owned Entreprise de Recherches et d'Activités Pétrolières (ERAP) concluded an agreement under which the French company acts as a contractor in the development of certain areas, rather than as a concessionnaire or associate. ERAP will pay for exploration, receiving reimbursement only if oil in commercial quantities is discovered. On discovery, ERAP will lend NIOC the funds necessary for developing the fields and in return will receive a large share of the oil on specified terms, together with the possibility of oil equipment supply and service contracts. Iran will be the owner of all oil discovered and produced. Aquitaine-Iran, S.A., has a minority interest in the agreement.

IRAQ The Turkish Petroleum Company (TPC) was formed before World War I to prospect for oil in what is now Iraq. Rivalry among British, Dutch and German commercial interests was resolved in 1914 and the ownership of the company became: Deutsche Bank, twenty-five percent; Anglo-Saxon Petroleum Company (Royal Dutch), twenty-two and a half percent; D'Arcy Exploration Company (Anglo-Persian), forty-seven and a half percent, and Calouste Sarkis Gulbenkian, five percent. Gulbenkian, an Armenian entrepreneur, had been instrumental in forming TPC.

The resolution of interests included what was called, from 1927 on, the Red Line Agreement. Under this agreement, the participants undertook not to act individually "directly or indirectly in the production or manufacture of crude oil" within an area embracing a large part of the Ottoman Empire as defined by a red line on a map. The area did not include Egypt, Kuwait or the Transferred Territories along the Ottoman-Persian frontier.

During the war Britain seized the Deutsche Bank's interest in TPC and, in a special oil agreement at the San Remo Conference of 1920, Britain placed the German shares at the disposal of France. The United States Government strongly objected to the exclusive nature of the exchange. In the meantime, interested American oil companies and TPC started direct negotiations. By the end of 1923 they had reached general agreement. Objections of Gulbenkian to some of the arrangements, however, deferred final agreement until 1928, when the composition of the TPC became: D'Arcy Exploration Company, Anglo-Saxon Petroleum Company, Compagnie Française des Pétroles and Near East Development Corporation, twenty-three and three-fourths percent each, and Participations and Explorations Company (Gulbenkian), the remaining five percent.

The Near East Development Corporation was held in equal shares by Standard Oil Company (New Jersey), Standard Oil Company of New York, Gulf Oil Corporation, Atlantic Refining Company and Pan American Petroleum and Transport Company. This marked the entrance of American oil companies into the Middle East. Some years later Gulf, Atlantic and Pan American sold their shares to Standard (New Jersey) and Socony-Vacuum, the reorganized Standard Oil of New York, now Mobil Oil Corporation.

The Iraqi Government granted a concession to TPC in March, 1925. As revised in 1931, the concession granted exclusive rights in northern Iraq east of the Tigris River, with the exception of the Transferred Territories. The large Kirkuk field was discovered in October, 1927. The company's name was changed to Iraq Petroleum Company (IPC) in 1929.

In 1932 Iraq granted the B.O.D. Company a concession for the area west of the Tigris and north of the thirty-third parallel. While the initials stood for British Oil Development, the company was largely composed of Italian and German interests. It spent considerable sums in unsuccessful exploration and came close to bankruptcy before the owners of IPC bought up the shares and took over the B.O.D. concession in 1941. The concession has since been held by Mosul Petroleum Company (MPC), which has the same ownership as IPC.

Producing fields in the MPC concession are Ain Zalah, which was discovered in 1939, but was not connected by pipeline until 1952, and Butmah, discovered in 1952 and connected by pipeline to Ain Zalah in 1953. Heavy oil in small quantities was discovered in the Qaiyarah area, but it has not been developed for export.

A concession covering southern Iraq was granted to the owners of IPC in July, 1938. It is held in the name of Basrah Petroleum Company (BPC).

Two important fields are now producing in this concession, the Zubair field discovered in 1948 and the Rumaila field discovered in late 1953. Most oil from these fields is exported through a deep water port at Khor al Amaya at the head of the Arabian Gulf, with some oil moving through the shallow-water Fao terminal at the mouth of the Shatt al-'Arab. Late in 1958 BPC relinquished its concession rights in Iraq's territorial waters in the Arabian Gulf.

IPC's fields in the north have continued to account for the greater part of Iraq's oil exports. Although two other fields, Bai Hassan and Jambur, have been discovered, the Kirkuk field has continued to be the principal producer. Much of IPC's postwar investment has been in the expansion of pipeline capacity to the Mediterranean. At the war's end, IPC began the construction of two sixteen-inch pipelines to the Mediterranean parallel to the two existing twelve-inch lines going from the Kirkuk oil field to Tripoli, Lebanon and Haifa, Palestine. The second Tripoli line was finished in 1951. The Palestine war forced the abandonment of the Haifa lines. To replace the loss of the Haifa outlet, a 30/32-inch pipeline to Banias, Syria was put into operation by 1952. It was supplemented by a parallel line of similar diameter completed in 1961.

The production of IPC was interrupted at the

Middle East Crude Oil Production 1967

(Thousands of Barrels Daily)

Year	Iraq	Iran	Kuwait	Bahrain	Qatar	Saudi Arabia	Abu Dhabi	Muscat-* Oman
1960	963	1,047	1,692	45	173	1,315		
1961	997	1,174	1,732	45	178	1,481		
1962	1,000	1,309	1,956	45	187	1,643	15	
1963	1,153	1,455	2,089	45	193	1,785	48	
1964	1,249	1,683	2,297	49	189	1,896	188	
1965	1,310	1,878	2,351	57	194	2,206	284	
1966	1,383	2,105	2,484	62	289	2,602	362	
1967	1,222	2,603	2,501	70	324	2,806	384	150

* Muscat-Oman daily average since production began in August, 1967.

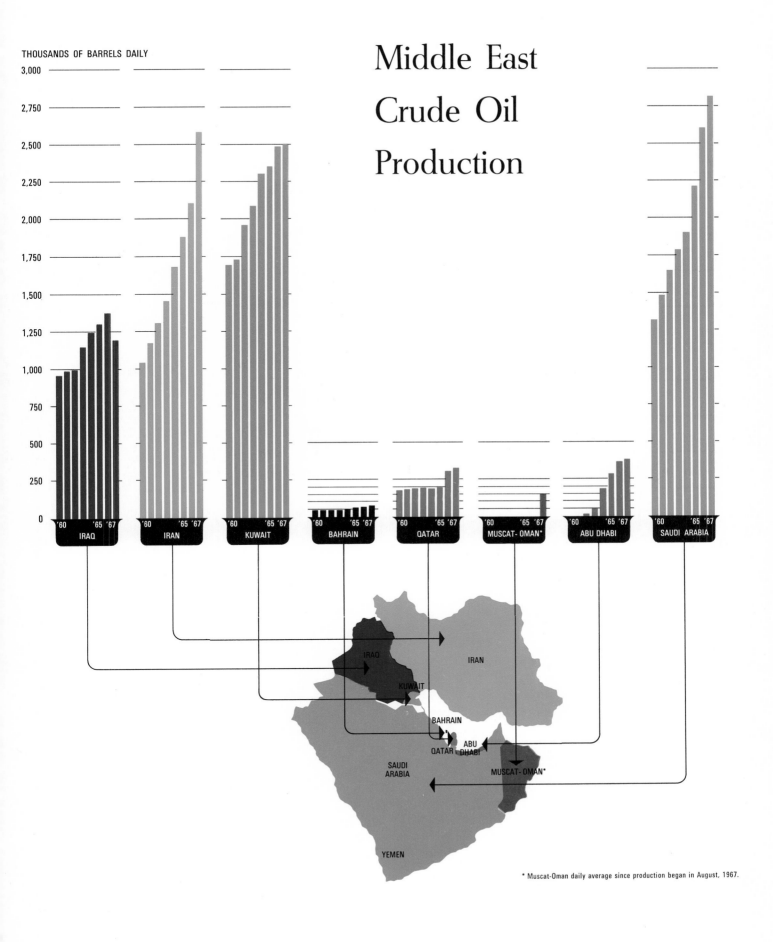

Middle East Crude Oil Production

THOUSANDS OF BARRELS DAILY

* Muscat-Oman daily average since production began in August, 1967.

time of the Suez crisis in November, 1956, when some of the pipeline facilities in Syria were destroyed. The flow was restored the following year. Iraq, along with other Arab states, halted oil production for several days during the Israel-Arab conflict in June, 1967. Earlier in 1967 the pipeline was closed during a dispute between Syria and IPC over transit fees.

A concession crisis erupted on April 6, 1961, when the Iraq Government prohibited IPC and its sister companies MPC and BPC from further exploration. Then on December 12 of the same year, the government published Law 80 expropriating more than ninety-nine and one-half percent of the concession area held by the companies and leaving them with only the areas where wells were in actual production. The government and IPC carried on prolonged negotiations and in 1965 a draft agreement was reached, but it never was ratified. On August 6, 1967, the government issued Law 97, assigning the exclusive right to the expropriated acreage to the government-owned Iraq National Oil Company (INOC). INOC may develop the areas in association with others, but each association must be approved by a law. Law 97 also prohibits INOC from developing any area through a concession or making any arrangement with others which would affect public ownership of petroleum or other hydrocarbons in the area.

IPC termed Iraq's action a "breach of international law, as it purports to deprive the companies of rights which cannot be legally taken away unilaterally. The remedy for settling disputes unresolved by negotiation is arbitration. The companies have protested to the government, and they and their shareholders will take every step available to them to prevent the future exercise by other parties of the companies' rights."

INOC announced three months later that it had entered into a contract with ERAP for the exploration and development of areas in central and southern Iraq totaling 4,170 square miles, including 695 square miles offshore in the Arabian Gulf.

96

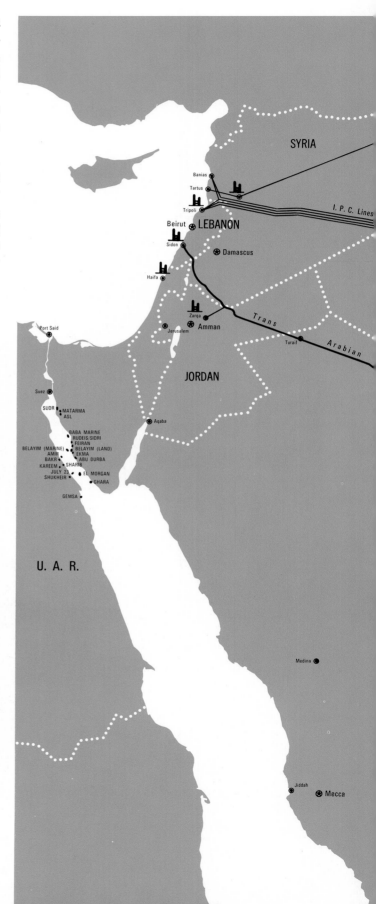

Middle East Oil Facilities

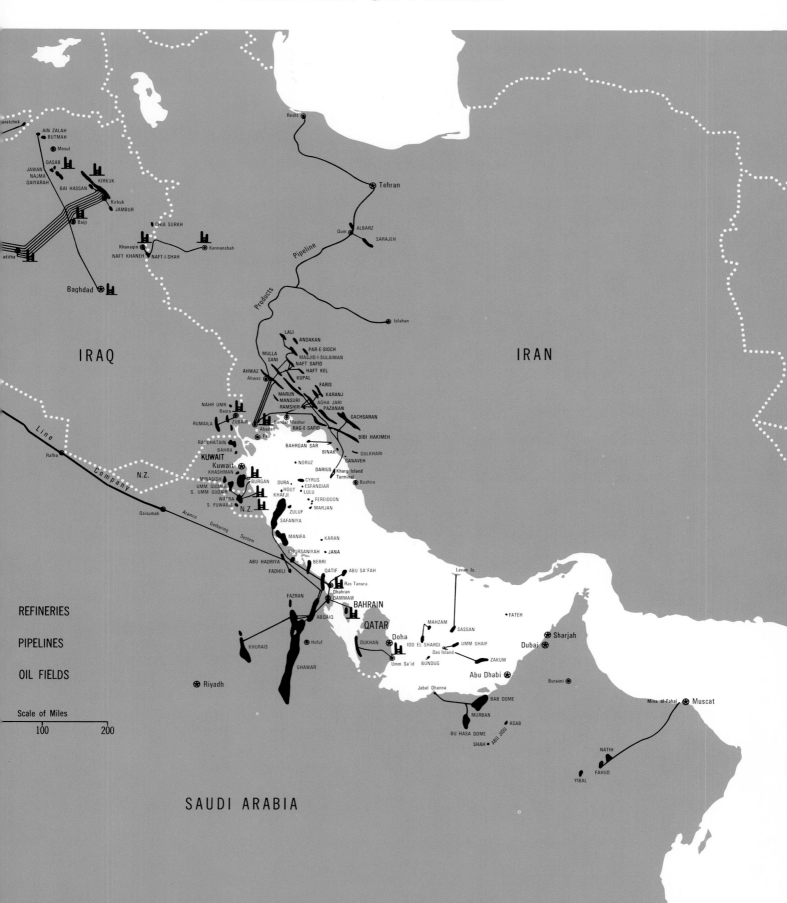

REFINERIES

PIPELINES

OIL FIELDS

Scale of Miles
100   200

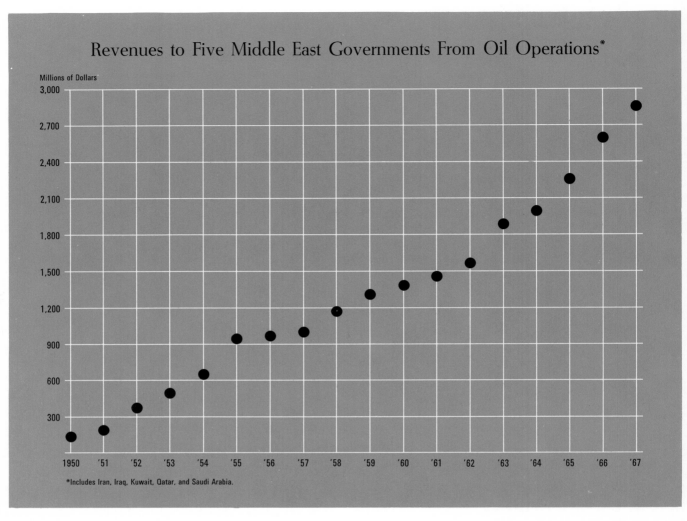

Revenues to Five Middle East Governments From Oil Operations[*]

Millions of Dollars

*Includes Iran, Iraq, Kuwait, Qatar, and Saudi Arabia.

ERAP will act as a contractor and the terms with Iraq follow a pattern similar to those that the French state-owned company made with the National Iranian Oil Company the previous year. The contract for exploration is for six years, with development and production over a twenty-year period. ERAP must surrender all acreage outside actual producing fields after six years. ERAP paid INOC fifteen million dollars, which is not recoverable, in consideration of the contract. But ERAP's exploration and other expenditures will be repaid in crude oil if petroleum in commercial quantities is found. ERAP may purchase a share of the production at an agreed price, and upon request will market a share of INOC's oil for a commission.

Near the end of 1967 Iraq and the Soviet Union agreed on a basis for Russian assistance to INOC in connection with oil exploration and development.

KUWAIT The postwar expansion of Kuwait's production for some years was the most spectacular in the Middle East. Installations idle during the war were reopened in 1945. Production jumped from 16,000 barrels daily in 1946 to over the million mark in 1955, and to more than two million in 1964.

Because of the half-interest which Anglo-Iranian

(which later became British Petroleum) held in the Kuwait Oil Company (KOC), Kuwait was the chief beneficiary when Anglo-Iranian's holdings in Iran were nationalized in 1951 and Anglo-Iranian had to turn to other sources of crude oil. Gulf owns the other half of KOC. From 1954 until 1966 when Saudi Arabia took the lead, Kuwait was the largest producer of crude oil in the Middle East.

Eight fields have been discovered: Burgan, Raudhatain, Minagish, Umm Gudair, Bahrah, Sabriya, Khashman and Dhahr.

All crude oil produced in Kuwait moves by pipeline to Mina al-Ahmadi. One of the world's largest oil terminals is located there, as are KOC's 250,000-barrel daily refinery, liquefied petroleum gas plant and bitumen plant.

In May, 1962, KOC voluntarily relinquished about one-half of the concession acreage it had held since 1934 and gave up another 386 square miles in 1967. Oil rights to the 3,576 square miles of released area were reserved for Kuwait National Petroleum Company (KNPC), which is owned sixty percent by the government and forty percent by private Kuwaiti interests.

KNPC was established in 1961 and a few months later took over marketing within the country. An agreement was concluded in May, 1967, between KNPC and a Spanish Government-sponsored group, Hispanoil, to form a joint venture (fifty-one percent KNPC and forty-nine percent Hispanoil) to explore and develop the former KOC acreage. A decisive factor in choosing Hispanoil over other bidders was the Spanish Government's guarantee that Kuwait would supply twenty-five percent of the Spanish market for crude oil for a fifteen-year period beginning in 1970. The Kuwait National Assembly must approve the new agreement.

KNPC is expanding into other activities. It has built a 95,000-barrel-a-day refinery at the Kuwait industrial complex of Shuaiba. It also owns a sixty percent interest in Kuwait Chemical Company's fertilizer plant at Shuaiba; a fifty-one percent interest in Kuwait Aviation Fueling Company,

which took over local aircraft refueling from British Petroleum Company in 1961; and a five percent share in Central African Petroleum Refineries, a small refinery near Umtali in Rhodesia.

SAUDI ARABIA-KUWAIT NEUTRAL ZONE Three oil companies have concessions in the Neutral Zone—two onshore and one offshore.

Onshore, the American Independent Oil Company (Aminoil) was granted Kuwait's undivided half interest in 1948, and Pacific Western Oil Corporation, later named Getty Oil Company, obtained the Saudi Arabian half share in 1949.

Aminoil, designated as the operating company, began exploration in 1949 and struck oil in 1953. The Wafra field thus discovered was the only onshore producing area in the Neutral Zone until March, 1964, when the South Fuwaris field, twelve miles to the south, was placed on stream. In late 1966 oil was discovered at South Umm Gudair, a southern extension of Kuwait's Umm Gudair field.

Getty Oil Company has a tanker terminal and a

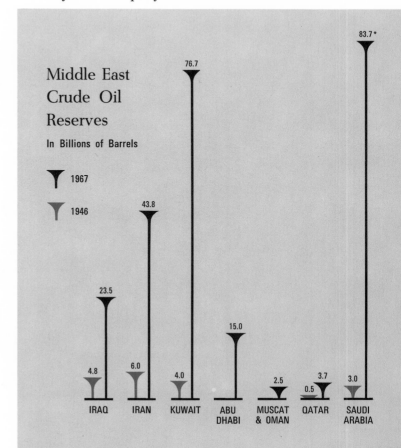

Middle East Crude Oil Reserves

In Billions of Barrels

▼ 1967

▼ 1946

	IRAQ	IRAN	KUWAIT	ABU DHABI	MUSCAT & OMAN	QATAR	SAUDI ARABIA
1967	23.5	43.8	76.7	15.0	2.5	3.7	83.7*
1946	4.8	6.0	4.0			0.5	3.0

Source: Oil and Gas Journal, December 25, 1967

*Aramco estimates its proved reserves at about 77 billion barrels as of December 31, 1967.

General Geology of the Middle East

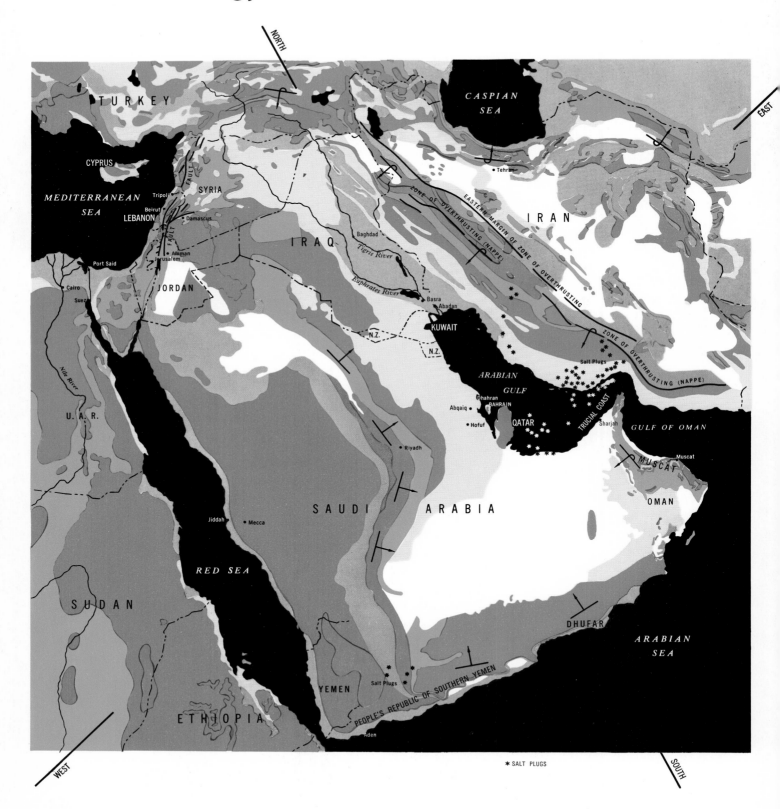

* SALT PLUGS

General Comparison of Stratigraphy

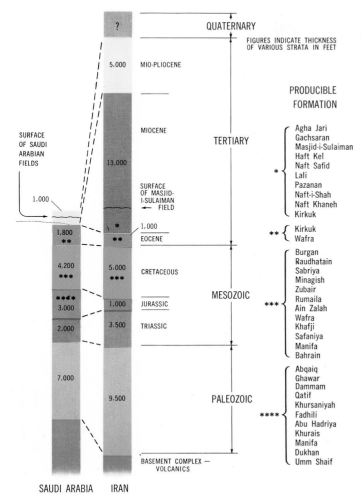

FIGURES INDICATE THICKNESS OF VARIOUS STRATA IN FEET

	SAUDI ARABIA	IRAN			PRODUCIBLE FORMATION

QUATERNARY

? — 5,000 MIO-PLIOCENE

13,000 MIOCENE — TERTIARY

* { Agha Jari / Gachsaran / Masjid-i-Sulaiman / Haft Kel / Naft Safid / Lali / Pazanan / Naft-i-Shah / Naft Khaneh / Kirkuk

SURFACE OF SAUDI ARABIAN FIELDS

1,000

SURFACE OF MASJID-I-SULAIMAN FIELD

1,800 ** / ** / 1,000 EOCENE

** { Kirkuk / Wafra

4,200 *** / 5,000 *** CRETACEOUS — MESOZOIC

*** { Burgan / Raudhatain / Sabriya / Minagish / Zubair / Rumaila / Ain Zalah / Wafra / Khafji / Safaniya / Manifa / Bahrain

3,000 **** / 1,000 JURASSIC

2,000 / 3,500 TRIASSIC

7,000 / 9,500 PALEOZOIC

**** { Abqaiq / Ghawar / Dammam / Qatif / Khursaniyah / Fadhili / Abu Hadriya / Khurais / Manifa / Dukhan / Umm Shaif

BASEMENT COMPLEX — VOLCANICS

SAUDI ARABIA   IRAN

50,000-barrel-a-day refinery in the Neutral Zone, while Aminoil sends its half share of oil production by pipeline to its tanker terminal and 110,000-barrel daily refinery at Mina Abdullah in Kuwait.

The Japanese-owned Arabian Oil Company obtained concessions in 1958 from both Kuwait and Saudi Arabia covering the offshore area of the Neutral Zone. These concessions provide that Saudi Arabia and Kuwait receive fifty-six and fifty-seven percent respectively of the profits obtained from each country's undivided half interest. Early in 1960 oil was discovered in the Khafji field.

A second offshore field, the Hout field, was discovered by Arabian Oil in 1963 about 15 miles north of the Khafji field. Early in 1967 the company drilled a discovery well, Lulu-1, near the median line of the Arabian Gulf offsetting IPAC's Esfandiar field in offshore Iran. This third offshore field discovery is apparently an extension of Esfandiar field across the undefined international boundary. A fourth field, Dura, was found in November, 1967, thirteen miles northeast of Hout.

Production averaged about 280,000 barrels daily in 1967. Arabian Oil has a 30,000-barrel-a-day refinery at Khafji.

Diagrammatic Cross Sections of the Middle East

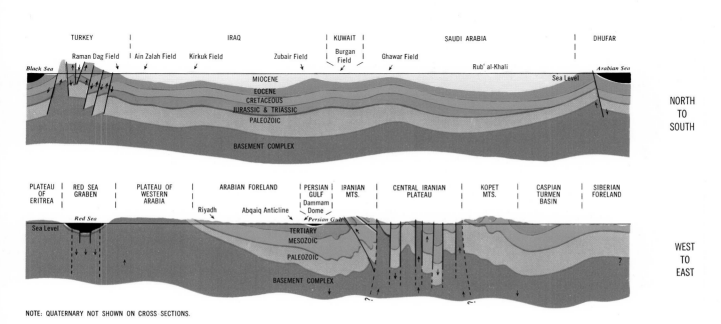

NOTE: QUATERNARY NOT SHOWN ON CROSS SECTIONS.

QATAR Field activities were resumed .in Qatar in 1947, after five years' suspension caused by the war. Production began in 1949 and rose steadily to an annual average of 115,000 barrels daily in 1955 and to 174,000 in 1958. The pattern of onshore production until 1964 was one of slight increases, interspersed with occasional years of decline. In 1967 annual production reached about 200,000 barrels daily. All production until 1964 came from the onshore Dukhan field of the Qatar Petroleum Company (QPC), an affiliate of IPC.

In 1952 Qatar gave an offshore concession to a Shell subsidiary later known as Shell Company of Qatar. This firm discovered oil in two fields, Id-el-Shargi and Maydan Mahzam. Its production jumped rapidly from 24,000 barrels a day in 1964 to a rate of more than 125,000 in 1967.

In 1963 Continental Oil Company obtained a concession in onshore areas which had been dropped by QPC and offshore areas which had been relinquished by Shell. Later Continental was joined in the venture by Pure Oil Middle East, Inc., a subsidiary of Union Oil Company of California.

MUSCAT AND OMAN After several years of exploration, three oil fields were discovered in Oman. The concession is held by Petroleum Development (Oman) Ltd., in which Shell is the majority stockholder with minority interests owned by Compagnie Française des Pétroles and the Gulbenkian Trust.

The fields, Fahud, Natih and Yibal, are some 150 to 200 miles inland on a plain southwest of the towns of Muscat and Matrah on the Gulf of Oman. A 30/36-inch line has been laid from the Fahud and Natih fields across the plains and over the coastal mountains through the Sumail pass 2,000 feet above sea level, a route that follows an old camel track. The 174-mile pipeline terminates at a harbor built at Mina al Fahal, a few miles west of the towns of Muscat and Matrah.

Production began from the Fahud and Natih fields in August, 1967 at 132,000 barrels daily and moved up within a short time to 160,000. At a later stage, the Yibal field, farthest from the coast, will be brought into production.

BAHRAIN The petroleum reserves of these islands are small compared with other Middle East countries, and increases in production have been gradual. From 30,000 barrels daily in 1948, production was lifted to 70,000 in 1967.

The concession is operated by Bahrain Petroleum Company, which is owned jointly by Standard of California and Texaco. A 200,000-barrel-a-day refinery processes Bahrain production and crude oil imported by pipeline from Saudi Arabia, twenty-five miles away.

Continental Oil Company of Bahrain holds a concession on two offshore blocks, including the Huwar Islands. The operating company is jointly owned by Continental and Pure Oil Middle East, Inc.

SAUDI ARABIA The French company Société Auxiliaire de l'Entreprise de Recherches et d'Activités Pétrolières (AUXERAP), a subsidiary of France's state-owned Entreprise de Recherches et d'Activités Pétrolières (ERAP), was awarded three blocks along Saudi Arabia's Red Sea coast early in 1965. If oil is discovered, the government's General Petroleum and Mineral Organization (Petromin) will hold a forty percent interest in the operating company. The first exploration well, a deep test in the southern block near Jaizan, was abandoned during 1967.

Late in 1967 Petromin was granted two concessions, one in the Rub' al-Khali in an area which Aramco had relinquished, the other along the Red Sea coast. Petromin, while retaining legal title to both concessions, assigned its rights and obligations in them to foreign companies. A contract for exploration and exploitation of the approximately 30,000 square miles in the Rub' al-Khali concession was entered into with AGIP Mineraria, S.p.A., a subsidiary of Ente Nazionale Idocarburi, an Italian state concern. If commercial oil production is discovered, Petromin has the option to acquire thirty to fifty percent of the operating company, depending upon the level of production reached.

The concession along the Red Sea coast was assigned to Sinclair-Natomas-Pakistan under similar provisions except that if oil in commercial quantities is discovered Petromin has the option of fifty percent participation.

ABU DHABI Abu Dhabi is fast developing into a major oil producer with output from both onshore and offshore wells. Petroleum Development (Trucial Coast), since 1962 renamed Abu Dhabi Petroleum Company (ADPC), an IPC affiliate, first

President Thomas C. Barger *of Aramco,* Shaykh Khalifah ibn Salman Al Khalifah, *Director of Finance of Bahrain, and* Shaykh Ahmed Zaki Yamani, *Saudi Arabian Minister of Petroleum and Mineral Resources, turn the valve that starts the oil flow from the offshore Abu Saʻfah field, whose revenues are shared by Bahrain and Saudi Arabia.*

found oil in commercial quantities at Murban in October, 1960. A loading terminal was built at Jabal Dhanna, seventy miles away on the Arabian Gulf coast, and exports of crude oil began there in December, 1963. Output for 1964 averaged 127,000 barrels daily and rose to 280,000 in 1967. Oil fields also were found on the Asab and Shah domes of the Abu Jida anticline, and at Sahil, about twenty-two miles northeast of Asab.

Early in 1967 the partnership of Phillips, ENI and Aminoil acquired concession rights to 4,997 square miles in four blocks which had previously been dropped by ADPC. Phillips is the operator.

Offshore, Abu Dhabi Marine Areas (ADMA), owned two-thirds by British Petroleum and one-third by Compagnie Française des Pétroles, first found oil in commercial quantities at Umm Shaif in 1962. Production averaged 61,000 barrels a day in 1964 and rose to 100,000 by mid-1967. Crude from Umm Shaif is transported by submarine pipeline for twenty miles to Das Island, where storage tanks and a tanker loading jetty have been constructed. A second field, Zakum, went into production in October, 1967, and is expected to reach 200,000 barrels daily in 1968. The discovery well of al-Bundug, the third offshore field, was completed in 1965.

A consortium of three Japanese firms—the Abu Dhabi Petroleum Development Company—was awarded at the end of 1967 a concession covering 1,705 square miles of offshore area that had been relinquished by ADMA.

DUBAI This shaykhdom's first oil was discovered by Dubai Petroleum Company in 1966 in an offshore field, fifty-five miles from the Dubai coast. Initial production was planned for 1968. The field, Fateh, is in a concession whose ownership is shared thirty-five percent by Dubai Petroleum Company (Continental), fifty percent by Dubai Marine Areas (two-thirds BP and one-third CFP), ten percent by Deutsche Erdöl and five percent Sun Oil Company.

Part 3

The

Aramco

Venture

THE ENTRANCE
INTO
SAUDI ARABIA

The story of how Aramco obtained its concession in Saudi Arabia begins on Bahrain, an island in the Arabian Gulf.

Standard Oil Company of California (Socal), as well as the other present owners of Aramco, was one of the American oil companies which made serious efforts to acquire an interest in oil reserves abroad following World War I. Although Socal was one of the largest producers of oil in the United States, its hunting abroad had not been successful. By 1930 Socal had drilled some thirty-seven wells in six foreign countries and had carried out exploration in a dozen other lands without finding any substantial oil production. Such are often the vagaries of oil prospecting.

While Socal was thus engaged, an energetic and amiable New Zealander named Major Frank Holmes was following the trail of oil prospects in the Arabian Gulf area. He went to Bahrain in the early Nineteen Twenties to assist in developing water resources, but his principal interest seemed to be in possible oil resources. In 1922 he crossed over to the Arabian mainland and negotiated with 'Abd al-'Aziz Al Sa'ud for a concession covering more than 30,000 square miles in al-Hasa Province in eastern Arabia. This concession was granted in 1923. In 1925 Holmes suc-

ceeded in obtaining an oil concession for Bahrain.

These concessions were taken in the name of the Eastern and General Syndicate, a British group with which Holmes was associated. The group was not made up of oil operators, but it hoped to interest British companies who were. In this effort it was unsuccessful. The concession in al-Hasa was allowed to lapse through failure to meet obligations. The Bahrain concession, which called for exploration during the first two years, was kept alive only by the syndicate's obtaining an extension. At length the syndicate turned to the United States and aroused the interest of Gulf Oil Corporation. Gulf took an option from the syndicate in November, 1927, and sent a geologist, Ralph U. Rhoades, to examine and map Bahrain.

Gulf, however, was faced with complications. At that time Gulf was one of the companies holding interests in the Iraq Petroleum Company, then known as the Turkish Petroleum Company. Under the so-called Red Line Agreement, these companies had agreed that none of them would act independently within a prescribed area, including Bahrain, in the Middle East.

Gulf referred the question to the Turkish Petroleum Company, whose board of directors decided the company was not interested in Bahrain but that the Red Line Agreement precluded Gulf from taking over the concession. Gulf then approached Standard of California and, at no profit to itself, brought Socal and the Eastern and General Syndicate together. Gulf's option was assigned to Socal on December 27, 1928.

The lack of interest in Bahrain and Arabia among British oil companies at that time does not indicate that their judgment was faulty. They had good reasons for their views and perhaps were not then prepared for expansion in uncertain ventures. The oil production in Iran and Iraq comes from formations which are not present in Bahrain and Arabia, and a test well on Qishm Island, off the coast of Iran, had not indicated that the formations found in Bahrain and Arabia would be productive. There have been examples in the United States, Venezuela, Libya and elsewhere of newcomers finding oil in places which other companies had condemned on similar geological grounds.

The proposed entrance of an American oil company into the Arabian Gulf region was not welcomed at first by Britain. By virtue of an undertaking signed in 1914, the Ruler of Bahrain had bound himself not to embark on the exploitation of possible oil resources within his territory or to "entertain overtures from any quarter" without British approval. Although the concession had been granted, the exploration period had to be extended if the concession was to be kept alive.

In November, 1928, a month before Gulf's option was assigned to Socal, British authorities informed the Eastern and General Syndicate that they would "advise" the Ruler of Bahrain to grant the extension only if the syndicate would give an undertaking that it and any company to which the concession might be assigned would be and would remain under British management and control. Only after months of negotiations was consent given in August, 1930, for the assignment of the concession to the Bahrain Petroleum Company, Ltd., a company which Socal owned and had formed for the purpose under the laws of Canada. Meanwhile,

in the spring of 1930, two Socal representatives, Fred A. Davies, later chairman of the board of Aramco, and William Taylor had examined the geological and operating conditions in Bahrain and had recommended a test well.

The venture in Bahrain naturally aroused the interest of Socal in the mainland of Arabia only twenty-five miles away. When Davies was in Bahrain he recommended that arrangements be made for him to visit the mainland. The only reason an approach to King 'Abd al-'Aziz was not made in the spring of 1930 was that the company had been convinced by Holmes that he, with his long acquaintance with the King, was better able to do so than anyone else.

Holmes, however, was preoccupied with other affairs. Among other things, he was conducting negotiations with the Ruler of Kuwait on behalf of Gulf. His promised visit to the King was postponed many times. Two years went by and in early June, 1932, oil was discovered in Bahrain. Socal decided to approach the Saudi Arabian Government without the assistance of Holmes. At that time, Socal learned that the British India Office had dissuaded Eastern and General Syndicate from promoting any interest of Gulf or Socal in Saudi Arabia.

Perhaps the time, however, had not been wasted. Socal was unknown to King 'Abd al-'Aziz when the Bahrain venture was started. Permission was requested through the Saudi Arabian minister to London in the autumn of 1930 for geologists to make a preliminary examination of al-Hasa and had been refused. By 1932, however, the Americans had established a good reputation in Bahrain. They had demonstrated, among other things, that their interests were confined to oil and involved no political entanglements or ambitions.

The first step in approaching the Saudi Arabian Government was made in early November, 1932, in a telegram to the well-known author and explorer, H. St. John B. Philby, who was then in Jiddah. Philby was asked to propose to the government that Socal make a preliminary geological examina-

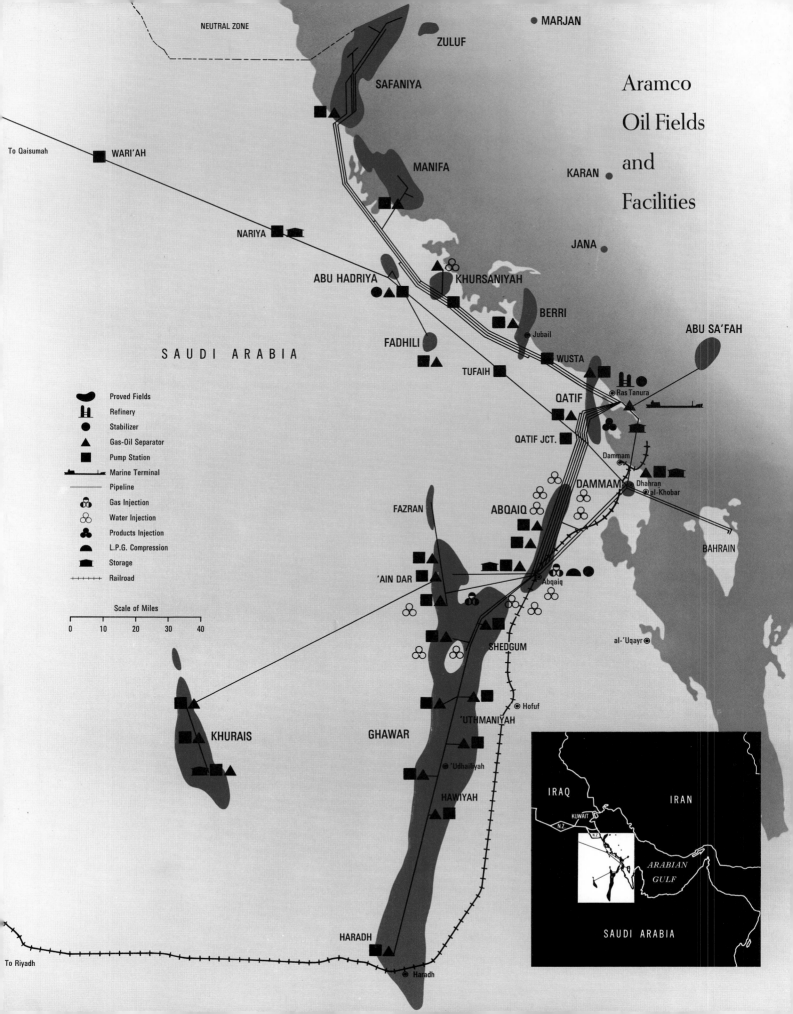

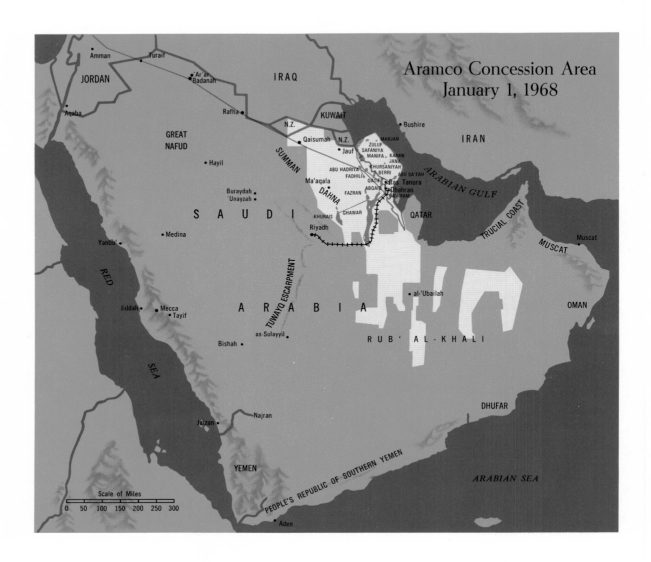

Aramco Concession Area
January 1, 1968

tion of al-Hasa with a view toward negotiating a concession if further exploration seemed justified. The government, however, wanted to negotiate a concession before any geological work was commenced.

Three months later a company representative, Lloyd N. Hamilton, was on his way to Jiddah. Negotiations began in mid-February, 1933. Hamilton was accompanied and assisted by Karl S.

Twitchell, who previously had investigated water and mining resources in Arabia. Twitchell later was largely responsible for the gold-mining activities of the Saudi Arabian Mining Syndicate in the Hijaz.

In the ensuing negotiations, Standard of California had to face the competition of the Iraq Petroleum Company group, whose representative was in Jiddah at the same time. Even Holmes put in an appearance for a few days as a competing

110

agent, but apparently received no encouragement.

The negotiations were proceeding during the darkest days of the post-1929 depression. One of the first acts of the new President, Franklin D. Roosevelt, in March, 1933, was to close all banks in the United States. There was doubt for a time whether the company could lay its hands on enough cash to make the original payments. Then, after agreement had been reached on all points, the United States declared an embargo on gold exports on April 20 and shortly thereafter went off the gold standard. This action required a renegotiation of the payments provisions of the Concession Agreement which had been expressed in terms of "pounds gold." It became necessary to provide for payments in dollars or sterling according to the rate of exchange between such currencies and the "gold pound." Later, in view of the highly unsettled world monetary conditions after the beginning of World War II, these provisions caused great difficulties of interpretation.

Otherwise, the Concession Agreement drafted by Hamilton in straightforward and simple language was a model of clarity. The agreement was signed in Jiddah on May 29, 1933, by 'Abd Allah as-Sulayman, then Minister of Finance, and by Hamilton for Standard of California. The agreement was ratified by the Saudi Arabian Government by a Royal Decree issued on July 7, 1933, and became effective on July 14 when it was published in the official gazette.

ARAMCO AND ITS OWNERS In November, 1933, the concession was assigned to California Arabian Standard Oil Company (Casoc), a company owned and formed by Standard of California under the laws of Delaware. The name of this company was changed on January 31, 1944, to the present more appropriate title—Arabian American Oil Company (Aramco).

By 1936 the production and position of Standard of California in the Middle East and the Netherlands East Indies (now Indonesia) called for

additional marketing facilities. On the other hand, marketing facilities which had been developed by The Texas Company (now Texaco Inc.) were in need of more accessible production. The two great companies combined their interests between Egypt and the Hawaiian Islands and in this way The Texas Company became a half owner of Casoc.

In late 1946, after Saudi Arabian petroleum reserves had been proved to be extremely large, calling for great market outlets and enormous capital investments for their full development, arrangements were made for Standard Oil Company (New Jersey) and Socony-Vacuum Oil Company (now Mobil Oil Corporation) also to become owners of Aramco. As these two companies were members of the Iraq Petroleum Company group, the perfection of these arrangements had to await modification of the same Red Line Agreement which partly was responsible for the opportunity given to Standard of California to enter the Middle East oil picture. The arrangements were completed in November, 1948.

Thus four leading American oil companies acquired a substantial independent interest in the great oil reserves of the Middle East. Since that time, shareholdings in Aramco have been: Standard of California 30 percent, Texaco 30 percent, Standard (New Jersey) 30 percent and Mobil 10 percent. As of the end of 1967, these four companies were owned by close to 1,500,000 individual stockholders.

THE CONCESSION AGREEMENT The agreement which 'Abd Allah as-Sulayman and Hamilton signed, as extended three times, runs for a period of sixty-six years from 1933.

In its essentials it grants the company the exclusive right within a so-called Exclusive Area to prospect for, drill for, extract, manufacture, transport, deal with, carry away and export oil and oil products, and to provide itself with the means and facilities with which to do so. Apart from certain initial payments, the government was to receive a royalty of four shillings gold, or its equivalent in dollars or sterling, per ton of net crude oil produced, saved and run from field storage. The government also was to receive without cost, at the expiration of the concession, all of the fixed facilities which the company had installed.

The Exclusive Area originally covered all of eastern Saudi Arabia as far west as the western edge of the Dahna, with extensions from the two ends of the Dahna running respectively North 30° West and South 30° East to the northern and southern boundaries of the kingdom. In 1939 a Supplemental Agreement extended the northern and southern parts of this area westward and granted rights with respect to Saudi Arabian interests in the two Neutral Zones, one with Iraq and the other with Kuwait. Following this agreement the exclusive concession area amounted to about 495,900 square miles, or roughly the size of Arizona, New Mexico and Texas combined.

In addition, as a part of the 1933 agreement, the company was given a preferential right in a region extending westward from the Exclusive Area. Part of this preferential area was relinquished in 1947 and the remainder in 1963.

Since 1939 the company has relinquished about three-fourths of the Exclusive Area as it then existed. In 1967 the concession area covered five tracts aggregating approximately 125,000 square miles. There are to be further relinquishments at five-year intervals of undeveloped areas so that the total area will be 20,000 square miles by 1993.

Aramco's financial arrangements with the government have also undergone change. Aramco was exempt from taxes under the original Concession Agreement. In 1950, however, when the government imposed its first income taxes, Aramco submitted to an income tax which, taken together with other payments to the government, equalled fifty percent of its gross income less operating expenses. Subsequent agreements have increased the government's income by altering the items that could be deducted as operating expenses.

THE GROWTH OF ARAMCO

The first oil prospectors stepped ashore at Jubail on September 23, 1933, less than four months after the Concession Agreement was signed. Geologists R. P. Miller and S. B. Henry came by launch from Bahrain with Karl S. Twitchell, who had met them there after driving across Saudi Arabia from Jiddah. The three wore beards and donned Arab dress to avoid appearing conspicuous to the townspeople, few of whom had ever seen a Westerner.

A small compound at Jubail and a house at Hofuf had been obtained for the geologists by 'Abd al-'Aziz and Hamad al-Gosaibi, prominent al-Hasa merchants who had been named company agents. These simple accommodations were to be home quarters for the men until 1936.

The afternoon of their arrival the geologists began to explore the coastal region south of Jubail, and on September 28 they came to the hilly area they had observed from Bahrain, twenty-five miles away. They found evidence of a domal geologic structure that could mean oil, and they called the structure the Dammam Dome.

With the aid of camel transport the first field camp was set up about five and a half miles south of the coastal village of Dammam. After J. W. Hoover arrived, he and Henry began mapping the dome. The area's most prominent hill is Jabal Dhahran.

To the geologists, the Dammam domal structure was so readily apparent that they felt future exploration work in Saudi Arabia was going to be a cinch. In time they learned that nature had guarded its oil secrets well. Except for the Dammam Dome the surface of the coastal region is largely covered by sand, marl or limestone deposits which mask the folding responsible for oil accumulations, leaving only obscure hints of what lies beneath.

After making a preliminary map of the Dammam Dome, the geologists began inspecting the rest of the concession. More geologists arrived—Art Brown, Tom Koch and Hugh Burchfield—along with Allen White, an engineer. Under Miller's direction, teams of two made excursions into more remote areas.

Working among a strange people in a land only vaguely and inaccurately mapped, these men had their troubles. At first field parties, often hundreds of miles from their bases, had no radio contact with the Jubail or Hofuf camps. They depended largely on camel transportation for supplies. The load limit for a good camel is about 400 pounds, so a sizable caravan was required to pack the provisions and gear required by the oilmen and their escort of ten soldiers and guides furnished by the government.

By the end of 1933 there were eight oilmen living in Saudi Arabia, counting Bill Lenahan, the liaison man in Jiddah. The small contingent stationed on Saudi Arabia's eastern shore could merely nibble

Dhahran, 1938: The limestone hills on Dammam Dome helped Aramco's pioneers to work out the structure.

'Abd Allah as-Sulayman, Finance Minister, and Lloyd Hamilton sign the Concession Agreement in 1933.

at the 320,000-square-mile concession area—and wait for word of the airplane that was promised them.

The airplane came unannounced the next spring, landing at Jubail on a strip that previously had been dragged in the sand. The plane had been borne by ship to Alexandria; then, after being turned back once by a sandstorm, was flown into Baghdad for fuel and on to Saudi Arabia. Aboard were Richard C. Kerr, a geologist, pilot and photographer, and Charley Rocheville, who claimed to be the company's ninth arrival in Saudi Arabia because he was in the nose of the plane when it touched down. With the plane, the men proceeded with the observations and aerial photographs which were necessary before detailed geological studies could begin.

As these explorers fanned out across the desert

sands and gravel plains, additional help was arriving. Saudi Arabia was attracting a select group, take-charge types who came with special training and quickly learned whatever new skills circumstances demanded. Many of them had worked in other foreign countries. Several had backgrounds with distinct dashes of daring in them, like Felix Dreyfuss, who had built and flown his own airplane back in California. And there was the much-liked Max Steineke, virtually a company legend before his death in 1952, a geologist who asked for the Saudi Arabia assignment after stints in Alaska, Colombia and New Zealand.

By the spring of 1935 a good start had been made in working out the stratigraphy of the country by surface examination, but no great progress had been made in deciphering the subsurface folding. Nevertheless, the geologists found enough evidence to suspect the presence of favorable structures in areas which are now oil fields.

Only the drill could confirm the geologists' belief that the Dammam Dome contained oil. The structure was similar to the one already yielding oil on Bahrain Island. So when the decision was made in the summer of 1934 to test the Dammam Dome, it was with great expectations.

Engineers, construction pioneers and drillers began arriving in December. Included in the initial group were Guy S. Williams, drilling superintendent; Floyd Ohliger, petroleum engineer; Walt Haenggi, rig builder; Joe Cartwright, camp clerk and paymaster; Claude Jared, Jack Schloesslin and George McCoy, drillers, and Bill Eltiste, a mechanic, driller and rig builder. Miller was named resident manager. The camp at the Dammam Dome was growing and, in time, would become Dhahran.

The small coastal town of Dammam to the north and the tiny huddle of fishermen's huts known as al-Khobar, to the south, offered neither living quarters nor supplies of food and other necessities for the oilmen. A supply line reaching more than 11,000 nautical miles to the United States was established to bring in every last item needed to explore and drill, to build quarters and to feed the crews.

Al-Khobar was selected as the port for unloading cargo. Before heavy materials could be received, Saudi crews built a rock pier from the shore through shoals into water deep enough to dock small boats and barges. A road, crude but passable, was constructed to the drilling site.

As the drilling equipment was installed, construction proceeded on the first Dhahran camp. It was not the usual wildcat camp, but rather more elaborate in keeping with the "assurance" of finding oil. Although later modified and enlarged, these

Some of Aramco's pioneers outside the Dhahran messhall in 1935: Walt Haenggi, Fred Davies, Floyd Ohliger, Bill Forkner, Felix Dreyfuss, Bill Eltiste, Bill Burleigh, Claude Jared, Woody Wilson and Guy Williams.

A rock pier was constructed at al-Khobar in 1934-35 so that small boats and barges could dock to unload heavy materials.

same buildings were in use as Dhahran District offices until late 1957.

Fresh water came from a spring under the sea between Dammam and al-Khobar through an eleven-mile pipeline. Basic accommodations at the camp were practically complete by the time Dammam No. 1 was spudded in on April 30, 1935.

Early testing of the Dammam Dome proved only that there are no sure shots in oil prospecting. Disappointments were laced only with enough encouraging news to warrant continued efforts. In the summer of 1935 a good showing of oil was found at about 1,900 feet, above the Bahrain producing zone, but the showing proved insubstantial. The main hopes were riding on what the drill would find in the zone which was the producer on Bahrain Island, but when the main Bahrain Zone was penetrated a few days before Christmas, it yielded only some gas and a little oil and water. The well was carried to 3,203 feet without results.

The Dhahran camp, as of 1936, was more elaborate than the usual wildcat camp. These buildings were used as offices until 1957.

116

Well No. 2 was started the following February in a different part of the structure. The early results from the Bahrain Zone were promising, but they did not hold up. Eight other wells drilled into or through the Bahrain Zone had no better results.

DISCOVERY OF OIL Although one deeper test —going beyond the Bahrain Zone—had found only larger quantities of gas and no oil, it was certain that, if the Dammam Dome held oil in paying quantities, it was much deeper than the drill had gone so far. Accordingly, Well No. 7 was started in 1936 as a deep test. It was halted while the Bahrain Zone was tested, but drilling was resumed in August of 1937.

This well turned the company's fortunes. Drilled to 4,727 feet, it encountered large quantities of oil in what is now called the Arab Zone. The well was completed in March, 1938, nearly three years after drillers had spudded in Dammam No. 1.

Dammam No. 1 (right), the first test, and Dammam No. 7, which discovered oil in commercial quantities.

Proof that the Dammam Dome was an important oil field turned loose construction plans already drawn and waiting. Now Dhahran would be transformed from a camp into a community. The residential area, started in 1936, was expanded. Family cottages and dormitories and apartments for men without families sprang up and were joined by a dining hall, clubhouse and swimming pool. A hospital and clinic were temporarily installed in three family cottages. With the addition of a commissary, storehouse, garage, laundry, repair shops, utility plants and a central air-conditioning plant, Dhahran became a self-contained community.

A small storage and shipping terminal was built at al-Khobar and a six-inch pipeline began carrying oil from Dhahran to al-Khobar in September, 1938, for barging to the refinery of the Bahrain Petroleum Company (Bapco). In this small way, export of crude oil began.

After geologists made maps and aerial photographs of possible marine terminal sites, Ras Tanura was chosen. Because charts of coastal waters were incomplete, the company conducted a hydrographic survey using a sonic depth finder. The British Admiralty supplied unpublished data, offered advice on the selection of a channel and sent a survey vessel to check the channel selected and the position of channel markers. In turn, the British incorporated the company's soundings into navigation charts.

By the spring of 1939 a ten-inch pipeline ran between the Dammam field and Ras Tanura. Terminal facilities included 177,000 barrels of tankage for crude oil, pumps, submarine loading lines and moorings for an anchorage 3,000 feet offshore. In Dhahran a 45,000-barrel-a-day stabilizer was completed to remove poisonous hydrogen sulfide gas from the crude oil.

KING VISITS DHAHRAN The arrival of the first tanker was the occasion also of the first visit to company installations by King 'Abd al-'Aziz Al Sa'ud. Two thousand persons accompanied the

King 'Abd al-'Aziz during his first visit to Aramco in 1939 is shown over oil installations by Floyd Ohliger.

King, including seventeen other members of the royal family, four government ministers and prominent merchants. The entourage was escorted by 400 soldiers. About 400 cars were used to bring the visitors, some of whom came from Jiddah and Mecca, more than 870 miles away. A camp of 350 tents was established near Dhahran for the guests. The celebration lasted several days.

The King's introduction to the company's oil operations came during the journey to Dhahran, when his party stopped at the geological outpost of Ma'aqala. After breakfast the geologists invited His Majesty to speak over their new voice radio to his finance minister, Shaykh 'Abd Allah as-Sulayman, who had gone on with others in the royal party to a camp at Abu Hadriya. Tom Barger, a geologist who would later become the company's president and chief executive officer, was among those who got the generator going and established radio contact with Abu Hadriya, amidst the usual static and squawks. Shaykh 'Abd Allah was waiting at the other end as the King was motioned to speak. His Majesty had only shouted—" 'Abd Allah!"—before static claimed the airwaves. The King and Barger continued to shout into the instrument, but in vain. The display of modern science had fizzled.

However, all proceeded smoothly at Ras Tanura. The royal party and company officials boarded the *D. G. Scofield* and the King turned the valve to begin loading the first tanker to bear a cargo of Saudi Arabian crude oil. The date was May 1, 1939.

In the meantime, exploration was moving ahead. By the time field work had to be discontinued in the early war years, the geologists had covered 175,000 square miles by preliminary reconnaissance and about 50,000 square miles by detailed mapping. A much smaller area had been subjected to gravity meter, seismograph and structure drill surveys.

Survey parties had penetrated remote areas, including northern portions of the Rub' al-Khali, as early as 1937. These hardy bands were taking the automobile where it had never been before, were prescribing remedies for the ailing who sought help at their camps and were dinner guests of Bedouins—eating in the customary Arab style as they sat on the floor, legs crossed, using the right hand as the sole utensil. The credentials that enabled a man to function in so many capacities—geologist, doctor, mechanic, linguist and radio operator—could only be earned on the job. These early crews worked, learned Arabic from their guides and, in the brief time left for leisure, were known to pore through rather ancient copies of magazines or toss around a well-worn football.

Although the work accomplished by so few in so little time was impressive, only a good start had been made. But the geologists were pinpointing some indicated structures for further study and perhaps drilling. No one proved to be more accurate than Max Steineke in tying together the stray bits of evidence that pointed to the possibility of oil.

Steineke was reputed to carry Saudi Arabia's known stratigraphy around in his head. Certainly his first-hand knowledge of the country's geology was immense. In a quick coast-to-coast trip across the Arabian Peninsula, from Arabian Gulf to Red Sea, he attached to the formations he saw many of the names still in use today.

But Steineke's particular effectiveness was the conviction he coupled with his keen sense of observation. He was one who insisted that Dammam Dome wildcatters go deeper, and the Arab formation subsequently discovered has been the main source of petroleum in all but one of the company's producing fields. About ninety percent of all the oil produced by Aramco has come from the four zones of the Arab formation. One of these zones, the Arab D, has yielded about eighty percent of the company's cumulative production.

THE ABQAIQ STRUCTURE On another occasion when Steineke was sure he "smelled" oil, he took Fred Davies on a bouncing, jostling ride into the open desert southwest of Dhahran. As Davies described the trip:

"We finally got out to about where Abqaiq is

now. Max got out just like a bird dog and started out through those sand dunes. Every one looked exactly alike to me and we finally landed up in a little cup between sand dunes in which there was an outcrop of Eocene limestone. Max bent over and knocked off a hunk of rock, held it up with great pride and said, 'See that, Fred, that's Eocene limestone.'

"The air was full of dust and sand. Max pointed: 'That's Jabal Dam.' It was five miles off. I couldn't see a quarter of a mile. Again he pointed: 'See that's Jabal Ghuraymil,' which was ten miles away. You know the chances I had of seeing that.

The expansion of oil facilities continues. Column of new crude topping unit is hoisted into place at the Ras Tanura Refinery.

119

"Oil, he said, in both of these places had to be below the ground, adding: 'So, therefore, we have a structure there and we ought to drill it.' I looked at him in astonishment, but I wouldn't dare contradict him and told him, 'You certainly may be right, but I can't even see what you're pointing at.' But Max's enthusiasm was such that in a short time we drilled right at that location and we found the big Abqaiq oil field."

That outcropping, or window, of older Eocene rock indicated to Steineke that an original domal structure at the surface had been covered by the action of the winds, water and seas over the centuries.

THE WARTIME LULL Following the outbreak of war in Europe in September, 1939, operations gradually came to a halt. Enemy action was never close enough for real jeopardy, but one light bombing by Italian planes did slight damage at Dhahran on October 19, 1940. Shipping became difficult, there were tanker shortages, enemy action made markets inaccessible and demand for unrefined crude oil dried up in the Indian Ocean area. With the curtailment of shipping, other operations were

cut back, and to make any evacuation easier the staff was decreased to a skeleton force. The last of the wives and children departed in May, 1941. The most important operation continued by the remaining employees was the production and shipment of 12,000 to 15,000 barrels of oil daily to the Bahrain refinery.

The well which found the Abqaiq field in November, 1941, remained shut in because of the war. Earlier that year, in March, a test started in Abu Hadriya in late 1938 encountered oil at 10,115 feet, but now it was necessary to suspend drilling on a second well. The original small 3,000-barrel-per-day "teakettle" refinery at Ras Tanura started up in January, 1941, but was shut down six months later.

But the employees who remained kept busy. The company assisted the Saudi Arabian Government in solving problems resulting from shortages of transportation and food. In the spring of 1941 Aramco engineers and geologists completed a study begun by the government on water resources and agricultural possibilities in the al-Kharj area, southeast of Riyadh. Later diesel-driven pumps were installed and an eleven-mile canal was con-

A Saudi Arabian company lays a new 40/42-inch pipeline extending forty-three miles across the desert between Abqaiq and Qatif.

Equipped with communications and a graphic panel showing Aramco's pipeline system, dispatchers in Abqaiq control oil movements.

These spheroids at the Abqaiq gas-oil separator plant No. 1 help reduce the gas pressure and serve as storage.

structed to the Bijadiyah area, which was brought under cultivation. Aramco employees supervised the work, which began in 1942 and was completed in 1944. To assist in the inland movement of food imports, a water well was drilled at al-Hani, located along the long, waterless route between the port of al-'Uqayr and Riyadh.

A severe drought reduced the number of transport camels and the government truck fleet could not be maintained. At the request of the King the company pressed into emergency food-hauling service a number of its dwindling supply of trucks.

The company experimented in large-scale camel transport to supplement its truck fleet. To drill a wildcat at Jauf in 1943, a well that proved to be dry and was abandoned, fuel oil, cement and other materials were moved by camel. But camel transport proved neither cheap nor satisfactory. Effort was concentrated to keep as many trucks running as possible; mechanics rigged up spare parts using ingenuity and whatever material was available.

Employees, to insure their own food supply, fattened cattle and sheep they bought in the local

markets. An air-conditioned cottage was turned into a brooder house where chickens were hatched in an incubator.

NEW REFINERY AND PIER By the autumn of 1943 the United States had become concerned about the enormous drain upon American oil fields due to the requirements of war. The U.S. government allocated materials for the construction at Ras Tanura of a 50,000-barrel-a-day refinery, to be financed by Aramco's owner companies. High priorities were assigned to steel and other materials. Trucks and construction equipment which could be spared were sold to the company. Military authorities cooperated in the movement of men and materials by air and sea transport.

The project included the refinery, storage tanks, loading lines, a T-shaped pier with tanker berths to supplement the offshore anchorage, and a submarine pipeline to Bahrain, where the Bapco refinery was being enlarged.

The quiet of Aramco's restricted operations turned into roaring activity. The pandemonium of

123

A diesel-electric rig drilling in the 'Ain Dar area.

Crude oil is stored at the Ras Tanura tank farm for loading aboard tankers at the piers or sea island.

any large construction project far from its base of supplies was intensified by wartime shortages and government control of material and transportation. Boat No. 8, containing a shipload of important supplies, was sunk by the enemy. Men arrived before they could be housed. Men and materials arrived in the wrong order.

But the men managed to proceed on schedule. The refinery was placed in partial operation in September, 1945, and was in full production in December, shortly after the end of the war. The pipeline to Bahrain went into use on March 2, 1945.

By the end of 1945 Aramco had discovered four fields—Dammam, Abu Hadriya, Abqaiq and Qatif—and now the company needed to develop its resources rapidly enough to claim its share in an expanding market.

Oil production was less than 20,000 barrels daily

125

The refinery at Ras Tanura operates around the clock.

Drilling a development well in the Hawiyah area of Ghawar.

before 1944. Production increased to more than 246,000 barrels daily in 1947, moved to more than 300,000 as 1948 began and was over 500,000 at the beginning of 1949.

Drilling at Abqaiq resumed in 1944 and proceeded rapidly. Oil was discovered at Qatif in June, 1945, at 'Ain Dar in June, 1948, and at Fadhili and Haradh in January, 1949. These finds brought to seven the number of oil fields in Saudi Arabia. Production was drawn from only three—Dammam, Abqaiq and Qatif—until the beginning of 1951, when 'Ain Dar was connected with the pipeline system.

WORLD'S LARGEST OFFSHORE FIELD Safaniya, Aramco's first offshore field and the world's largest offshore reservoir, was found in May, 1951, in the Arabian Gulf about 150 miles north of Dhahran. A month earlier, drilling at 'Uthmaniyah appeared to open up a separate field, south of 'Ain Dar. Oil from this area was needed immediately and seven wells were completed by the end of the year. In 1952 further exploration in the 'Uthmaniyah and the 'Ain Dar areas, in addition to a discovery at Shedgum in August, showed that the oil reservoir was continuous among these three areas.

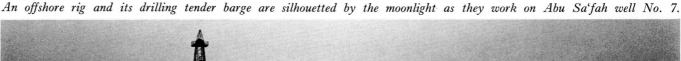

An offshore rig and its drilling tender barge are silhouetted by the moonlight as they work on Abu Sa'fah well No. 7.

126

Mobile drilling platform 2, Aramco's largest piece of offshore drilling equipment, with helicopter landing area in foreground.

Exploratory wells drilled in 1953 and 1954 at Ras Hawiyah and Haradh left little doubt that a single reservoir extends from Haradh in the south to the northermost point of 'Ain Dar. This field, now known as Ghawar, is 150 miles long and up to twenty-two miles wide, the world's largest onshore.

Important new discoveries were made at Khursaniyah in June, 1956, at Khurais in October, 1957, and at Manifa in November, 1957. The Khursaniyah discovery well was located sixty miles up the coastline from Ras Tanura. Khurais Well No. 1 located an inland oil reservoir 120 miles southwest of Abqaiq and ninety miles east of Riyadh. The Manifa field, the company's second offshore field, was found by a well drilled nine miles offshore, between the Safaniya field to the north and Khursaniyah to the south. In March, 1957, the drilling of an exploratory well ten miles north of the 'Ain Dar area discovered a northern extension to Ghawar, which is called Fazran.

Another offshore field, Abu Sa'fah, was found in 1963 by an exploratory well drilled twenty-eight miles off the coast of Ras Tanura. Berri, a reservoir which underlies both land and water, was found in 1964 about thirty-two miles northwest of Ras Tanura.

A well to probe the perimeter of the Safaniya field in 1965 located a new reservoir distinctly separate from Safaniya. The new field was named Zuluf. Three more offshore fields were discovered in 1967. A well to delineate Zuluf found still another field which was labeled Marjan. An exploratory well drilled in the central Arabian Gulf, directly east of the Manifa field, located what was named the Karan field, and south of Karan and east of Jana Island the Jana field was found.

Safaniya oil began moving through a 131-mile pipeline to Ras Tanura in April, 1957, and Khursaniyah was brought into production in 1960 after the field was tied into the Safaniya-Ras Tanura line. Abu Hadriya began producing in 1962.

Construction was scheduled in 1968 for a pipeline to bring Khurais crude oil into Abqaiq. Oil has been withdrawn from Khurais since 1963 and taken by truck to Riyadh to fuel electric power plants.

The offshore Abu Sa'fah and Manifa fields and the northward extension of the onshore Qatif field

Drillers at work at an offshore rig during development of the Abu Sa'fah field.

The pipelines and columns of the refinery at Ras Tanura make up a disciplined industrial pattern.

were brought into production in 1966. Berri became the company's twelfth producing field early in 1967.

Production forecasts made in 1962 and 1963 clearly indicated that wells would have to be drilled at a faster rate than in previous years. Changes were made in equipment, support services, manpower levels and crew organization, and the number of wells drilled went from nineteen in 1963 to thirty-five in 1964, fifty-three in 1965 and sixty-two in 1966.

Diameters of pipelines installed during the early

A sand buggy carries a seismograph crew across the desert sands.

The Aramco Board of Directors at the fall, 1967 meeting. Seated, from left, are Henry C. Moses, *Mobil Oil Corporation;* Harvey Cash, *Texaco Inc.;* George T. Piercy, *Standard Oil Company (New Jersey);* George L. Parkhurst, *Standard Oil Company of California;* Shaykh Ahmed Zaki Yamani, *Minister of Petroleum and Mineral Resources of the Saudi Arabian Government;* Thomas C. Barger, *President and Chief Executive Officer; and* Robert I. Brougham, *Senior Vice President. Standing, from left,* Joseph J. Johnston, *Secretary and General Manager, U.S.A. Offices;* Paul H. Arnot, *Senior Vice President;* Liston F. Hills, *Vice President;* John P. Lunde, *Vice President;* William R. Chandler, *President, Trans-Arabian Pipe Line Company;* Daniel J. Sullivan, *Vice President; and* Dr. Abdulhady Hassan Taher, *Governor of the General Petroleum and Mineral Organization. With the exception of the Secretary and General Manager, U.S.A. Offices, all other Aramco personnel pictured live in Saudi Arabia.*

development of production were as small as ten and twelve inches. In 1948 a thirty-inch line, largest laid up to that time, was completed from Abqaiq to Qatif Junction. A 40/42-inch diameter pipeline was completed between Khursaniyah and Ras Tanura in 1965 and in the following year the line was extended to Safaniya. At the end of 1967 the company had a crude oil pipeline network in Saudi Arabia of 1,416 miles, and a gas, liquefied petroleum gas and petroleum products pipeline network of 281 miles.

CURRENCY PROBLEMS Finding reserves and making petroleum available to world markets are difficult and expensive endeavors. Because this energy source is not evenly divided across the earth's surface, external factors—such as international economics and politics—have continued to play a role in shaping the nature and extent of the industry's development. Thus Aramco's production and rate of development have reflected in varying degrees the economic and political climate in producing and consuming countries.

In the late Nineteen Forties, many nations lacked sufficient U.S. dollars or other convertible currencies to pay for their oil and other needed imports. Economic activity slackened in 1949, resulting in a small reduction in world oil consumption. To meet this situation, Aramco and its affiliated companies worked out arrangements to sell oil for nondollar currencies, and used these currencies to buy supplies and services from nondollar areas.

Then world demand for petroleum took a sudden upward surge in the spring and summer of 1950. The industry, including Aramco, was not altogether

130

he headquarters of the Arabian American Oil Company in Dhahran.

The Consolidated Shops in Dhahran (above) covers a square block. Its specialists (below) can repair almost any piece of equipment.

prepared for this new demand. The Korean War was partly responsible for the unexpected increases.

Aramco had established in November, 1948, a wholly-owned subsidiary which could play a major role in meeting the nondollar currency problem. The Aramco Overseas Purchasing Company, later called Aramco Overseas Company (AOC), was created at a time when the immensity of the construction efforts by Aramco and its affiliate, the Trans-Arabian Pipe Line Company (Tapline), required a separate purchasing and engineering organization which would be closer to nondollar suppliers. AOC first had its headquarters in Rome, then moved to The Hague in Holland in 1954. AOC maintains branch offices in Beirut, Lebanon; Sydney, Australia; and Tokyo, Japan.

Although currency convertibility is no longer the serious problem it was in the late Nineteen Forties, Aramco still maintains an active purchasing program in such areas as Western Europe, Japan and Australia, all of which are large purchasers of oil from the marketing affiliates of Aramco's owners.

GROWTH IN OIL PRODUCTION Production increases were moderate for the years 1955 through 1958 as compared with most of the postwar years. Production in 1956 and 1957 was adversely affected by the closing of the Suez Canal from the end of October, 1956, until mid-April of 1957, and by an embargo on oil shipments to Bahrain, Britain, France and certain other areas between November, 1956, and March, 1957. A tanker shortage also depressed liftings. Crude oil production, which had averaged more than one million barrels daily in October, 1956, dipped to about 665,000 barrels daily in January, 1957.

The reopening of the Suez Canal was followed by production of 1,209,757 barrels daily in July, 1957, then a one-month record, but output then leveled off because of a worldwide surplus in producing capacity and a temporary economic recession in some major consuming countries. Production began to climb again in 1959 with the end of the recession

and substantial increases in Eastern Hemisphere demand. At the same time in 1959, Tapline's deliveries from Sidon fell to the lowest point since 1956 because an oversized world tanker fleet had drastically reduced shipping rates between the Arabian Gulf and the Mediterranean Sea.

Year-to-year increases in crude oil production since 1959 have ranged upward from less than six to eighteen percent. Daily production exceeded 2,000,000 barrels for the first time in 1965 and increased eighteen percent the following year to nearly 2,400,000 barrels daily.

In June, 1967, war broke out in the Middle East for the third time since 1948. For the second time in eleven years the Suez Canal was closed, forcing Europe-bound shipments from the Arabian Gulf to go around Africa's Cape of Good Hope. A shortage of tankers quickly developed and transportation charges rose sharply for crude oil cargoes from the Arabian Gulf to Europe. Aramco production,

The headquarters of Aramco Overseas Company in The Hague.

Growth in Annual Production of Crude Oil

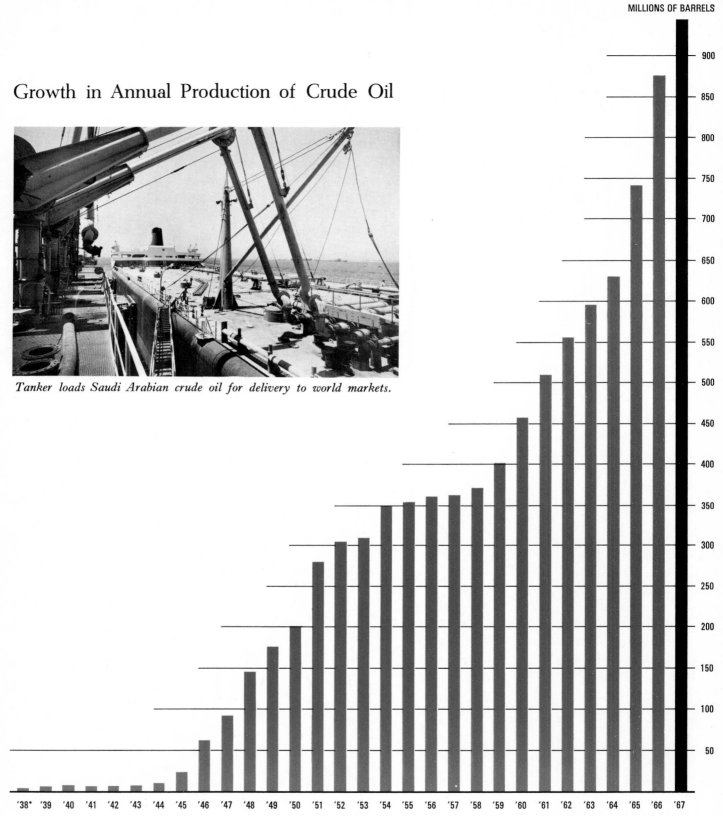

Tanker loads Saudi Arabian crude oil for delivery to world markets.

MILLIONS OF BARRELS

'38* '39 '40 '41 '42 '43 '44 '45 '46 '47 '48 '49 '50 '51 '52 '53 '54 '55 '56 '57 '58 '59 '60 '61 '62 '63 '64 '65 '66 '67

*Commercial production declared October 16, 1938.

Cumulative production of crude oil to December 31, 1967 — 9,103,077,606.

Annual Production of Crude Oil

YEAR	BARRELS DAILY	TOTAL BARRELS
1938	1,357	495,135
1939	10,778	3,933,903
1940	13,866	5,074,838
1941	11,809	4,310,110
1942	12,412	4,530,492
1943	13,337	4,868,184
1944	21,296	7,794,420
1945	58,386	21,310,996
1946	164,229	59,943,766
1947	246,169	89,851,646
1948	390,309	142,852,989
1949	476,736	174,008,629
1950	546,703	199,546,638
1951	761,541	277,962,605
1952	824,757	301,860,885
1953	844,642	308,294,245
1954	953,000	347,844,850
1955	965,041	352,239,912
1956	986,129	360,923,384
1957	992,114	362,121,478
1958	1,015,029	370,485,754
1959	1,095,399	399,820,590
1960	1,247,140	456,453,173
1961	1,392,518	508,269,201
1962	1,520,703	555,056,388
1963	1,629,018	594,591,671
1964	1,716,105	628,094,543
1965	2,024,870	739,077,565
1966	2,392,737	873,349,148
1967	2,597,563	948,110,468

refining and terminal facilities were shut down for five days during the crisis and for fourteen weeks no tankers were loaded at Tapline's Sidon terminal. Crude oil production for the first five months of 1967 averaged 2,843,000 barrels daily, about sixteen percent above the production rate for 1966. However, production fell off substantially after the June hostilities.

Crude oil was produced in 1967 at the record rate of 2,597,563 barrels daily, down from what had been anticipated earlier in the year, but still 8.6 percent greater than the 1966 production rate. One-day records were established in total deliveries of crude oil, 4,158,794 barrels on May 5; production of crude oil, 3,468,881 barrels on May 8; and refinery throughput of crude oil, 373,386 barrels on December 10. Cumulative production at the end of 1967 was 9,103,077,606 barrels. Proved petroleum reserves were seventy-seven billion barrels, more than nineteen percent of the total estimated reserves in the world.

DIRECTING THE OPERATIONS Aramco maintains its headquarters in Dhahran where the chief executive officer and most of the company's management make their homes. In addition to its other operations centers in the Eastern Province, the company has offices in Riyadh, the capital, and in Jiddah, the main city in the Western Province, principally to facilitate the company's contacts with government agencies.

A company office in New York provides support for the Saudi Arabian operations. The New York office deals with the offtaker companies and obtains data on shipping schedules and other information from them needed for planning the production of crude oil and refined products in order to meet export demand. The New York office also performs vital purchasing, traffic and recruiting functions.

The Vice President-Government Relations (USA) and his staff have a small office in Washington, D.C.

SEA ISLAND BERTHS
FOR
GIANT TANKERS

The marine terminal at Ras Tanura has grown from a single pier capable of docking two small tankers into a major oil port able to load the giant supertankers of today.

The terminal's original pier, the South Pier, now can berth four ships and a North Pier can berth six ships. To provide more berths for bigger ships, the company went offshore a mile from the terminal to construct its first tanker-loading sea island. Two berths were placed in service early in 1966, and extensions brought the number of berths at the sea island to six. Five of these berths in deeper water enable the company to load tankers of up to 200,000 deadweight tons. The sixth berth is designed to load tankers of up to 400,000 deadweight tons.

Because of such variables as weather and scheduling of tankers, the loading capacity of the marine terminal is usually higher than Aramco's production. As a result, at times more than three million barrels of crude oil and products have been pumped aboard tankers in a single day.

The capacity of the Ras Tanura refinery was substantially increased in 1949 to 127,000 barrels daily from a plant originally designed for only 50,000 barrels a day. By 1954, with changes and additions, throughput of crude oil was nearly 218,000 barrels daily and in 1967 had risen to 325,000 barrels a day.

Through the years new processing plants have been added at the refinery to improve the quality and variety of products.

The first exports from the Middle East of refrigerated liquefied petroleum gases (propane and butane), commonly known as LPG, began in December, 1961. First produced from refinery process gases, the supply of LPG was expanded by a plant constructed in Abqaiq to extract raw propane and butane from the gases produced with crude oil. These gases are then sent to Ras Tanura for further processing. The propane and butane separated from the refinery gases and the raw LPG from Abqaiq are treated and cooled to a liquid state, stored at low temperatures in insulated tanks at the marine terminal and exported aboard refrigerated tankers. Refrigerated LPG export capacity was 3,400 barrels daily in 1961, but enlargement of plants at Abqaiq and Ras Tanura increased capacity to 42,000 barrels daily in 1968.

Storage tanks at the marine terminal and refinery can hold more than 21,000,000 barrels of crude oil, petroleum products and refrigerated LPG. A 400,000-barrel tank, one of the world's largest tanks for refrigerated LPG, was completed in 1967.

Stabilization plants at Ras Tanura, Abqaiq and Abu Hadriya remove poisonous hydrogen sulfide gas from crude oil delivered to Tapline and to tankers at Ras Tanura. Crude oil going to the

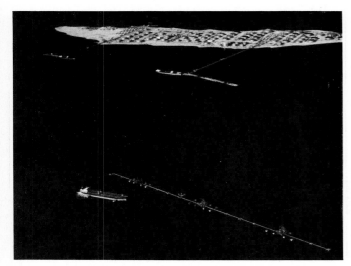

Sea island, piers and tank farm at the marine terminal.

refinery does not require this stabilization, as the hydrogen sulfide is removed in the refining operations.

Plants at Abqaiq, Ras Tanura and Dhahran feed electrical power into a grid which extends as far as Safaniya in the north and 'Udhailiyah in the south. At the end of 1967 this system had a rated capacity of 153 megawatts and was providing power for twenty-five gas-oil separator plants and pump stations and light and air-conditioning for Aramco communities and was being used, along with natural gas and steam, for power for stabilization and refinery processes.

A power dispatching center in Dhahran coordinates power generation and transmission among the three main generating plants.

At the North and South Piers of the marine terminal in Ras Tanura ten tankers can be berthed and loaded at the same time.

OIL EXPLORATION
IN THE DESERT

Air-conditioned trailers and helicopters have replaced the tents and camel caravans of Aramco's early oil explorers. A few of the men who range the desert still cultivate beards, but most face the day clean shaven.

The basic tools of the explorer are the same, but these tools have been sharpened by technical advances and by the use of computers for sophisticated interpretation.

Exploration of the concession has gone through several stages. First the area was roughly mapped and, along with that, detailed maps were made of areas where geologic formations were apparent at the earth's surface. In those areas where structural features were hidden by layers of sand and sediment the geologists drilled shallow holes to penetrate into the substrata. From this work emerged a reasonably accurate picture of the location of shallow geologic structures. Studies then turned to the deeper structural features, more difficult and costly to find, but which also can contain sizable accumulations of oil. One method of detecting these deeper structures was to drill deeper holes, and Aramco conducted an extensive program of structure drilling.

The gravity meter and the magnetometer are the least expensive tools used by oil hunters. They were used extensively by exploration parties of the company until 1958. Gravity meter and magnetometer surveys were run concurrently. The gravity meter measures small variations in the force of the earth's gravity pull which are, in some instances, related to distortions of the earth's crust, and enables the geologist to interpret roughly some of the major structures in the subsurface. The magnetometer measures variations in the earth's magnetic field across an area and contributes information related to structural features.

The seismograph, although a more expensive geophysical method of exploration, is able to give more precise and reliable subsurface information. The company began using this method in 1937.

Seismograph work involves sending shock waves into the earth and recording their return from the rock layers below. These shock waves may be generated by charges of explosives or by mechanical means. Aramco explorers use the big bang of heavy explosives to run widely spaced seismic lines in what is known as refraction surveying. For intensive surveying of a suspected structure they may use light charges of explosives, but more often they use the comparatively gentle mechanical jolts delivered by a Dinoseis. The Dinoseis is a special vehicle carrying a gas-driven chamber which can deliver a sharp thump onto the ground. Several Dinoseis units normally work together and pop simultaneously, covering an area intensively in what is known as a reflection survey.

In either case, the rebounds of the shock waves are recorded on tape. In a seismic data processing center, the tapes are run through computer programs to enhance the recordings and to filter out or dampen unwanted noise. The final result can give a picture of a cross section through the earth showing a series of structures in their correct relationship.

Seismic field parties may consist of more than a hundred men. Convoys of large air-conditioned trailers for sleeping, eating and office work are towed to camp locations by heavy-duty trucks equipped for desert travel.

Exploration teams have penetrated remote areas of the Rub' al-Khali. This great desert, whose Arabic name means The Empty Quarter, had been crossed by only two Westerners before Aramco geologists began probing its vast expanse in 1937. Concentrated efforts began in the northeastern portions in 1950 and 1951 and have been extended gradually toward the western, southern and south-eastern edges.

Most of the region is covered with sand. Both heavy and light vehicles can be used if equipped with proper sand tires, but it is often necessary to follow circuitous routes to avoid the worst sand conditions.

In 1966 helicopters and sand buggies were used for the first time by parties operating in the Sand Mountains of the Rub' al-Khali, where dunes rise from 500 to as high as 800 feet. The sand buggy is the desert adaptation of a vehicle more widely known for its use in exploring swampy areas. Oversize, low pressure tires, more than five and one-half feet high, give the sand buggies high traction in soft sand.

Although personnel and some supplies are flown to these remote areas, monthly truck convoys carry the bulk of the freight, usually taking about twenty-three days for a round trip between Dhahran and the Sand Mountains. Convoys must cross what is known locally as the "Transition Zone" to arrive in the Sand Mountains. This twenty-five-mile-wide barrier is truly trackless desert, where normal sand dune patterns and natural travel routes are

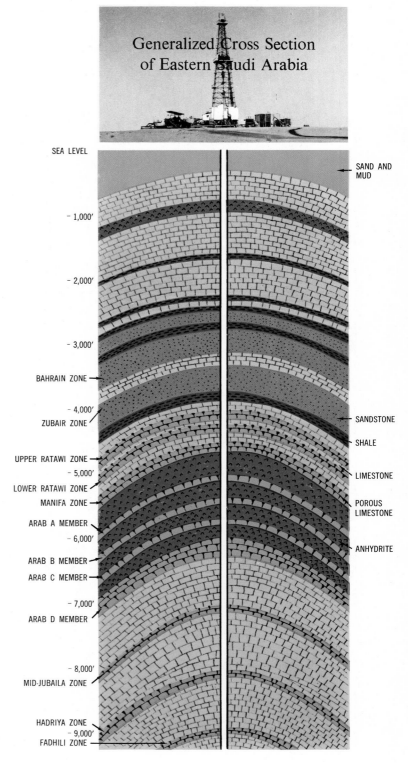

Generalized Cross Section
of Eastern Saudi Arabia

SEA LEVEL

SAND AND MUD

- 1,000'

- 2,000'

- 3,000'

BAHRAIN ZONE

- 4,000'
ZUBAIR ZONE

SANDSTONE

SHALE

UPPER RATAWI ZONE

LIMESTONE

- 5,000'
LOWER RATAWI ZONE

MANIFA ZONE

POROUS LIMESTONE

ARAB A MEMBER

- 6,000'

ANHYDRITE

ARAB B MEMBER

ARAB C MEMBER

- 7,000'

ARAB D MEMBER

- 8,000'

MID-JUBAILA ZONE

HADRIYA ZONE

- 9,000'

FADHILI ZONE

139

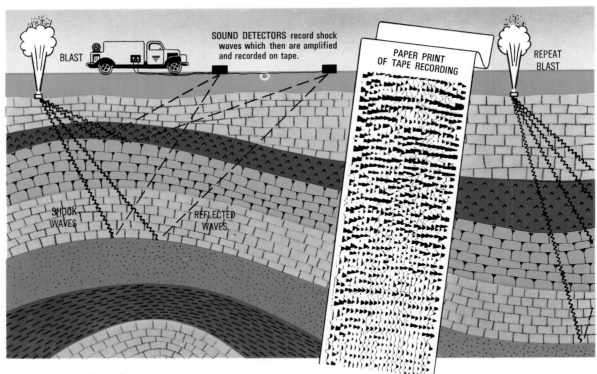

BLAST

SOUND DETECTORS record shock waves which then are amplified and recorded on tape.

PAPER PRINT OF TAPE RECORDING

REPEAT BLAST

SHOCK WAVES

REFLECTED WAVES

Seismic Exploration

Sensitive instruments pick up the minute variations from reflected shock waves and record them on tape.

Dinoseis trucks set off shock waves for seismic crew.

nonexistent because of conflicting winds which sweep the area. Drivers seldom use the same crossing point twice and a tractor is always stationed in the area to free the huge trucks when they get stuck in the sand.

Through the end of 1967, Aramco's exploration efforts had led to the discovery of sixteen oil fields, including the Safaniya field, largest offshore reservoir in the world, and the 150-mile-long Ghawar, world's largest onshore oil field.

Under the sponsorship of the Saudi Arabian Government and the U.S. Department of State, geographic and geologic maps have been published of the Arabian Peninsula. This work was a joint effort of the U.S. Geological Survey and Aramco.

ree geysers of sand rise in the air simultaneously as charges are set off to obtain a seismic record of subsurface structure.

A drilling rig working in the Rub' al-Khali sand mountains.

Computers process seismic data from field parties.

Helicopters transport men and materials from exploration base camps to outlying work parties in the vast Rub' al-Khali sands.

ECONOMIC PRODUCTION
OF CRUDE OIL

The money and time spent to find and develop an oil field make it imperative that, once found, the petroleum will be withdrawn in a manner that will yield the most economic production over the life of the reservoir.

Crude oil produced by Aramco is not pumped. Combinations of oil, gas and water expansion within the reservoir force the oil to the surface. These energies are augmented by gas and water injection.

When several oil companies compete to take oil from the same field, these natural reservoir pressures may be wasted, resulting in lower recovery of oil over the life of the field. Aramco can plan its oil production to gain the most economic return that science and technology can provide.

The Abqaiq field, Aramco's main source of oil between 1946 and 1952, was brought under a pressure maintenance program in 1954, when the company's first gas injection plant was completed. Dissolved gas produced with oil from the Abqaiq field is separated out, compressed to a pressure of about 2,500 pounds per square inch and returned to the oil-bearing formations through injection wells on the higher part of the structure. A second gas injection plant was installed at 'Ain Dar in 1959, and by 1967 it was possible to inject as much as 350,000,000 cubic feet of gas daily at both plants.

The injection of water around the edge of a reservoir also has proved an effective means of maintaining the production level and increasing the ultimate recovery of oil in some types of fields. In such instances, non-potable water is introduced into the producing formations by drilling injection wells which extend to the flanks of the oil producing formations below. In many injection wells, the water flows by gravity from the water formation into the oil reservoir. In some instances, water from deeper wells is forced by high pressure pumps into the oil producing formations.

The water injection program began in 1956, when 40,000 barrels of water daily were injected through three water injection wells on the northern flanks of the Abqaiq field. Through 1967, fifty-eight water injection wells had been drilled in three fields—Abqaiq, Ghawar and Khursaniyah—and injection averaged more than 1,400,000 barrels daily.

For practical purposes, gas, oil and water do not mix, but are kept largely separated by interfacial tension. This tension is similar to the force that holds a drop of water on a window pane. Because of this interfacial tension, some oil is left in the pore spaces of the rock structures after they have been swept by either gas or water. If these interfacial tensions did not exist, all the oil in the swept pore spaces could be recovered. One method of injection which neutralizes these interfacial tensions in some formations is called the miscible displacement process. This process can be

144

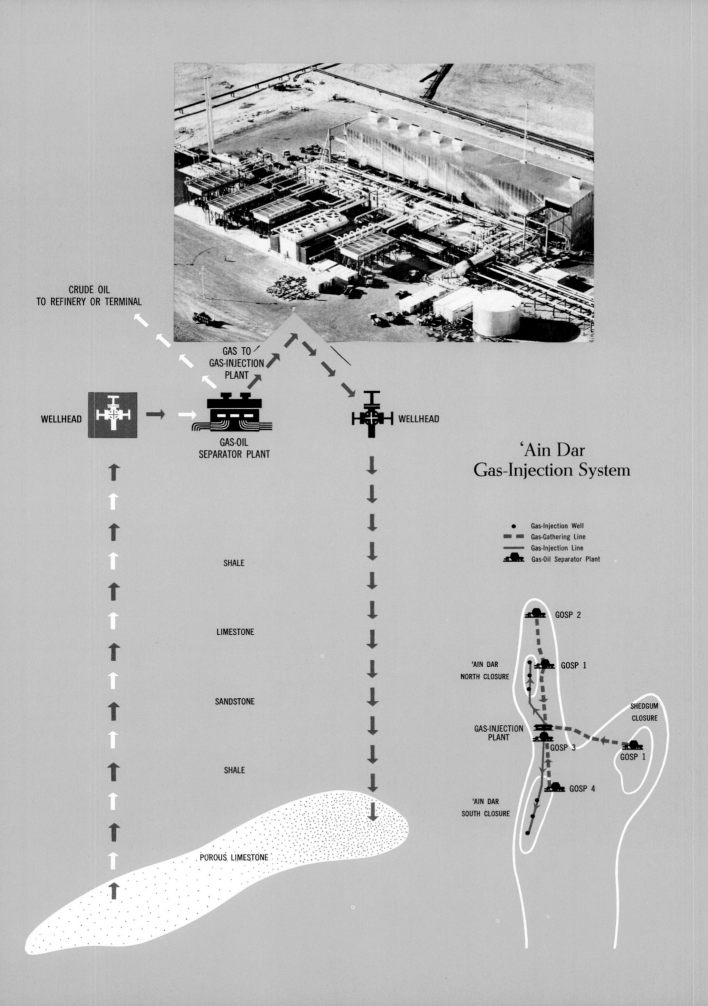

CRUDE OIL
TO REFINERY OR TERMINAL

GAS TO
GAS-INJECTION
PLANT

WELLHEAD

GAS-OIL
SEPARATOR PLANT

WELLHEAD

SHALE

LIMESTONE

SANDSTONE

SHALE

POROUS LIMESTONE

'Ain Dar
Gas-Injection System

• Gas-Injection Well
--- Gas-Gathering Line
— Gas-Injection Line
Gas-Oil Separator Plant

GOSP 2

'AIN DAR
NORTH CLOSURE

GOSP 1

SHEDGUM
CLOSURE

GAS-INJECTION
PLANT

GOSP 3

GOSP 1

GOSP 4

'AIN DAR
SOUTH CLOSURE

achieved by mixing light hydrocarbon liquids with natural gas and injecting the mixture into the crude oil formation. A plant was put in operation in Abqaiq in November, 1961, to remove light hydrocarbon liquids from low pressure gases collected from gas-oil separator plants. These liquids, which contained liquefied petroleum gas (LPG) and natural gasoline, were mixed with natural gas and injected into the 'Ain Dar and Abqaiq fields. The injection averaged 20,000 barrels daily, the equivalent of 30,000,000 cubic feet of gas daily.

Additional studies and cost analysis indicated that while the miscible process improved recovery from the 'Ain Dar field, it was more desirable to sell the LPG than inject it. In October, 1963, the raw LPG portion of the light hydrocarbon stream was removed at Abqaiq and sent by pipelines to Ras Tanura for further processing and sale. In September, 1967, the natural gasoline portion also was removed and shipped to Ras Tanura for blending and export. When sales of LPG and natural gasoline drop below the Abqaiq plant capacity, the excess is injected.

The application of advanced engineering and scientific principles to studies of reservoir conditions upon which gas and liquid injection programs are based requires much theoretical and laboratory analysis. To aid in this research an electric model, called a network analyzer, was built which simulated the reservoir characteristics of the Abqaiq field. The device assisted in predicting reservoir behavior under various programs of production and pressure maintenance. This device later was replaced by computer programs. Production engineers also rely on computers to work out the hundreds of permutations involved in deciding where and when to drill wells, how many wells will be needed for a given development and when and to what extent pressure maintenance should be introduced.

Some of the boiler stacks at the Ras Tanura power plant.

Refrigerated liquefied petroleum gas frosts loading pi

TAPLINE

Since much of Aramco's oil production is destined for European markets, a pipeline shortcut across northern Saudi Arabia and its neighboring Arab states to a Mediterranean port had long been considered as a cheaper means of transportation than the long journey by tanker around the Arabian Peninsula and through the Suez Canal. The world-wide shortage of tankers and of steel for their fabrication during and immediately after World War II led to a decision by Aramco's owner companies to undertake this major pipeline venture. In July, 1945, they incorporated a company in Delaware for this purpose, the Trans-Arabian Pipe Line Company, a name shortened almost immediately to "Tapline." Conventions giving Tapline the right of transit were negotiated with Saudi Arabia, Jordan, Syria and Lebanon, and construction of the pipeline was authorized in March, 1947.

A HOSTILE ROUTE An area more hostile to man and his works than the region in which Tapline was to operate is hard to imagine. Much of the line crossed desert lands where there were no roads, no water and no permanent habitations. The only inhabitants were Bedouin tribes on the move in search of water and grazing. The original surveyors and water-well drillers were the first Westerners to set foot on a great part of the route. Temperatures vary from the extremes of a freezing 10°F to a summer high of over 120°F. At places whole years may pass without a drop of rain, but occasional heavy winter rains inundate the desert. The pipeline route crosses terrain ranging from rolling dunes to gravel or rocky plains interspersed with an occasional dry water course in Saudi Arabia, through broken lava beds and intermittent dry lakes in Jordan, encountering the first signs of agriculture in the plains of southeastern Syria, scaling the steep terraced slopes of the rugged Anti-Lebanon and Lebanon mountains, and terminating on a rocky hillside overlooking the Mediterranean Sea a few miles south of the ancient city of Sidon in Lebanon.

Construction of the pipeline through this remote area, a distance of 754 miles from Sidon to Qaisumah, the eastern terminus of Tapline, plus another 315 miles in Aramco's related gathering system, was a massive effort in logistics, involving the movement of greater tonnages and more men for longer distances than had ever been undertaken on a single project in peacetime. Roads and camps

An innovation in pipelining, nearly half of Tapline was constructed above ground, avoiding costly rock excavation and reducing construction costs.

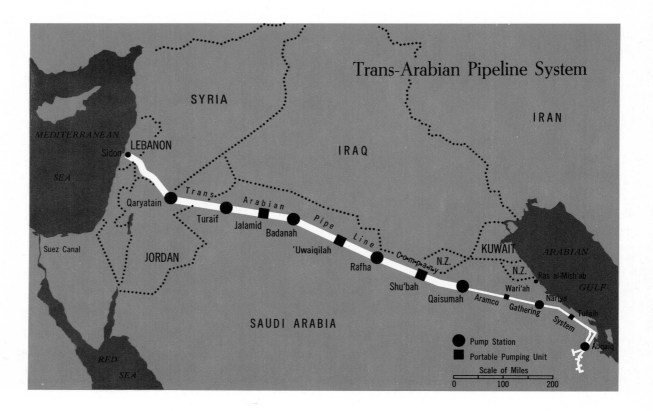

Trans-Arabian Pipeline System

had to be built. Deep wells had to be drilled to find water. More than 350,000 tons of pipe, equipment and materials had to be shipped halfway around the world, then trucked long distances overland. At the peak of construction more than 16,000 men were employed, over 3,000 pieces of motor and construction equipment were in operation, and 10,000,000 ton-miles of pipe and other cargo were hauled monthly.

INNOVATIONS IN PIPELINING To do the job at a cost that would assure the pipeline a competitive advantage over tanker shipment through the Suez Canal required innovations in pipelining. These innovations began with the shipment of the pipe itself. Two sizes were used, thirty and thirty-one-inch, permitting the nesting of one length of thirty-inch pipe inside a length of thirty-one-inch pipe, halving shipping costs. Another was the use of thinner, stronger pipe which would withstand higher operating pressures than the usual industry practice. Perhaps the most important was the construction of the line above ground, supported

in ring girders resting on concrete supports, in areas where the rocky surface would have made orthodox buried pipeline unusually costly. This method was unique in that no expansion bends were provided, and efforts of the pipe to expand or contract by reason of temperature changes were "restrained" and borne by carefully designed stresses in the pipe itself. Over half the line in Saudi Arabia was constructed in this manner, which required precise control of construction, but at a saving of millions of dollars.

Although it was originally planned to begin construction at both ends at about the same time, political disturbances resulting from the Palestine dispute delayed work on the western end until the autumn of 1949. Meanwhile, construction in Saudi Arabia started at Abqaiq in January, 1948, and proceeded steadily westward, operating from a new port and base camp built for the purpose at Ras al-Mish'ab on the Arabian Gulf, some 160 miles north of Dhahran.

The final weld connecting the western and eastern sections was made on September 25, 1950, and the

150

Remotely controlled auxiliary pumping units which require no attendants are spaced midway between main pump stations.

Four main pump stations in Saudi Arabia form the heart of the Tapline system. Each has housing, medical, recreation facilities.

first tanker was loaded at the four-berth Sidon terminal a few months later, on December 2.

The main Tapline pump stations located at Qaisumah, Rafha, Badanah and Turaif, all in Saudi Arabia, provided an initial capacity of 320,000 barrels daily. In 1957 the capacity was increased to 450,000 barrels daily by installation of auxiliary pumping units midway between the main stations. Driven by 5,000-horsepower combustion turbines which burn crude oil taken from the pipeline, these units are remotely controlled and require no attendants. Continuing technical improvements permitting operation at unusually high pressures raised the line's capacity to nearly 480,000 barrels daily by 1967. The two-billionth barrel of oil was received at the Sidon terminal in October, 1966.

NEW COMMUNITIES The remote, uninhabited area of the pipeline imposed upon Tapline the necessity of building complete communities at the main pump stations, with repair shops, supply depots, airstrips, communications, housing, hospitals, schools, feeding and recreation facilities and utilities—everything needed for self-sufficiency. Offices and accommodations had to be provided

nearby for government officials needed to administer the newly opened region. A gravel road was built across the desert to connect the pump stations. The road, the pump stations and the availability of water and medical care provided the stimulus for the development and growth of the northern area of Saudi Arabia. The road along the pipeline gradually was improved and became a main artery for truck transport of commodities from Lebanon, Syria and Jordan to eastern Saudi Arabia and to Kuwait. In agreement with the Saudi Arabian Government a road improvement program was launched in 1963 and paving of the 514 miles of road between Qaisumah and Turaif was completed in 1967. New communities have grown up near the Tapline stations, some as large as 20,000 people.

Since its inception, Tapline has found it necessary on two occasions to increase substantially the transit fees to countries traversed by the pipeline. Meanwhile tankers which compete with Tapline have become larger and more efficient, resulting in lower tanker transportation costs. The 16,500-deadweight-ton tanker which was the main competitor of 1950 has been replaced by the 50,000-tonner through the

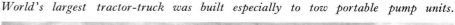

World's largest tractor-truck was built especially to tow portable pump units.

152

Heavy rubber hoses are hooked into the manifold of a tanker to load a cargo of crude oil at Tapline's terminal near Sidon .

Suez Canal and by much larger vessels rounding Africa's Cape of Good Hope to Europe. The closing of the Suez Canal as a result of the June, 1967, Middle East conflict and the resulting transportation crisis set off an unprecedented rush of orders for giant tankers in the 150,000-ton class and larger. Tapline is engaged in an intensive effort to maintain its pipeline shortcut route from the Arabian Gulf to the Mediterranean Sea as an economic means of moving Saudi Arabian crude oil to European markets in the face of higher transit payments and great reductions in competitive tanker costs.

Manifold for switching oil in and out of tanks and on to ships.

THE EMPLOYEES
AND THE COMMUNITY

For most of Aramco's Saudi Arab employees, life in the Eastern Province is roughly similar, in some ways, to life in a Western suburb. They commute to work, buy their homes on monthly payments and watch television in the evening. They even grumble with a touch of pride about the petty annoyances accompanying the seemingly unending construction of improvement projects: streets, water and sewage systems, parks and schools. In towns like al-Khobar, once a village of palm frond huts, shops bulge with consumer goods from all over the world—from American automobiles to Italian fashions to Japanese stereo sets. And what was the former fishing village of Dammam now is the province's main commercial port, the provincial capital—and the home of a growing number of light industries.

A FAR DIFFERENT LAND The two American geologists who landed on the coast of the Arabian Gulf in September, 1933, found a far different land. Almost everything they needed to begin their search for petroleum they either brought with them, or imported later.

The few inhabitants of the area roamed the desert in search of pasturage for their camels, sheep and goats, or lived in villages scattered along the gulf coast or grouped around oases. A man earned his livelihood by shopkeeping, date growing, fishing, pearl diving or shepherding his flocks. Although the Saudi Arabs were well-known throughout the area for their mercantile shrewdness, the large commercial houses were with few exceptions concentrated in the Hijaz, where the annual task of handling an influx of pilgrims led to the development of transport companies, shipping offices, import agencies and some banking operations. An established commercial structure of this nature was almost entirely absent in the Eastern Province. Technical and clerical skills needed by an oil company were in scarce supply. For a long time to come, the company looked to the outside for its supplies and its skilled workmen.

As the tempo of oil prospecting increased, the requirements of the enterprise and its people far outpaced the existing provincial economy. The company built offices, shops, roads, clinics and recreation facilities. It acted as the employees' grocer and banker, laundryman and dry cleaner, and even cobbled shoes. Now a growing business community provides most of these services. The thriving business communities found in the Eastern Province are the result of a concomitance of factors including the appearance of a number of competent local entrepreneurs, encouragement from the Saudi Arabian Government and a deliberate policy by Aramco to look to the local economy as much as possible for its service requirements.

It was, in fact, the sheer variety and magnitude of such needs that eventually gave rise to certain

154

company decisions that were to have a great impact on the Eastern Province. In the belief that its own well-being would be best sustained in a strong local economy, the company gradually instituted employee training programs, began giving technical and financial assistance to business and industrial concerns, helped in the development of agriculture and medical care, offered home loans to employees and increasingly encouraged Saudi Arabian companies to import and stock necessary supplies. Inevitably there were some failures and misunderstandings, but many ventures flourished.

TRAINING In the early days, the training of Saudi Arab employees was informal; drillers, craftsmen and office workers taught their particular specialities on the job. Schools in the province were scarce and literacy, particularly among the Bedouins, was rare. Although on-the-job training worked well and still is used by the company, a more intensive effort was needed to achieve the level at which seven of

every ten Saudi Arab employees are now supervised by their fellow countrymen.

The answer was formal training in academic and craft-shop classrooms, plus a policy which gives employees an opportunity for higher education or advanced vocational training abroad. Abqaiq, Dhahran and Ras Tanura each has an Industrial Training Center which offers instruction in Arabic and English, mathematics, the sciences, social studies and the operation of business machines. Training Center courses are available both during regular working hours on company time and in early evenings on the employee's own time.

Classroom instruction in the crafts is also provided, whereby employees learn on company time how to become better electricians, instrument repairmen, refrigeration mechanics and machinery and air-conditioning maintenance men.

The training program is far from static. Courses, academic standards and the teacher complement all evolve with the company's changing operating

The Industrial Training Center for employees in Dhahran.

155

NATIONALITY OF ARAMCO EMPLOYEES IN SAUDI ARABIA

	1952	Percentage of Total	1967	Percentage of Total
Saudi Arabs	14,819	61.7	9,813	81.3
Americans	3,235	13.5	1,284	10.6
Other Arabs	2,254	9.4	328	2.7
Indians	1,110	4.6	408	3.4
Pakistanis	1,320	5.5	227	1.9
Others	1,268	5.3	13	.1
Totals	24,006	100.0	12,073	100.0

In 1952 during a period of extensive construction of operating and support facilities, the company had 24,006 employees in Saudi Arabia, of whom only 61.7 percent were Saudi Arabs. Fifteen years later, even with increasingly active oil operations, the number of employees was 12,073 but the percentage of Saudi Arabs had increased to 81.3. A steady reduction in the number of American and other foreign employees was possible because of the development of Saudi Arabs with the requisite skills. The jobs held by Saudi Arabs range from roughnecks on drilling rigs to surgeons in the company's health centers; they maintain equipment all the way from bulldozers to aircraft.

In the same fifteen-year period the number of Saudis in professional and the higher level supervisory jobs rose from six to more than 200; the number of skilled workmen increased tenfold; the number classified as unskilled declined to one-tenth of its former total. In 1952 Saudi Arabs constituted thirty-one percent of the employees classified as semiskilled or higher. In 1967 more than eighty percent of such jobs were held by Saudi Arabs.

As an American company, Aramco has depended upon Americans for management direction, advanced technical knowledge and oil industry experience. The company, however, through training and supervisory development, seeks to give Saudi Arabs the greatest possible opportunity to participate in company operations. Another measure of the development of Saudi Arab employees is the number of supervisory jobs held by them—approximately 800 of the 1,400 such positions.

Although small in number—eight percent of the total in 1967—employees other than Saudi Arabs and Americans have provided skills which still are in short supply in Saudi Arabia. In this group are medical personnel from India, accountants from Pakistan, teachers from Jordan and translators from Lebanon.

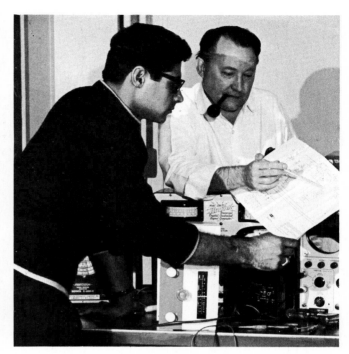

Laboratory trainee prepares sample rock core for testing. *Instructor goes over electronics problem with employee.*

requirements and the level of skills available. Even more important, the company has benefitted in recent years from the rising standards of schools and vocational institutes. Government emphasis on education has now given rise to a school system which has enabled Aramco to demand and get candidates for employment with the equivalent of a ninth-grade education.

Such progress has enabled the company to become more selective in its training practices and concentrate on the development of employees of promise. For example, a number of young employees, assigned to Abqaiq and Ras Tanura, have been enrolled in the Technical and Supervisory Program, which takes about ten years to complete. The curriculum in both districts is similar, except that in Abqaiq the accent is on drilling, and in Ras Tanura on refinery operation. Students are put in a training cycle in academic subjects and crafts for a minimum of a year, then work on the job for a year. Those who complete the program

successfully will attain supervisory responsibility. Qualified candidates who need advanced training not available locally are sent abroad, usually to the United States. A good example of such training is advanced electronics work.

A program of some years standing gathers Saudi Arabs who are supervisors or candidates for positions of leadership to improve their communications and supervisory skills. Courses being taught or planned, which would take up to 1,200 hours to cover, begin with basic elements of supervision and go through advanced seminars on organization and functions of the company. A newer offering, "Human Relations in Industry," gives groups of Saudi Arabs and Americans, working with an outside specialist as leader, an opportunity to sharpen their supervisory skills around the same table. Meeting twice weekly for eighteen sessions, the groups use the case study approach in attempting to resolve actual personnel problems taken from the files.

Each year selection boards choose a number of

157

This school in Dammam is one of thirty built and maintained by Aramco under its agreement with the Saudi Arab Government.

158

Saudi Arab employees recommended by their supervisors to go abroad for further education, practical work experience or a combination of both. Some employees work toward an associate degree while others try for a bachelor of arts or science degree. Employees in the Analytical and Budget Department might be sent to the Bentley College of Accounting and Finance in Boston. Others whose jobs require a broader educational background may attend such institutions as Antioch, Bucknell, George Washington University or San Francisco State.

This encouragement of education goes beyond the company's ranks. By a long-standing agreement with the government Aramco has built schools in Eastern Province cities and towns for both the children of its employees and the population at large. Thirty schools for boys and girls in the primary and intermediate grades have been constructed. Additionally, maintenance and operating costs are paid by the company, but each school becomes an integral part of the government's educational system.

Aramco also offers scholarships for college study abroad to Saudi Arab men and women. Recipients of the sixty scholarships are chosen by the Ministry of Education, and the scholarships are administered jointly by the government and the participating universities and colleges.

HOME OWNERSHIP In the early days of the Aramco enterprise most Saudi Arab employees lived as bachelors in company quarters. Originally there was a heavy turnover in employees as men who had previously lived pretty much as they pleased decided whether they wished to meet the daily demands of working in a modern industrial enterprise. The employee group gradually stabilized and by 1967 the average Saudi employee had been with Aramco for more than sixteen years.

Employees study actual cases from personnel files in training courses on supervisory techniques.

This home in Dammam was built by an Aramco employee with a loan obtained from the company's Home Ownership Program.

With this growing stability, Saudi Arab employees in increasing numbers began to bring their families into the operations area. To head off a proliferation of shanty towns and substandard housing, the company in 1951 instituted a home ownership program. The distinctive feature of the Aramco plan is its reliance on the development of natural communities. Rather than build, operate and maintain living areas for its Saudi Arab em-

ployees separate from the general population, the company, with government cooperation, began to encourage employees to build or purchase homes in existing communities.

The basis of the plan is an interest-free loan from the company to Saudi Arab employees. The company forgives twenty percent of the total amount of the loan, which includes a five percent service charge, and the employee pays the balance through

160

monthly deductions from his pay. At the end of 1967 a total of 6,780 Saudi Arab employees had used this plan to buy their own homes. In building a home, the employee chooses his own contractor and his own house design.

The company also took specific steps to foster the development of modern communities. Interest-free loans totaling eight and a half million dollars were extended to Dammam and al-Khobar for construction of municipal water and sewage systems. Financial and technical assistance was given to electric companies in the area. A branch of the Ministry of Interior which directs town planning and municipal development has also played a decisive role in the orderly growth of these communities. Although many employees buy their building lots, the government has assisted by granting free title to some land.

A Saudi Arab employee who has acquired a home under this company program has the assurance after his retirement of the possession of a good home in a local community among his friends and relatives. As an additional element of security, if a Saudi Arab employee dies or is totally disabled before paying off his home loan, the balance is forgiven so that his house is free of debt.

One important by-product of Aramco's encouragement of employee home ownership has been to strengthen the local economy by creating a substantial market for all types of building materials and home furnishings. Locally manufactured cement, concrete building blocks and iron grill-work go into the construction of these houses, and the builders putting them up are getting solid experience which they can put to use in other types of construction projects.

TECHNICAL ASSISTANCE Out of a nucleus of American employees who took an interest in helping some Saudi Arab friend fix a piece of equipment or launch a small business has grown an Aramco organization, the Arab Industrial Development Department, which greatly affects people's lives

in the Eastern Province. The plentiful vegetables in the local *suq*, or market, as well as the paper bags in which customers carry them away; uniforms worn by Dammam dock workers and Saudi Arab Boy Scouts; the growing electric system; business firms that can construct a highway, put up a school or drill a water well are examples of the products and services that have their origins in this department.

Aramco had reason for wanting to help local enterprises get off to a good start. The company wished to divest itself of many supply and service sidelines so it could concentrate more of its energies on the production of petroleum.

Over the years the men trying on behalf of the company to help strengthen the local economy have worked out several guidelines. The types of businesses they recommend for company financial or technical assistance tend to provide life's necessities or increase the comfort and convenience of

An al-Khobar plant makes ice cream, other dairy products.

At the al-Qahtani concern in Dammam, pipe is oiled, wrapped and coated with cement for use in underwater pipelines.

the local populace, make the greatest use of local labor and materials, or supply some basic ingredient upon which other businesses depend.

The kind of proposition receiving high priority for company assistance is one which contributes to economic takeoff. A good example is electric power. An Aramco study, plus technical and financial assistance, led to the establishment of a single electric company for Dammam and Al-Khobar and resulted in reduced electric rates.

A printing press in Dammam, which for some time had been handling jobs ranging from business cards to pamphlets, now prints the company's high-quality, Arabic-language monthly magazine and the company's four-color annual review. A paper products company expanded into plastic sheeting and tubing, and sacks for cement, lime and chicken feed. A plant in al-Khobar makes ice cream, reconstituted milk, yogurt and buttermilk. Local concerns have built dwellings, offices and

warehouses, laid pipelines up to forty-two inches in diameter and installed chilled-water systems for air-conditioning on land and oil-producing platforms offshore.

Other Saudi Arab companies operate buses on which employees commute between home and job, and lease fleets of vehicles to the company. Many of these businesses got their start under the aegis of Aramco. The important thing is that they now provide services of which many Saudi Arabs as well as foreigners take advantage.

LOCAL PURCHASING In various offices throughout Aramco there are sets of thick books, their spines permanently secured to racks, much like the sets of books in public telephone booths which serve many large cities of the world. Like these public phone directories, most of the thick reference books found in the company have a well-thumbed look. They are catalogues listing the 73,000 or so

An agriculture expert discusses the first grain crop with a farm worker at the Al-Faysal Settlement Project at Haradh.

163

Poultry raising, relatively new in the Eastern Province, has proven to be a highly successful agricultural industry.

items Aramco must have in stock to support its oil operations in Saudi Arabia.

For many years Aramco obtained all of its supplies directly from abroad. Now the company makes a concerted effort to build strong and dependable sources of supply among Saudi Arab businessmen. The company's aim is to do as much of its shopping locally as is practical, and looks to the day when fully eighty to eighty-five percent of its purchases are made from Saudi Arab merchants. In 1967, goods and services purchased through local agencies totaled $62.5 million.

There are, of course, special items from time to time which cannot be covered by a standard company stock number. Examples range from docking tugs, mobile cranes and launches for use of offshore drilling crews to lathes, electric motors

and transformers, all of which have been purchased through Saudi Arab channels.

AGRICULTURAL AID There always have been farmers in the Eastern Province working their small plots in the oases of Qatif and al-Hasa and raising such traditional produee as dates, watermelons, squash, and the yard-long, thin so-called snake cucumbers. The limited variety and uneven quality of their harvests were understandable because the farmers worked in climatic and soil conditions which are among the world's least favorable for agriculture. The same adverse environment had a similar effect on poultry raising.

Before 1958 carrots, cauliflower, celery, parsley, red radishes, green beans, peas and corn were not grown and rarely consumed in the Eastern

164

Province. Nowadays, these vegetables and many more are readily available in season—and the season for many of them is being extended all the time. It all started when Aramco decided to do something about the dearth of fresh vegetables and hired an agriculturist to help farmers in nearby oasis communities solve their problems. The agriculturist and his staff give advice and put on field demonstrations to illustrate the value of chemical fertilizers, insecticides, improved seeds and small tools and equipment. They watch the progress of the growth of crops, advise on marketing methods and ask cooperating farmers to pass along new methods to their neighbors.

Although this agricultural plan was set up initially to fill the fresh vegetable needs of employees and to give an economic boost to local farmers, the company saw from the beginning that if the program succeeded, benefits would reach a much broader section of the people. And that is exactly how things have turned out. Aramco bought about ninety percent of the first small crops of vegetables raised by the farmers. Now the crops of produce have grown so that Aramco buys less than five percent; the rest goes to local markets, and, more recently, to neighboring countries.

Egg production in the Eastern Province in 1960, the year the company began to take an active interest in poultry, was a mere fifty thousand dozen. With help similar to that Aramco was giving truck farmers, poultrymen quadrupled their egg yields over the next three years. Then the company's agriculturalists got a group of poultry farmers together to form a cooperative and resulting egg production has been climbing precipitiously ever since, to more than one and a half million dozen a year. Aramco's egg purchases, meanwhile, have been dropping in proportion and most of the eggs are sold on the local market.

On other projects the company's experts made a preliminary study and then usually brought in a consultant to draw up detailed specifications and cost estimates. The findings were reported to the

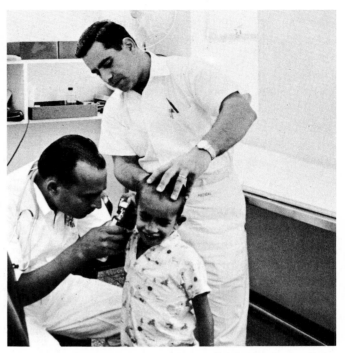

A doctor examines an employee's son at the Dhahran clinic.

A technician prepares a denture in the Dhahran dental clinic.

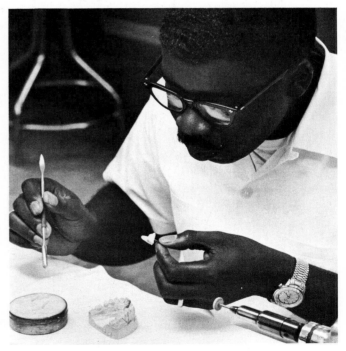

165

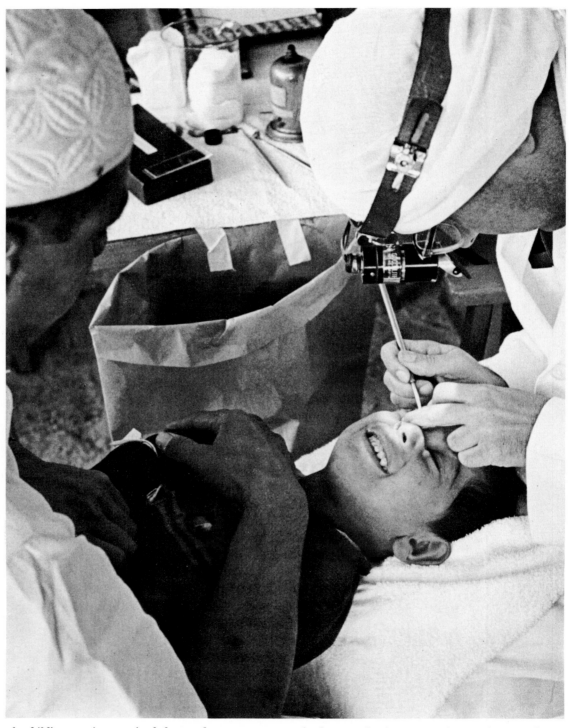

A child's eye is examined by a doctor as part of the search for a vaccine against trachoma.

166

Ministry of Agriculture. If ministry officials approved the project, the government bore the responsibility—and the cost—of carrying it out.

With the company's active interest, an experimental farm was established just north of Hofuf, the Qatif Oasis was crisscrossed with engineered drainage and irrigation systems, an enormous sand dune field which once seriously threatened the existence of several al-Hasa villages was stabilized and a 10,000-acre desert tract in remote Haradh, known as the Al-Faysal Settlement Project, was laid out for conversion into farms and villages on which Bedouins will be offered a settled existence. On the Haradh project, the company drilled irrigation wells and leveled and planted the first 100-acre pilot plot.

MEDICAL SERVICES The Dhahran Health Center is the focal point of Aramco's efforts in curative and preventive medicine. The center houses nursing, administrative, preventive medicine, clinical and surgical staffs, a dental section and 130 beds. Small health centers of fourteen beds each are maintained in Ras Tanura and Abqaiq.

The company assists two private hospitals in al-Khobar—ash-Sharq and as-Salamah. About sixty percent of the employees requiring hospitalization are cared for in ash-Sharq and as-Salamah hospitals at company expense. As a result of this arrangement, a Saudi Arab community has two medical institutions which give high-quality hospital care not only to Aramco patients but to the general public as well.

The reputation the Dhahran Health Center enjoys for the quality of its care has over the years generated a heavy demand for its services among the population at large. While the creation of the two new hospitals in al-Khobar, the establishment of the government's Dammam Central Hospital and a great increase in the number of private physicians in the area have all helped to ease this pressure, about 420,000 clinic visits by company employees, their dependents and members of the general public are still being made each year to the company's health centers, which, taken together, have one of the largest out-patient loads in the world.

While the company provides employees and their dependents with care when they are ill or injured, it places equal stress on preventive medicine. Wives of employees receive prenatal care and are taught practical and up-to-date methods of child care. Under a nurse's watchful direction a new mother may prepare and give food to her child and learn how to take care of him when he is ill. Such instruction has reduced markedly the incidence of malnutrition and diarrhea, formerly the commonest causes of infant mortality. In addition, mothers and children receive appropriate immunizations.

In the early Nineteen Fifties it was common to see teams of men in Eastern Province towns and villages spraying nooks and crannies of buildings with DDT. The company had joined with the government to fight the mosquito, which had been causing malaria in the region for centuries. Malaria now is rare and the government has assumed responsibility for keeping it that way with regular spraying. The good results brought by the first efforts against malaria demonstrated that widespread diseases which the people used to accept as their lot can be brought under control if attacked vigorously at their source.

Pulmonary tuberculosis is a case in point. Largely because of regular X-ray examinations and skin testing to detect the disease, followed by effective treatment, the number of cases of pulmonary tuberculosis among employees decreased seventy-five percent between 1956 and 1966.

Another weapon used to control communicable diseases is the needle. Men, women and children had been trooping into company clinics to get their shots long before, but in 1960 Aramco formalized its immunization program and began to keep detailed records. Since 1960 an average of 140,000 immunizations have been given to employees and their families each year. These include procedures

167

against diphtheria, typhoid, tetanus, whooping cough, polio, tuberculosis and, most recently, measles in the young.

The newest disease holding the attention of company medics is schistosomiasis, or bilharzia, widely seen in Egypt and Iraq. The disease results from the infestation of the bloodstream by a parasitic worm which breeds in fresh water. In Saudi Arabia apparently some kind of natural barrier separates the fresh-water breeding grounds, such as wells, from the non-infected areas. This barrier runs roughly down the middle of the country, which leaves the Eastern Province practically unaffected.

But since one-third of Aramco's Saudi Arab employees have their origins in the western part of the country and make vacation trips home, employees who visit infected areas are watched carefully for signs of the disease. Water sources known to harbor schistosomiasis are charted on a special map, as are any new sources moving in the direction of the Arabian Gulf.

TRACHOMA RESEARCH Since 1954 Aramco has been involved in one medical effort which, if its goal is met, will benefit vast populations of the world. In that year, the company joined forces with the Harvard School of Public Health to study trachoma in the hope of finding a vaccine against this blinding eye disease. Thus far the company has spent more than a million dollars in the quest. Research teams working in the Dhahran Health Center and in Boston have made experimental vaccines which were tested in the field, with moderately encouraging results.

Trachoma researchers are at the stage where they are attempting to discover, for example, how many types of trachoma organisms there are in a given Eastern Province community, whether every member of an infected family has the same type, and if a trachoma victim carries the same strain at every stage of the disease. Teams of Arabic-speaking nurses visit villages to study victims of the

disease, who in Saudi Arabia are first infected in infancy or childhood.

A project to improve health service in the Eastern Province has been undertaken jointly by the Ministry of Health and the World Health Organization (WHO), with some assistance from Aramco. The plan uses Dammam Central Hospital as a main base hospital and a satellite community health center in Safwa, between Dhahran and Ras Tanura. The company pays the costs of the team of international experts from WHO.

Company specialists in health education distribute posters and pamphlets to surrounding government schools and show health films in school assemblies and social clubs. Using demonstrations and motion pictures, they conduct a series of informal courses with groups of village women on such topics as the elements of nutrition and the eradication of insects and rodents.

ARAMCO TELEVISION When Aramco television goes on the air every night, it is estimated that there are about 380,000 Arabic-speaking viewers. The station, HZ 22 TV, broadcasts an average of thirty-seven hours a week. Each evening's schedule begins with a reading from the Quran, followed by features especially selected for children. About one-third of the programs fall into the educational category and include films dealing with popular science and travel and local shows on, say, health, highway safety, home economics and Middle Eastern literature. For entertainment, Aramco TV imports from the United States situation and comedy shows and full-length movies, all of which have been dubbed so that viewers hear Lucille Ball, Edmond O'Brian, Doris Day and Cary Grant speaking fluent Arabic. English-speaking viewers can simply turn down the television sound and pick up the film's original sound track on a special radio frequency.

Trees, lawns and hedges transform the desert in Aramco communities as in this residential area of Dhahran.

168

The station also broadcasts motion pictures produced in the Middle East, documentaries and newsreel-type specials made by the station's film unit, and big-time sports events filmed abroad. The station's staff can judge accurately the viewing tastes of their preponderantly Saudi Arab audience because nearly every member, including the station manager, is a Saudi Arab.

PUBLICATIONS Several periodicals inform Arabic and English-speaking readers about what is going on in the company, and on the traditions, geography and people of the Middle East in general and Saudi Arabia in particular. The weekly *Qafilat az-Zait* (Oil Caravan) carries company news for Saudi Arab employees. The monthly edition of *Qafilat Az-Zait* is an Arabic-language magazine carrying in-depth features about oil operations and articles on scientific advances, Islam and the Arab heritage, poetry, and regular columns of special interest to Arab readers. The well-designed periodical has become a favorite medium of expression for noted Saudi Arab and other Middle Eastern writers. Surveys indicate each issue is read by as many as 200,000 persons all over the Arabic-speaking world.

Each Wednesday the *Sun and Flare* is distributed to the Aramco community, carrying company news and topical features written for American and other English-speaking employees. *Aramco World*, a magazine edited and published six times a year in Beirut, focuses exclusively on the Middle East and on the influence that area has had on other parts of the world. By far the greatest proportion of its complimentary subscriptions goes to the United States, where readers of the magazine have an opportunity to become acquainted through its pages with the Middle Eastern scene—its people, history, religious beliefs and social development, its notable sites and the oil industry which touches so many lives in that vital region.

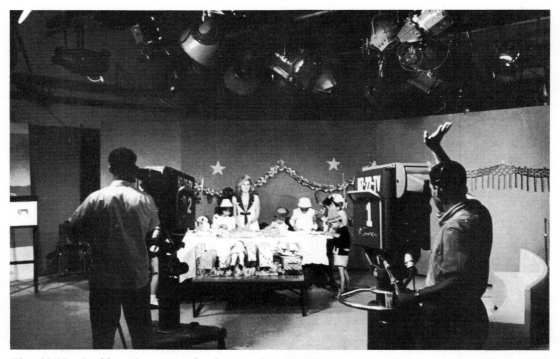

The Children's Show is among the features broadcast by Aramco television station HZ 22 TV.

Soccer is the most popular sport in Saudi Arabia and the company maintains fields in all three districts for teams of employees.

171

Part 4

Saudi Arabia:

The Government

The People

The Land

THE ARABIAN PENINSULA

Saudi Arabia occupies about four-fifths of the Arabian Peninsula, which is bounded by the Red Sea on the west, the Gulf of Aden and the Arabian Sea on the south, and the Gulf of Oman and the Arabian Gulf on the east.

The length of the peninsula from the Gulf of Aqaba to the Arabian Sea is about 1,400 miles. The width through the narrower northern part between the Red Sea and the Arabian Gulf is about 750 miles, but across the southern part between the Red Sea and the Gulf of Oman it is about 1,200 miles.

The area of the peninsula is slightly more than a million square miles, or about one-third the size of the continental United States.

BOUNDARIES Saudi Arabia stretches from the Red Sea to the Arabian Gulf in the northern half of the peninsula, but in the wider southern part it is bordered by several neighboring states. To the southwest on the Red Sea is Yemen. About a hundred miles east of the southwestern tip of the Arabian Peninsula is the port city of Aden. Aden and its hinterland were administered by Britain as the Eastern and Western Protectorates for many years. Britain withdrew on November 29, 1967, and the area became the People's Republic of Southern Yemen. The eastern part of the new nation encompasses the famous valley of Hadhramaut. Northeast of Hadhramaut is the Sultan of Muscat's province of Dhufar.

The northern border of Yemen with Saudi Arabia, running from the vicinity of Najran to the Red Sea, has been defined and marked, but not so the border running south from Najran. From Yemen to Qatar, in a great arc swinging around the sands of the Rub' al-Khali, the boundaries of Saudi Arabia have never been agreed upon.

Almost all the small states which lie along the southeastern periphery of the Arabian Peninsula have close treaty relations with Great Britain, and for over twenty-five years Saudi Arabia and Britain have made intermittent efforts to settle various boundaries in this region. The Arabian Peninsula's eastern bulge, part of which has long been referred to as Oman (generally east of 56°E), includes the seven small British-protected shaykhdoms of the Trucial Coast. In 1955 the Sultan of Muscat, who as Ruler of Muscat had until then administered only small strips of coast on the Gulf of Oman, using British help, extended his rule westward over the mountainous area to the sands of the Rub' al-Khali and northward to the Buraimi Oasis. This area had comprised the Imamate of Oman for centuries, and Saudi Arabia has continued to recognize the Imam's claim to it. Sovereignty over the Buraimi

Comparative Areas

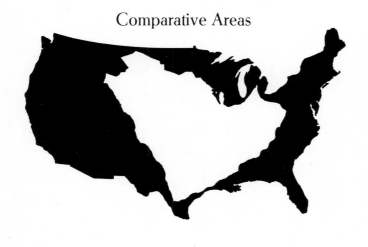

Oasis is in dispute between Saudi Arabia on the one hand and Britain, representing Muscat and Abu Dhabi, on the other. An arbitration tribunal was disrupted in 1955 by the withdrawal of the British member. British-led forces proceeded to occupy the area under dispute in the name of the Ruler of Abu Dhabi and the Sultan of Muscat. The region of az-Zafrah is similarly in dispute between Saudi Arabia and Abu Dhabi.

Southeast of Dhahran, site of Aramco's headquarters, lie two British-protected shaykhdoms, the peninsula of Qatar and the Bahrain Islands. An offshore boundary between Saudi Arabia and Bahrain was agreed upon in 1958, and the governments of Qatar and Saudi Arabia reached an agreement on their common boundary in 1965.

North of Saudi Arabia lie Jordan, Iraq, Kuwait, and two areas designated as Neutral Zones. Saudi Arabia shares equal rights with Iraq in one Neutral Zone and with Kuwait in the other. Boundaries with Kuwait and Iraq were defined at al-'Uqayr in 1922, at which time the two Neutral Zones were created. The boundary with Iraq and the limits of the Saudi Arabia-Iraq Neutral Zone have been surveyed but not marked. Ambiguities in the original agreement have led to disagreement over the precise course to be taken in the demarcation. The boundary with Kuwait and the limits of the Saudi Arabia-Kuwait Neutral Zone were surveyed

and demarcated in 1965 and a boundary agreement was signed and ratified by the two governments. Saudi Arabia and Jordan concluded a boundary agreement in 1965, which involved a minor exchange of territory, giving Jordan additional territory near its sole port of Aqaba.

Saudi Arabia considers as territorial waters a belt twelve miles wide around its coasts, including many island possessions, and asserts jurisdiction over areas of seabed and subsoil beyond this belt. With one exception, Bahrain, Saudi Arabia's offshore boundaries vis-à-vis that of its neighbors have yet to be established. The southern offshore boundary of the Saudi Arabia-Kuwait Neutral Zone has been agreed upon in principle, with the northern boundary to be submitted to a qualified commission for resolution.

Of increasing importance is the question of jurisdiction over the seabed and subsoil in the Arabian Gulf beyond the twelve-mile limits of the bordering countries. The existence of oil-bearing structures in such areas has led to development of a median line approach under which ownership of minerals lying beneath international waters would be determined. This approach was used as the basis for a median line agreement between Iran and Saudi Arabia, initialed in December, 1965. By the end of 1967, however, the agreement had not been formally signed by either government.

PROVINCES AND DISTRICTS The Kingdom of Saudi Arabia is divided into geographical districts, which have been subdivided into administrative districts or provinces. These geographical divisions, which are essentially topographical and by no means identical with the modern administrative structure, include the Hijaz, Najd, 'Asir and al-Hasa.

NAJD Traditionally Najd, which contains the capital, Riyadh, and covers a large part of the interior of the country, is divided into a number of subdistricts. The northernmost part of Najd, just south of the Great Nafud, is the district of Jabal

176

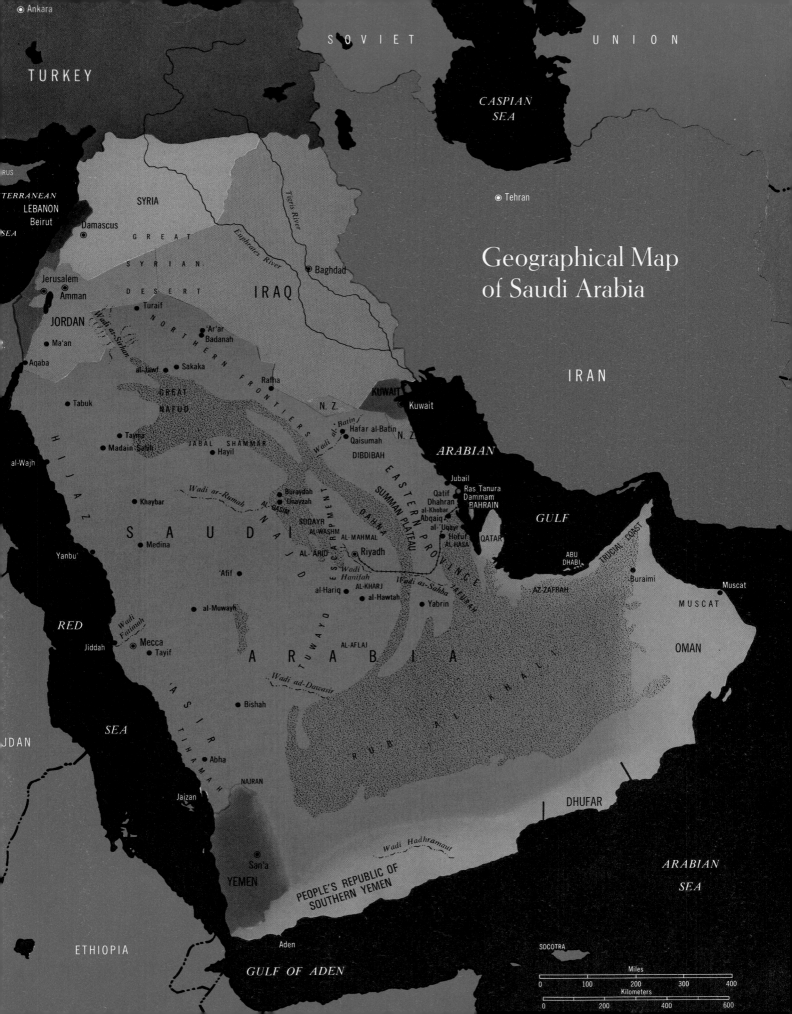

Geographical Map
of Saudi Arabia

Ankara

SOVIET   UNION

TURKEY

CASPIAN
SEA

RUS

TERRANEAN
LEBANON
Beirut

SEA

SYRIA

Damascus

Tehran

GREAT

Tigris River

SYRIAN

Euphrates River

Jerusalem
Amman

DESERT

Baghdad

IRAQ

JORDAN

Turaif

Wadi ar-Sirhan

'Ar'ar
Badanah

NORTHERN FRONTIERS

IRAN

Ma'an

al-Jawf   Sakaka

Aqaba

Rafha

Tabuk

GREAT
NAFUD

N. Z.

Wadi al-Batin

KUWAIT

Kuwait

Hafar al-Batin

ARABIAN

Tayma

Qaisumah

N. Z.

Madain Salih

JABAL SHAMMAR

DIBDIBAH

EASTERN

Jubail

Ras Tanura

al-Wajh

Hayil

Khaybar

Wadi ar-Rumah

SODAYR

Buraydah
Unayzah

AL-QASIM

Wadi al-Sahba

SUMMAN PLATEAU

Qatif
Dhahran
al-Khobar
Abqaiq
al-'Uqayr

Ras Tanura
Dammam
BAHRAIN

GULF

HIJAZ

DAHNA

PROVINCE

Medina

AL-WASHM

AL-MAHMAL

Hofuf
AL-HASA

QATAR

SAUDI

NAJD

ESCARPMENT

AL-'ARID

Riyadh

ABU
DHABI

TRUCIAL COAST

Buraimi

Muscat

Yanbu'

'Afif

Wadi
Hanifah

NAFURAN

AZ ZAFRAH

MUSCAT

al-Hariq
al-Hawtah

AL-KHARJ

Wadi as-Sahba

Yabrin

TUWAYQ

RED

Wadi
Fatimah

al-Muwayh

OMAN

Jiddah

Mecca
Tayif

ARABIA

AL-AFLAJ

RUB   AL   KHALI

SEA

'ASIR

Wadi ad-Dawasir

JDAN

SEA

TIHAMAH

Bishah

Abha

NAJRAN

ARABIAN

Jaizan

DHUFAR

SEA

Wadi Hadhramaut

San'a

YEMEN

PEOPLE'S REPUBLIC OF
SOUTHERN YEMEN

ETHIOPIA

Aden

SOCOTRA

GULF OF ADEN

Miles

0   100   200   300   400

Kilometers

0   200   400   600

Shammar, which takes its name from one of the most powerful tribes of the north. Jabal Shammar was the domain of the House of Rashid, which during the second half of the last century contended with the House of Sa'ud for mastery over the interior of the peninsula.

Southeast of Jabal Shammar in Najd is the district of the Qasim, athwart the course of Wadi ar-Rumah. The large towns of 'Unayzah and Buraydah in the Qasim are the home of an industrious and talented people famous from India to Egypt as traders. Southeast of the Qasim is the district of Sudayr, the original home of the well-known Sudayri family. The capital of Sudayr is al-Majma'ah.

In the many districts of Najd which are administered from Riyadh, most of the settlements are located in oases in the valleys which cut through the Tuwayq Escarpment. North of Riyadh are the districts of al-Washm and al-Mahmal. Riyadh itself is situated in the district of al-'Arid, where Wadi Hanifah is the principal valley. Wadi Hanifah runs southward and then eastward to the district of al-Kharj, the site of unusual spring-fed pools of water and a government farm. Following the line of the Tuwayq Escarpment south of Riyadh are the oases of al-Hawtah and al-Hariq, the district of al-Aflaj, and the long valley of Wadi ad-Dawasir, named after a large tribe which has distributed its nomadic and settled members over much of eastern Arabia.

THE HIJAZ The Hijaz, which contains the holiest cities in Islam—Mecca and Medina—was a separate kingdom until conquered by 'Abd al-'Aziz in 1924-25. The Hijaz includes much of the western portion of Saudi Arabia and in modern usage, along with 'Asir, is sometimes called the Western Province. Jiddah is the country's main port on the Red Sea and a center of banking and commerce. Generally speaking, the Hijaz includes the modern administrative areas governed from Mecca, Medina, Tabuk, Ranyah, Bishah and al-Baha.

'ASIR In the 'Asir area, Jaizan, a town on the Red Sea just north of Yemen, is the capital of the low-lying coastal district of Tihamah. Abha, some 8,000 feet above sea level, is the capital of the highland district of 'Asir proper. Najran is a cluster of fertile little oases in the interior. Saudi Arabia's possession of this area was confirmed as a result of a brief war with Yemen in 1934.

AL-HASA Al-Hasa is the former geographical title of a portion of the present Eastern Province, the region along the Arabian Gulf where the oil fields are located. Al-Hasa took its name from the oasis of al-Hasa, in which the former provincial capital, Hofuf, is located. The principal towns of al-Hasa include, in addition to the oasis of al-Hasa, the Qatif Oasis and Tarut Island, the modern provincial capital of Dammam, the cosmopolitan town of al-Khobar, and Aramco's towns at Dhahran, Ras Tanura and Abqaiq and its facilities in Nariya, Qaisumah, Safaniya, Manifa and other producing areas. The present Eastern Province also includes large sections of the Rub' al-Khali—the Empty Quarter.

MODERN ADMINISTRATIVE DISTRICTS There are eighteen administrative districts in the kingdom. Five of these—the Eastern Province, the Riyadh and Mecca areas, Hayil and the Northern Frontiers—are considered major amirates or provinces. The Medina area and the Qasim in Najd are administered like the five major amirates, though they are not considered to be as important. These seven amirates make up the largest portion of the kingdom, roughly seven-ninths of the total land mass, and include most of the cities and large towns. The governors of these provinces report directly to the Minister of Interior. Governors of the other provinces and districts report to the Deputy Minister of Interior. During the reign of King 'Abd al-'Aziz, the provincial governors—amirs—administered their provinces semiautonomously, in the King's name. Although many of the provincial

King Faysal ibn 'Abd al-'Aziz Al Faysal Al Sa'ud.

Crown Prince Khalid ibn 'Abd al-'Aziz Al Faysal Al Sa'ud.

governors are leading members of the royal family and powerful figures in their own right, the provinces are closely tied into the central government in Riyadh and are under the jurisdiction of the Ministry of Interior. At one time local officials of central government agencies were subordinates of the provincial governor; now most of these officials report to their respective ministries in Riyadh, though they receive nominal supervision from the governor. Provincial department heads, who represent central government ministries, such as education, finance, health and agriculture, coordinate their activities with the provincial governor. Local government organizations—municipalities and the governorates of towns and villages—report to the provincial governor through his local amirs or subgovernors and not to a central government agency. Municipal councils and village and town headmen, *'umdahs*, are locally elected and are under the jurisdiction of local subgovernors.

179

MODERN SAUDI ARABIA

When Faysal became King of Saudi Arabia in November, 1964, he assumed the throne of a kingdom that had been shaped to a great degree by his father, 'Abd al-'Aziz. Before his death in November, 1953, King 'Abd al-'Aziz had brought the kingdom to essentially its present boundaries and had established the character of its administration. Saudi Arabia has no single formal constitution like that of the United States. The *Shari'ah*, which is the law of Islam, is officially the country's constitution. This system of law, which goes back to the beginnings of Islam, is based on the Quran and the traditions of Muhammad, his companions, and the first generation of Muslims.

The rights, duties and obligations of both the ruler and the ruled are set forth in Islamic law. Basic rights, such as equality before the law, the sanctity of private property and the right to "life, liberty and the pursuit of happiness," are integral parts of this constitution. Besides regulating what a Westerner would consider purely religious questions, the laws of Islam provide a system of private law, civil and penal norms, laws of war and part of the system regulating relations with non-Muslims. The interpretation of this law is a function of the *Shari'ah* judiciary and the Ulema, a college of learned religious men. Since the sources of the *Shari'ah* are considered to be divine, the judiciary in Saudi Arabia, perhaps even

more than that in the United States, is independent of the executive and legislative branches of government. With its various levels of courts—ranging from trial courts through courts of appeal—Saudi Arabian law provides an accepted and readily available means of settling disputes.

In matters not expressly prohibited or made obligatory by the *Shari'ah*, residual authority to enact regulations reposes in the monarch, who acts through the Council of Ministers. In the administration of the relatively large body of secular regulations which cover such areas as public health, customs, commerce and labor, commissions with judicial powers have been established to rule upon disputes. These bodies are comparable to Western administrative tribunals and regulatory agencies. They complement the *Shari'ah* courts, which continue to deal with matters traditionally within their jurisdiction.

ADMINISTRATIVE DEVELOPMENT Saudi Arabia's strict adherence to its Islamic tradition continues side by side with the country's economic and administrative development. Both economically and administratively the country has developed along lines quite familiar to Westerners. Administrative development aims at building an efficient, modern system of government. In 1952, shortly before his death, King 'Abd al-'Aziz

180

established a Council of Ministers under the presidency of what in practice is a prime minister. Under Faysal, Saudi Arabia is rapidly modernizing its administrative machinery. Foreign experts, primarily provided by the United Nations and the Ford Foundation, have worked with trained young Saudis on this problem. Like most other developing nations, Saudi Arabia faces a constellation of problems in forming its administrative structure. One of the greatest problems has been the lack of trained personnel, a deficiency which the country faces in almost every area of its development. However, the nation's massive investment in education and educational facilities since the late Nineteen Forties is making this problem somewhat more amenable to solution. The dependence upon foreign experts and advisors, while still great, is becoming less each year as more and more Saudi Arabs obtain technical, vocational, college and graduate educations both within the country and abroad.

HUMAN RESOURCES The country has invested a sizable proportion of its income in the development of its human resources. Government allocations for health, welfare, education and social services have been increasing rapidly. This buildup has been slowed only once in recent years; the 1967-68 budget reflected a drop in such allocations because of increased financial obligations resulting from the June, 1967, Middle East conflict.

Most of Saudi Arabia's population is concentrated in widely scattered towns and villages. Population density is on the order of five persons per square mile—a figure roughly comparable with U.S. population density in 1790. Distances between most populated areas are relatively great. Economic development was hampered by the lack of good communications between population centers. Agricultural products of an oasis, for example, often could not be transported to distant markets and there was little incentive to expand production.

Riyadh University was the first institution of higher learning established in Saudi Arabia and still is being developed.

TRANSPORTATION One of the first projects to improve transportation was the construction of the 375-mile Saudi Government Railroad. Built by Aramco for the government's account, the railroad linked the new Arabian Gulf port of Dammam with Riyadh, the capital. Though this achievement may have appeared spectacular when the first train reached Riyadh in 1951, it was to be dwarfed by later highway construction projects.

In the early Nineteen Sixties, the Saudi Arabian Government began work on a major road program, aimed at linking towns and cities with each other and with their rural hinterland. By late 1967 some 3,250 miles of major highway had been paved and opened for traffic. Another 2,800 miles were under construction. In 1967 the first transpeninsular highway—a 950-mile asphalted road connecting the Arabian Gulf port of Dammam with Riyadh and the Red Sea port of Jiddah—was opened. A portion of a second transpeninsular highway, linking the Eastern Province with Jordan, was opened to traffic between Qaisumah and Turaif in 1966. This section of the northern highway was paved by the Trans-Arabian Pipe Line Company under an agreement with the Saudi Arabian Government.

Plans call for some 7,500 miles of paved roads by the early Nineteen Seventies. Roughly forty-three percent of this road program was completed by late 1967.

A Saudi Arabian airline, originally attached to the Ministry of Defense, has been flying for many years. Since the airline was separated from the ministry and made into a semiautonomous corporation in 1963, its services have been expanded and its performance record sharply improved. This improvement has been due partially to a technical and management arrangement between the airline and Trans World Airlines (TWA), but primarily it reflects the modernization and rapid development taking place in all aspects of the nation's economic and educational systems. Major cities and towns are connected by rapid, dependable and regular air transportation. Saudi Arabian Airlines also serves other Middle Eastern cities and India, Pakistan, North Africa and Europe. Airline operations are supported by radio communications between all airports and airline headquarters in Jiddah. The airline maintains a training center in Jiddah which prepares young Saudis for careers in all aspects of airline operations.

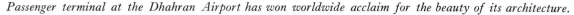

Passenger terminal at the Dhahran Airport has won worldwide acclaim for the beauty of its architecture.

The spectacular Mecca-Tayif highway, opened in 1965, has 174 curves in its fifty-four miles, averaging more than three curves a mile.

TELECOMMUNICATIONS The Saudi Arabian Government has also been modernizing its communications network in other areas. An automatic telephone network will tie the major cities and towns together by 1970. This telephone network will ultimately permit direct dialing between Dammam, Riyadh, Jiddah and other large population centers.

Telecommunications have come a long way since the late Nineteen Twenties when King 'Abd al-'Aziz was said to have had verses from the Quran read over the radio in order to convince religious scholars that the instrument could be a means for moral betterment. The country, a member of the International Telecommunications Union, is covered by a radio and telegraph network. Aramco, through its leased circuits, has virtually instant communications between its headquarters in Dhahran and its offices in New York and The Hague. Saudi Arabia, with the assistance of foreign experts, is laying the groundwork for the use of communications satellites to further improve and modernize its international communications.

The kingdom, which had one radio broadcasting station for its Radio Mecca service in 1962, now has stations in Jiddah, Riyadh and Dammam, which broadcast a wide variety of educational and entertainment programs. Television stations were completed in Jiddah and Riyadh in 1965 and additional stations will provide television service throughout the country.

PORTS AND AIRPORTS Efforts have been made to modernize and improve existing ports and airports. On the Red Sea, a modern port at Yanbu', north of Jiddah, was completed in 1966 to serve the Medina area. The Jiddah Port is being expanded at a cost of almost thirty million dollars, and the port at Dammam was enlarged. Other gulf ports, at Qatif, Jubail and al-Khobar have been improved and handle specialized smaller vessels, such as fishing fleets and coastal ships.

Saudi Arabia has three major international airports—Dhahran, Jiddah and Riyadh. Smaller airports at Tayif and Medina can handle jet traffic. Most cities and the larger towns are served by airports. The Jiddah Airport can handle some forty jets daily and will be enlarged to accommodate more than one hundred jet flights daily.

ECONOMY Before the discovery of oil, the nation's economy was based upon oasis agriculture of a simple and primitive type, small-scale fishing along the coasts, pearling in the Arabian Gulf, nomadic herding, commerce and Mecca pilgrimage income. With the discovery of oil, the petroleum industry rapidly became the major industry, providing more than eighty-five percent of the government's income. This expanding industry undoubtedly will continue to provide the bulk of the government's income for some time to come. In recent years the government has placed increasing emphasis upon the development of other sources of income.

Dammam port extends seven miles out into the Arabian Gulf.

184

Business center of Jiddah, principal port on the Red Sea.

AGRICULTURE This emphasis has been in two areas —agriculture and industry—both of which offer good prospects for development. Traditionally, agriculture in Saudi Arabia has been limited to the few areas with adequate water supplies—in oases, along wadi beds and catchment basins and in the relatively high-rainfall region in the southwest. In the Qatif and al-Hasa Oases in the Eastern Province, water for agriculture was obtained from deep hand-dug artesian wells, which flowed freely and provided sufficient water for the major traditional crop, dates. Some years ago, in areas where underground water had to be lifted to the surface, the job was done by camels and donkeys traveling monotonously back and forth on runways to raise and lower skin buckets. In most of these areas, the camels and donkeys have been replaced by mechanical pumps.

The date has become less valuable as a crop in recent years. Traditional dietary habits have changed because of increased prosperity, introduction of new foods and methods of food preservation, altering tastes and notions of nutrition. Dates have become, for many Saudi Arabs, a supplemental food instead of a basic item of diet. The date gardens have declined in importance and a gradual shift to other forms of agriculture began. Encouraged by Aramco in the Eastern Province and by the Ministry of Agriculture in the rest of the nation, farmers have begun to plant vegetables, melons and other truck garden crops, as well as fodders like alfalfa. The change has been so

A network of drainage canals in the Qatif Oasis helps to leach from the soil salts left by stagnant water.

Bees in the Qatif Oasis produce excellent quality honey.

Experts from Taiwan have introduced new strains of rice.

successful that in early 1967 tomatoes from the Eastern Province and from Buraydah in Najd were exported to Lebanon, one of Saudi Arabia's main suppliers of fruits and vegetables. Aramco has, for many years, purchased vegetables from nearby producers.

This agricultural expansion has taken place primarily in the traditional agricultural areas. However, a large-scale program is under way to study and develop water resources for agricultural development. A hydrological survey, a long-range program being carried out by international consulting firms, is designed to provide the government with the basic data needed to develop its agricultural resources. Much of the country is wasteland. Potentially, some of this wasteland can, with time and capital, become rich agricultural land. Vast aquifers—water-bearing formations—underlie many sections of the country. The Wasia aquifer, first studied by Aramco, lies under a large area of northeastern Saudi Arabia and contains more water than there is in the Arabian Gulf, some thirty trillion barrels of which are believed to be suitable for household use. In an area some thirty miles square east of Riyadh, there are about one trillion barrels of potable water at depths between one and two thousand feet. If only twenty percent of this water were recovered, it could supply Riyadh with more water than the city would need over the next hundred years.

As part of the hydrological survey, soil and fertility tests are under way to determine the best areas for agricultural projects. The first large agricultural development project is at Haradh, near the southernmost tip of Aramco's Ghawar oil field. This project, planned as a Bedouin resettlement project, will reclaim some 10,000 acres of desert land, which will be irrigated from deep wells and cultivated by small landowners under the direction and supervision of foreign consulting firms and the Ministry of Agriculture and Water. An integral part of the project is an agricultural experiment station.

187

BEDOUINS AND HERDING Most of the desert will continue to be unsuitable for agriculture. Traditionally these desert areas have been the preserve of Bedouins, who move about the country in a planned and deliberate pattern to take advantage of rain-filled wells and pastures for their herds of camels, sheep and goats. Saudi Arabia, while usually thought of as a land of nomads, has a surprisingly small Bedouin population. Perhaps as little as twenty percent of the population is Bedouin, and this percentage is decreasing steadily as young Bedouins obtain education and shift to urban life. Many of Aramco's most highly skilled technicians were originally Bedouins. The Bedouins have made and continue to make a substantial contribution to the Saudi Arabian economy, supporting themselves and producing a surplus of animal products for the settled population. Yet Saudi Arabia is

Sheep and goats are the primary sources of meat and milk.

The Bedouins, moving their flocks with the season, efficiently crop the sparse desert vegetation to produce meat and milk supplies.

still a net importer of meat and animal products. Studies by United Nations and other experts indicate that with modern methods of range management the country could easily become self-sufficient in animal products and might develop an exportable surplus. The hydrological survey will provide basic data for such range management programs, and a feed grain storage project is designed to store livestock fodder in strategic locations. Herd size is dependent upon pasturage and water, and water is becoming increasingly more important as the Bedouins have shifted from camels to sheep and goats in response to changing food consumption patterns. Camels can range for up to five days without water, but sheep and goats must be watered daily. With truck tankers now hauling water from wells, sheep and goats increasingly are being pastured at greater distances from water sources. The government's large-scale well-drilling program in recent years has provided additional water for Bedouins. Increased water resources, the shift from camel to sheep and goat herding, improved communications, additional motor transport in the desert, fodder storage programs, mobile health and education units and drought relief programs have brought about basic changes in Bedouin habits. Increasingly, Bedouin families are settling on the outskirts of towns and cities and are becoming integrated into urban society. Members of these families or their shepherds still graze the flocks in the desert. Although there are still many Bedouins who have not adopted this pattern, most of these move in relatively isolated areas, like the Rub' al-Khali. But even in the vast sands of the Rub' al-Khali, the number of trucks in use is increasing.

The buildings of government ministries line one of the main boulevards in the growing Saudi Arabian capital of Riyadh.

Shrimp netted from the Arabian Gulf are quick-frozen and exported to the United States and Japan and consumed locally.

MARINE RESOURCES Marine resources of the Arabian Gulf have been developed as a result of private investment, Aramco guidance and government encouragement. Arabian Gulf shrimp, processed and frozen in Dammam, are exported to American and Japanese markets. The Ministry of Agriculture has undertaken studies of fishery resources and the Ministry of Commerce and Industry has classified fishery companies as national industries entitled to tax and customs relief.

Pearling was long one of the principal occupations in the Arabian Gulf and yielded from early times some of the finest pearls in the world. Both the Bible and the Quran contain references to pearls, which may have been inspired by gems from the gulf.

The Bahrain Islands still are the main center for gulf pearling. From there the pearls go mainly to the markets of India and Paris. The people of Bahrain were almost entirely dependent upon pearling for their livelihood before the development of oil resources. Jubail on the mainland and Darin on the island of Tarut were the principal Saudi Arabian pearling ports on the gulf. Jaizan, on the Red Sea, was also famous for its pearling and mother-of-pearl industry.

The Arabian Gulf pearl industry flourished until about 1931, when the price of pearls declined. The slump was due partly to the world-wide depression in the Thirties and partly to the appearance on the market of Japanese cultured pearls. The industry has never recovered from this slump and only relatively small numbers of Saudi Arabian and Bahraini pearlers are still active.

INDUSTRY Modern industry appeared in Saudi Arabia relatively recently, but it is developing steadily along with other commercial activity. Industry, traditionally, was of the cottage and handicraft type with different districts being noted for specialty products. Hofuf in the al-Hasa Oasis, was famous for its *bishts*—Arab cloaks, which were handwoven from wool in different weights and colors and decorated with gold embroidery around the collar. Goldsmiths, silversmiths and other craftsmen were found in virtually every city and town, and the carpenters of the Hijaz were noted for their intricately carved lattice work screens, panels and doors.

These handicrafts largely have been replaced by industries processing plastics, steel, cement, clothing and tiles.

To encourage industry the government has provided low-cost industrial sites in major cities, special tax and customs incentives, a firm commitment to the free enterprise system and a fully convertible currency.

Plastic bags and sheeting now are being manufactured by the National Paper Products Company near Dammam.

A teacher goes into the problems of mechanical drawing during a class at the College of Petroleum and Minerals, opened in 1964 near Dhahran

192

COLLEGE OF PETROLEUM AND MINERALS In 1963 the Saudi Arabian Government established the College of Petroleum and Minerals in an area adjacent to the company's operations in Dhahran. The college is a separate government entity with its own budget from the state and a board of directors of which the Minister of Petroleum and Mineral Resources is the chairman. In addition to Saudi officials the board also includes distinguished educators from the United States and France, reflecting its international orientation.

The first students entered the college in 1964 and the successful candidates from that class are now abroad, principally in the United States, where they are completing their courses in engineering and the sciences at the university level. Plans envisage that future students will be able to complete their studies in Saudi Arabia.

Although the college has modern classrooms and living quarters at the present time, construction of a new campus was started so that the increasing enrollment can be accommodated. The enrollment of 142 students for the 1967-68 year is expected to grow to 2,800 students by 1985.

PETROMIN A major element in the industrialization drive is the General Petroleum and Mineral Organization, or Petromin as it is more familiarly called. Petromin was established in 1962 as an independent agency of the government and was charged with the development of industries based upon petroleum, minerals and natural gas. Petromin may carry out projects itself or in conjunction with others. Petromin sees itself as a catalyst in industrial development. The governor of Petromin has described his organization as a state corporation with a difference. He has set forth the philosophy of the organization in this way: "Petromin is not a substitute for private enterprise. Rather, it works in collaboration with private investors, foreign firms for the most part, in undertaking large projects for which private capital on the required scale is not available locally."

The Jiddah iron and steel plant illustrates one aspect of the Petromin approach to industrial development. The ultimate aim is to use iron ore deposits in western Saudi Arabia. Stage one involved construction of a steel mill in Jiddah to roll imported steel billets into steel reinforcing rods and other products. Stage two involves construction of a plant to process imported pig iron into steel billets for the steel rolling mill. The final stage envisions making pig iron from iron ore mined in western Saudi Arabia. In this project, Petromin will establish an integrated industry in relatively small and manageable stages. Capacity can be increased as the industry gains experience and as demand increases. No attempt is being made to make the country self-sufficient in iron and steel, nor is the project being carried out merely for prestige.

As for the oil business, Petromin has taken a diversified approach. For example, two of its operating affiliates are the Arabian Geophysical and Surveying Company and the Arabian Drilling Company, both of which are joint ventures with foreign firms. In addition, Petromin is particularly active in the domestic marketing field, a function which received its main impetus from the purchase of Aramco's bulk plant in Jiddah in 1964. This plant was the wholesale supplier for most of the petroleum products sold in western Saudi Arabia. Petromin purchased most of the remaining portion of Aramco's local marketing facilities in mid-1967 and, as a consequence, is now the primary wholesaler throughout Saudi Arabia of petroleum products. Petromin and private shareholders also own a small refinery in Jiddah.

The Saudi Arabian Fertilizer Company in Dammam was organized by Petromin to make urea and ammonia for fertilizers and extract sulfur from natural gas supplied by Aramco. Part of the stock of this company is owned privately.

As the government's agent, Petromin has entered into agreements with foreign oil companies for joint ventures in various areas of the country.

SOCIAL AND ECONOMIC PROGRESS Saudi Arabia has been following a deliberate and evolutionary policy of development. A spirit of change is in the air and the changes that have been made are apparent to all. Standards of living have risen sharply. Gross national product is reported to be increasing at about ten percent a year. Per capita income is estimated to have risen from the subsistence level in the late Nineteen Forties to about $280 in 1966. Present estimates indicate that per capita income holds the promise of being doubled every seven years. Admittedly, gross national product and per capita income figures can only be rough estimates, for Saudi Arabia is just beginning to develop the statistical information necessary for accurate estimates. However, such figures can serve as a rough yardstick to compare the country with other developing nations.

The cities of Saudi Arabia reflect most clearly the sharp rise in social and economic conditions. The city of al-Khobar, a few miles from Aramco's Dhahran headquarters, is a case in point. In the early Forties, al-Khobar was little more than a collection of huts. It has become a prosperous, modern city with paved streets, street lighting, water and sewage systems, department stores, modern homes and buildings, and traffic problems. The population is cosmopolitan, with sizable foreign elements drawn from Europe, the United States, Canada, Pakistan, Japan, India and the other Arab states. A short distance from al-Khobar is the town of Thuqbah. This town started as a collection of Bedouin huts and tents in the early Nineteen Fifties. Thuqbah, too, grew rapidly into a modern town. It already has paved streets and modern homes served by municipality-operated water and sewage systems. Schools, hospitals or clinics, and other public facilities can be found in all but the smallest hamlets and settlements.

The pace of progress is accelerating year by year. Each improvement sets the stage for other changes; each change accelerates the pace. Saudi Arabia has crossed the threshold into the modern world and is rapidly taking its place in that world.

Al-Khobar, whose shops display goods from all over the world, is a favorite shopping center for employees of Aramco.

194

THE CLIMATE

During the last Ice Age, which ended some 15,000 years ago, Arabia is known to have enjoyed a more temperate climate with greater rainfall than at present. Much of the desert was then grassland, and the great wadi systems still seen in Arabia testify to the eroding power of the runoff from the highlands. Experts now generally agree that the climatic changes at the end of the Ice Age resulted in a weather pattern in Arabia that has altered little to this day.

The intense heat of the summer months is now the best known feature of the Arabian climate. Temperatures in the shade frequently exceed 120° Fahrenheit over much of the peninsula. Furthermore, the summer is longer than in more temperate regions. The dryness of the interior makes the heat more endurable there, but along the coasts the humidity is high, particularly at night. The effects of the severe summer heat are mitigated in the urban centers by the increasingly common use of air-conditioning equipment in many homes, institutions, offices, shops and automobiles.

While the summers of Arabia have their forbidding aspects, the rest of the year has its attractive features. As in other desert regions, the climate in the spring and fall is pleasant with cool nights and sunny, balmy days. The nights, with their bright stars or brilliant moonlight, are delightful. In December, January and February, temperatures drop below freezing in central and northern Arabia, but snow and ice are uncommon except in the highest places. The desert Arabs mark the changing seasons by the changing stars and constellations in the heavens. Each period, characterized by its own winds and temperatures, has its ruling constellations. In the late summer Bedouins and townsmen alike watch eagerly for the rising of *Suhayl* (Canopus), which traditionally marks the end of the most trying hot and humid portion of the Arabian Gulf summer.

The winds of Saudi Arabia vary greatly, being affected by the surrounding seas. In the Eastern Province the prevailing wind comes from the north-northwest. This wind, the *shamal*, frequently whips up sandstorms in its path, but it cools the land somewhat. In the Arabian Gulf the south wind, the *kaws*, is the sailor's enemy because of the fierce storms it stirs up without warning.

RAINFALL AND WATER RESOURCES The monsoons of the Indian Ocean affect the southern fringe of the Arabian Peninsula and account for the relatively abundant rains of about twenty inches a year in 'Asir. In the northern half of the peninsula periodic rains are brought by the systems of low atmospheric pressure that move in from the Mediterranean basin. These rains are scattered, however, and may be almost completely lacking in some years. The unpredictable and local nature of the rainfall is a characteristic of most desert

A mild shamal, *or sandstorm, obscures an exploration camp on the plains of northern Saudi Arabia.*

regions. Dhahran has an average seasonal rainfall of about three inches, but in some seasons may have almost seven inches and in others less than one inch. The rains in the Eastern Province usually start in November or December and end in May. Tapline pump stations in northern Saudi Arabia normally receive more rain than Dhahran.

Parts of the great sand mass of the Rub' al-Khali have been known to be without rain for ten years at a time. When rain does fall in the country, it is likely to come in torrential downpours, causing flash floods which do considerable damage to homes and cultivated fields. Rainfall over most of the peninsula is not sufficient to support much vegetation. However, in many areas water collects in underground strata and can be produced by wells.

As a result of rainfall seeping into the ground in the interior, fresh artesian water is found trapped under a cover of impervious rock at various places in the Arabian Gulf region. When the rock is penetrated by drilling or digging, water rises in the hole and in many instances flows to the surface. The large supply of water in the oases of al-Hasa and Qatif and on the Bahrain Islands has been obtained through the centuries from hand-dug wells reaching into the water-bearing strata. Numerous sweet-water seepages also are found in the sand-covered areas of the coastal region and in the floor of the Arabian Gulf itself. Arab sailors still fill their waterskins from fresh-water springs at the bottom of the gulf. For these reasons the water supply of this region is much better than that in many other parts of the peninsula.

Westward to the sands of the Dahna, where the

196

elevation above sea level ranges from 700 to 1,200 feet, water is scarce and watering places are confined mainly to small basins where water accumulates after rainfall. Some wells have been dug by hand to a depth of 200 feet or more. An abundant supply of good water usually can be found in this area by drilling 500 to 800 feet to the water table, but the water must be pumped to the surface. In many places it is too saline for people to drink. At Tapline pump stations in northern Arabia, water is obtained at depths of from 500 to 1,200 feet.

Great quantities of good quality water are available from deeper aquifers known to lie below much of eastern and northern Arabia. Aramco studies have shown that one of the more prolific of these natural underground reservoirs—the Wasia—contains more water than the Arabian

Gulf. The use of this water for supplying cities and new settlements will require the installation of large capacity pumping systems.

Between the Dahna sands and the igneous rocks of central and western Arabia, water is found most commonly at the foot of a series of long, gradual slopes tilting to the east from the crests of imposing escarpments that face west. The greatest of these escarpments is Tuwayq. Down its eastern watershed runs the underground water that supports the irrigation works of al-Kharj.

Watering places in the central plateau region are few and widely separated, even though the elevation of 3,000 to 4,000 feet draws more rainfall than that of the region to the east. Water is fairly abundant in the mountainous districts of the Hijaz, where it supports wild and cultivated vegetation.

197

PLANT AND ANIMAL LIFE

The great belt of desert which extends from the west coast of North Africa 6,000 miles eastward to the Indus Valley is a natural geographical unit with homogeneous terrain and climate. The plant life of this zone, set apart by the plant geographers as the North African-Indian desert floristic region, is quite uniform. All of the Arabian Peninsula, except the mountains of Oman and the extreme south, including Yemen and the 'Asir highlands, lies within this region and shares in the common biological heritage of the Saharan and Indian deserts.

The vegetation of the North African-Indian desert region has several distinctive features well demonstrated in Arabia. Most of the plants are small annual herbs or small shrubs; true trees are rare, and there are no forests. Plants have adapted to the rigorous desert climate either by leading an active life only in the temperate rainy season and assuming the protected form of seeds to evade the heat and dryness of summer or by accumulating structural or chemical changes that enable them to withstand desert conditions. These adaptations include the ability to store water, reductions in leaf surface area and the growth of special coverings, such as hairs, to reduce water losses. Adaptations in internal chemistry enable some species to tolerate salty soil that would kill most plants.

Another characteristic of the vegetation is the small number of species. The Eastern Province of Saudi Arabia has probably not more than 370 native plants, as compared to the smaller Lebanon-Palestine area, which borders on several floristic regions and has perhaps 3,500 species. The small number of desert species reflects the difficulties faced by plants in adapting to such a harsh environment. A third feature of the Arabian desert vegetation is the rarity of endemic species, plants which are peculiar to it and which are not found elsewhere. Most of the species seem not to have originated here but to have migrated from adjacent regions.

The number of different plants that form a conspicuous part of the perennial vegetation is quite small. In eastern Arabia a sedge (*Cyperus conglomeratus*) and a perennial grass (*Panicum turgidum*) are common in the coastal sands. The 'arfaj shrublet (*Rhanterium epapposum*) is dominant over hundreds of square miles further inland, and the *rimth* saltbush (*Haloxylon salicornicum*) covers wide areas of poorly drained soil. Both 'arfaj and *rimth* are important pasture plants, the saltbush furnishing the salt required by grazing livestock. Visitors to Saudi Arabia accustomed to the desert landscape of the southwestern United States will look in vain for their familiar cacti. The cactus family belongs almost exclusively to the New World and the few species of prickly pear (*Opuntia*) now found in coastal areas of the Middle East are generally believed to have been introduced. The

Picris saharae, *a desert bee-fly feeds on tiny drops of nectar among its petals.*

Iris sisyrinchium, *a foot-high wild iris, is found in desert hollows after rains.*

Salsola subaphylla, *a desert saltbush, has papery wings on its half-inch fruits.*

Anagallis arvensis, *the scarlet pimpernel, is found on moist ditch banks in oases.*

Anthemis deserti, *four-inch high annual, is a close relative of the camomile.*

Gagea reticulata, *a dwarf lilly, sprouts from a tiny bulb after winter rainfalls.*

striking cactus-like euphorbias and stapelias of southwestern Arabia belong to altogether different families.

The southwestern highlands of Arabia are classed as part of the East African Highlands floristic region and not as part of the desert. True forests of juniper *(Juniperus procera)* and wild olive *(Olea chrysophylla)* cover parts of the higher slopes of 'Asir, and recent forestry work undertaken by the Saudi Arabian Government is protecting and developing these important resources.

None of the wild desert plants is important as food for humans, although a score or more different herbs are occasionally eaten by the Bedouins. Desert truffles are a delicacy in season, and *samh,* the seeds of *Mesembryanthemum,* are collected in northern Arabia and made into bread. The Bedouins have medicinal uses for many desert plants. Some of these remedies have scientifically proved value; others probably provide only psychological aid. Frankincense and myrrh, transported to the West more than 2,000 years ago over the Incense Road from south Arabia, still grow wild in Dhufar and Hadhramaut. The greatest economic value of the desert vegetation, however, lies in its role as forage for the Bedouins' livestock.

Most desert flowers are small but, contrasting with their often barren surroundings, they have a beauty out of proportion to their numbers and size. Bright and fragrant spikes of broomrape color the spring roadsides in eastern Arabia and the delicate desert camomile grows in scattered carpets on the sand. Farther north, on the gravel plains and rocky steppes, dense growths of wild iris brighten the depressions where rain pools have lain. The fruiting of the 'abal bush *(Calligonum comosum)* marks the height of the spring flowering season on the deep sands. This leafless woody shrub, valued as firewood by desert travelers, has a pleasing symmetry when its bone-white branches are dry. The winter rains bring out pale pink flowers and by late spring the bush is covered with a brilliant trimming of scarlet fruits.

CULTIVATED PLANTS The date palm *(Phoenix dactylifera)* is the most important single cultivated plant of the entire North African-Indian desert region. The limits of distribution of this palm, like those of the Arabian camel, almost exactly coincide with the boundaries of this zone. The fruit is a staple food and the tree provides valuable wood and fibre by-products.

Wheat, barley, sorghum and millet are the chief grains grown in Arabia. Alfalfa is a common oasis crop; cotton, rice, melons and some tree fruits are cultivated on a smaller scale. Coffee grows on the high terraces of 'Asir and Yemen, once the principal source of coffee for the Western world. The more profitable *qat* (*Catha edulis*) is grown in the same area for the people of Aden and Yemen who chew its mildly narcotic leaves. Henna and, in southern Arabia, indigo are cultivated for dyestuffs. The food habits of Saudi Arabian townsmen are gradually but markedly changing. Dates are becoming a less important food item, and more land is being devoted to garden vegetable crops to satisfy the changing tastes of the growing middle class.

Where water is available for irrigation, as in the oases and in Aramco communities, almost anything can be grown in Arabia that grows in similar latitudes elsewhere. The clear, deep springs of the oases, with a rich flora that includes maidenhair fern and water ferns, are beauty spots frequented by townsmen. Aramco's communities are green with trees, lawns and hedges. Saudi Arabian municipalities have planted their avenues with trees. Mesquite and Jerusalem thorn, both originally from the New World, and eucalyptus, an Australian native, are popular ornamental trees. Tamarisks are often planted as windbreaks.

The graceful gazelle has been almost exterminated in Arabia.

WILD ANIMALS Gazelles, graceful members of the antelope family, were once seen on the plains of Arabia in herds of hundreds. In recent years they have been almost exterminated by hunting parties in trucks and cars, except in the most isolated areas. Three species or subspecies of gazelles are recognized by the Bedouins: the *rim*, the *'ifri* and the *idm*. Each of these forms, identifiable in the field by color and markings, is characteristic of a certain terrain type or geographical area. In some areas their ranges overlap. An adult buck weighs about thirty-four to forty pounds. The oryx (*wudayhi*) is a large species of the antelope family that is now almost extinct. A few specimens still roam the southern Rub' al-Khali. Mature oryx weigh up to 200 pounds and have almost straight, tapering horns more than two feet long. It has been suggested that the sight of the animal in profile gave rise to the legend of the unicorn. Ibex or mountain goats live in some mountains of Arabia.

The wolf, striped hyena and rarer cheetah occur throughout the peninsula. Jackals are common around inhabited areas. Troops of baboons may be seen in the mountains of southwestern Arabia. Smaller mammals found in Arabia are the fox, ratel or honey badger, coney, mongoose, porcupine and hedgehog. Hares, smaller than the American jack rabbit, are found throughout the country and are hunted intensively by the Bedouins. The jerboa, described by Charles Doughty as "a small white aery creature in the wide waterless deserts, of a pitiful beauty," leaves its burrow at night to hop about kangaroo-fashion on long hind legs. Other small rodents of the desert are the gerbils and jirds (sand rats).

BIRDS The ostrich has become extinct in Arabia in recent years. One of the last on record was shot near the Iraq boundary in 1938. It weighed 300 pounds and ran with nine-foot strides. Fragments of ostrich egg shells still are sometimes found in the desert. Eagles, hawks and falcons fly wild, and falcons are trapped and trained for hunting. Falconry is the sport of ordinary Bedouins as well as of kings and nobles in Arabia. The falcons, after laborious training, are used for hunting *hubara* (Macqueen's bustard), a heavy bird with a wingspread of about three feet. Other game birds are the sandgrouse (*qata*), the stone curlew (*kirwan*), doves, quail and the courser *(darajah)*.

Vultures, owls and ravens are common in Arabia. The Bedouins say that the owl was originally a "wailing woman, seeking her lost child in the wilderness." Flamingos, egrets and pelicans are found along the coasts with many shore birds. Many birds of Europe pass through Arabia on their north-south migrations; cuckoos, thrushes, warblers, swallows and wagtails are seasonally common. The white-cheeked bulbul is the best known songbird of the oases, and the plaintive voice of *Umm Salim*, the two-striped lark, is familiar to desert travelers.

REPTILES At least five species of harmless snakes are known in eastern Arabia: the sand boa, Gray's whip snake, the Arabian leaf-nosed snake, the variable sandsnake and the Moila snake. The sand viper *(Cerastes cerastes)* is venomous and fairly

common, but nearly all victims of snakebites attributed to this small viper recover without special treatment. The name "horned viper" often applied to this species is something of a misnomer, for less than half of the individuals of both sexes have the characteristic horn-like raised scales over the eyes. This snake moves in the sand in the fashion of the sidewinder of the American southwest and is seldom seen except at night. The track left by this viper in the sand is very distinctive; the trace is discontinuous and consists of a series of evenly spaced marks, each resembling an elongated letter "J". There is no authenticated record of the occurrence of the Arabian hooded cobra in northeastern Arabia. The Moila snake, or Arabian rear-fanged snake *(Malpolon moilensis)*, is frequently mistaken for a cobra. Although it belongs to a different family, it reacts when disturbed by dilating its neck and raising its head in a cobra-like attitude. The Moila snake has a mild venom effective against small rodents but is not considered dangerous to man. The black hoodless cobra, however, has been captured in eastern Arabia. It is extremely rare. The sea snakes of the Arabian Gulf are

The tiny, inquisitive hedgehog is a favorite children's pet.

Giant sea turtles breed on the islands in the Arabian Gulf.

venomous, but they bite only to catch their food and are not dangerous to swimmers.

There are no poisonous lizards in Arabia. The *dabb*, or spiny-tailed lizard, is a heavy, plant-eating species that grows to about twenty inches. Its meat is sometimes eaten by Bedouins. The longer but slimmer *waral*, or desert monitor, is carnivorous and is not eaten. Among the smaller common lizards are geckos, several lacertids, the tiny *tuhayhi* agamid, and a shiny, sand-swimming skink. A pink legless lizard (*nadus*) that lives under the sand is frequently mistaken for a small snake when accidently uncovered. The Caspian turtle is often seen in oasis irrigation ditches and a common frog represents the amphibians in similar habitats.

FISH A killifish *(Aphanius dispar)* is found in springs in the Qatif and al-Hasa oases and where water from springs collects to form small lakes. These fish reach a length of about four inches. Their small size minimizes their usefulness as food, though they are occasionally caught for that purpose.

A Dhahran child examines sand-swimming skinks in the desert.

The seas around the Arabian Peninsula are rich in fish and many employees of Aramco are avid sports fishermen.

The most common game fish found in the Arabian Gulf are:

Hamur, a dark-colored grouper, slightly speckled and similar in form to a bullhead. The biggest weigh about thirty pounds and the meat is like that of the sea bass. This fish lives under rock ledges near the coasts.

Kan'ad (often pronounced *chan'ad*), a silver-colored king mackerel. It reaches twenty pounds and is a hard fighter on the line. The meat resembles that of the halibut in color.

Qidd (often pronounced *jidd*), the barracuda. It attains a length of four feet and a weight of twenty pounds.

Sayyafi, the sawfish. It weighs up to several hundred pounds and is caught near the shore during the spawning season.

Other fish commonly caught by trolling are the *subayti*, or grouper, and the *jihabah*, a variety of tuna. The *subayTi* (with a heavy T) is a porgy sometimes caught with hook and line but more commonly by spearing.

Whales and dugongs occasionally enter the Arabian Gulf from the Indian Ocean, and dolphins are very common. Sea turtles nest each year on some of the small sandy islands of the Arabian Gulf. Sharks and sardines are caught in great numbers off the southern coasts of Arabia. Surveys of marine life in the gulf indicate the presence of more than 200 species of fish.

INSECTS Insects of economic importance in the Arabian Peninsula have been the subject of recent scientific study. Locusts are a scourge; they breed in the desert and under favorable conditions their eggs hatch by the millions. Descending upon cultivated areas they devour every living green thing in sight. Among the Bedouins locusts are a food delicacy; they may be roasted and eaten immediately or boiled, dried in the sun and stored. The Saudi Arabian Government has cooperated

Salukis hold a special place among the Bedouins in the desert. *The Arabian wildcat,* Felis margarita, *is occasionally captured.*

since 1942 with neighboring states and international agencies in the fight against the desert locust.

Aramco has worked closely with the Saudi Arabian Government in suppressing flies and mosquitoes in the Eastern Province. A joint residual spraying program begun in 1948 successfully brought malaria under control.

Perhaps the most commonly seen desert insect is the awkward-flying dung beetle, which industriously collects balls of dung in which it lays its eggs. Among the arachnids are the scorpion, the velvety red rain mite and the hairy *shabath*, an enormous but harmless sun spider, or solpugid. This nocturnal stroller has been mistaken by more than one terrified desert traveler for a tarantula.

DOMESTICATED ANIMALS The Arabian camel or dromedary, the universally recognized symbol of Arabian desert life, still plays an important role in the Bedouin economy, although it has been supplanted by the motor truck as a carrier of commercial goods. Recent research has proved that the camel does not have any special water storage ability. It can go for long periods without drinking primarily because of its ability to tolerate wide ranges of body temperature without cooling itself by sweating heavily. A camel may lose more than twenty-five per cent of its body weight in water without suffering the fatal reduction in blood volume that occurs in other animals under great heat stress.

Camels can drink water too salty for human consumption and provide valuable milk. They are seldom slaughtered by the Bedouins for meat. There are many recognized strains of camels, some famous for their milk production, others as riding animals.

The black, fat-tailed sheep and the long-eared breed of goat are the primary milk and meat producers of the desert wherever their water and pasture requirements can be met. Both wool and goat hair are used in weaving the tents of the Bedouins; camel hair is not strong enough for this purpose.

The *saluqi*, a pure-bred hound, is widely used for hunting and is considered to be in a class by itself, far above the lowly status of other dogs in Arabia. Most Bedouins keep heavy watchdogs of mixed breed.

The donkey is the most important beast of burden in oasis areas, and the large white breed of al-Hasa is famous throughout eastern Arabia. Some cows of Indian type are kept in settled areas. The local bantam chicken has now been largely supplanted by larger improved varieties.

The Arabian horse is famous for its beauty and endurance, but there are not many horses in Arabia today. The law and order established by the ruling House of Sa'ud eliminated their importance as mounts for desert raiders. The breed is now being preserved in the Ministry of Agriculture Stables at Riyadh and by a number of private fanciers, some of them Aramco employees.

HIGHLIGHTS
OF THE GEOLOGY

From time to time in long-distant ages, going back hundreds of millions of years, the Arabian Gulf (or seas that can be said to have been its ancestors) covered a much larger area than now. These seas sometimes reached out to and partially covered an ancient mountainous land mass or shield in what is now the central part of western Saudi Arabia. They also extended around the northern side of this land mass in the region now occupied by northern Saudi Arabia, Iraq, Jordan, Syria and Lebanon.

In these ancient seas were deposited limestones, muds and sands which, in their hardened rock form, are seen today on the surface of the land as far west as, and in some areas beyond, the Tuwayq Escarpment. From their western extremity eastward the thickness of these deposits increases gradually below the surface until, on the western shore of the Arabian Gulf, they probably are about 30,000 feet thick. Farther out in the gulf, and still farther eastward, they may exceed 40,000 feet.

The teeming plant and animal life of some of these ancient seas was the source of the petroleum which is found so abundantly in the Arabian Gulf-Mesopotamian region. The organic material of their bodily structure, which sank to the sea bottom and was collected and preserved, together with the marine sedimentary deposits accumulating at the same time, was transformed into liquid petroleum by a slow process of nature.

The marine deposits, which in the beginning were laid down almost horizontally, have been tilted gently in an easterly direction by a general and gradual sinking of the Arabian Gulf basin. In

many places the sediments also have been warped into bulges, known as anticlines or domes, in which collections of oil have been trapped in the limestones and sandstones under high pressure. The present oil fields are in such areas.

Saudi Arabia contains two great sections or provinces which are in distinct contrast from a geologic viewpoint.

The first of these geologic provinces is the ancient land mass or shield in the central part of western Saudi Arabia. This old land mass once extended across the Red Sea into Africa. It consists of highly folded and compressed ancient sediments whose internal structure and form have been fused and altered by the great pressures and heat of ancient mountain building. These rocks are cut in many places by intrusions of granite and other igneous rocks, including a number of both old and comparatively recent lava flows. They represent the stubs of ancient mountain ranges, which have been worn down gradually by erosion to the general level of the region.

The other principal geologic province of Arabia is occupied by sedimentary rocks; that is, by the deposits of the seas which, although also ancient, are much more recent than the old shield, against and over which they spread. The western boundary of the sedimentary province swings around the ancient land mass in a great arc roughly following the configuration of the large sand-covered areas beginning with the Great Nafud on the north and coming down to Nafud ad-Dahi. The sedimentary strata slope or dip gently away from this old land mass, to the northeastward in northern Saudi

204

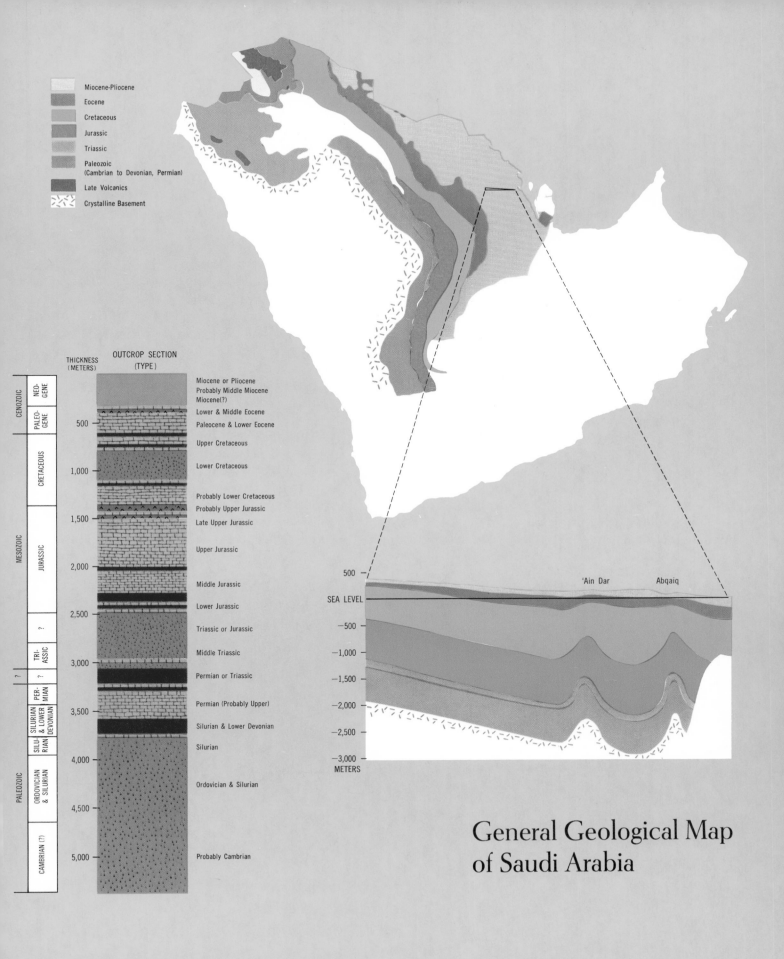

General Geological Map of Saudi Arabia

Legend:
- Miocene-Pliocene
- Eocene
- Cretaceous
- Jurassic
- Triassic
- Paleozoic (Cambrian to Devonian, Permian)
- Late Volcanics
- Crystalline Basement

THICKNESS (METERS)

OUTCROP SECTION (TYPE)

CENOZOIC	NEO-GENE		Miocene or Pliocene
			Probably Middle Miocene
			Miocene(?)
	PALEO-GENE	500	Lower & Middle Eocene
			Paleocene & Lower Eocene
			Upper Cretaceous
MESOZOIC	CRETACEOUS	1,000	Lower Cretaceous
			Probably Lower Cretaceous
		1,500	Probably Upper Jurassic
			Late Upper Jurassic
	JURASSIC		Upper Jurassic
		2,000	Middle Jurassic
			Lower Jurassic
	?	2,500	Triassic or Jurassic
	TRI-ASSIC		Middle Triassic
	?	3,000	Permian or Triassic
PALEOZOIC	PER-MIAN		Permian (Probably Upper)
	SILURIAN & LOWER DEVONIAN	3,500	Silurian & Lower Devonian
	SILU-RIAN		Silurian
	ORDOVICIAN & SILURIAN	4,000	Ordovician & Silurian
		4,500	
	CAMBRIAN (?)	5,000	Probably Cambrian

500 —
SEA LEVEL
-500 —
-1,000 —
-1,500 —
-2,000 —
-2,500 —
-3,000 —
METERS

'Ain Dar   Abqaiq

Arabia, to the eastward in eastern Saudi Arabia and to the southeastward into the Rub' al-Khali basin in southern Arabia. For a long period these strata have been wearing away or eroding. Many of the harder members, which are more resistant to erosion, now rise above the level of the general terrain in the form of escarpments. The most notable escarpments are the impressive group of westward-facing hills known as the Tuwayq Escarpment.

As the limestones and other strata seen on the surface in central Arabia are tilted gently to the east, they are found thousands of feet below the surface in the vicinity of Abqaiq and Dhahran, where some of the members yield oil. The limestones found on the surface at Dhahran likewise outcrop again at a much higher elevation to the west. The water that they take in from rainfall in their westerly outcrop is the source of the water that they produce along the coast.

The ancient basement complex of igneous and metamorphic rocks, exposed in the central part of western Arabia, appears again in the eastern portion of the Iranian mountains. These rocks are Precambrian in age; that is, they represent an early period in the geological history of the earth, perhaps before any form of life existed. The region between

these two outcrops of Precambrian rocks is a great basin. The trough of this basin now is occupied by the valleys of the Tigris and Euphrates Rivers and by the Arabian Gulf.

Different invasions of the sea within this region were separated by long periods in which the seas withdrew and in which the sedimentary deposits were eroded.

The first deposits upon the old basement complex were of the early Paleozoic age (Cambrian, Ordovician, Silurian and Devonian). They range up to a few hundred feet thick in central Arabia and may reach from 5,000 to 10,000 feet in the deeper portions of the basin.

The next deposits found in central Arabia are much younger (late Paleozoic and early Mesozoic). This fact indicates a break of many million years between the deposition of the two groups. In certain areas in Saudi Arabia the late Paleozoic rocks rest directly upon the basement complex. Interruptions of deposition occurred in the Mesozoic epoch, but beds of the Triassic, Jurassic and Cretaceous ages are represented.

Overlying the Cretaceous in eastern Saudi Arabia are limestones of early Tertiary age (Eocene), and resting upon these unconformably are strata of much younger Tertiary age (Miocene). Limestones of an age between these two groups (Lower Miocene) are found in southwest Iran and Iraq and are the main producers of oil in those areas, but have not been found in Saudi Arabia.

The existing deformation of these strata took place mainly in Cretaceous and Eocene times and was related mainly to the formation of the great mountain ranges of Iran. At the beginning of the late Tertiary period the Iranian mountains started rising as a result of powerful, deep-seated pressures exerted from the east, while at the same time the eastern Arabian Gulf region was sinking. The Arabian mainland was little affected except for being tilted slightly toward the Arabian Gulf basin. Deposition continued in the Arabian Gulf while these great movements, which occurred slowly, were in progress. The result was that the sedimen-

An escarpment in Saudi Arabia where the powerful forces of erosion have clearly exposed a series of sedimentary strata.

The Tuwayq Escarpment, on the road from Riyadh to Jiddah, is capped by limestone originally laid down in ancient seas.

tary strata were thrown up into high mountain ranges in Iran, where the eroded remnants of these strata reach 14,000 feet in elevation. The oil fields of southwest Iran and eastern Iraq are in anticlines along the western flank or foreland of these mountain ranges.

On the western side of the Arabian Gulf the older deformation was much less pronounced, and the folds in eastern Saudi Arabia are of a broad, gentle type, generally trending north and south. One of the longest folds is the En Nala axis which extends from the southern end of Ghawar north to include, probably, Fadhili and Khursaniyah—a distance of more than 250 miles. All of the known oil accumulations in Saudi Arabia, with the exception of Dammam and possibly Khursaniyah, are in this type of gentle fold. Dammam is thought to be a deep-seated salt plug.

THE TERRAIN

From a geographical standpoint the Arabian Peninsula may be considered as divided into a number of regions, each characterized by distinctive terrain. These regions are described here in turn, starting with the Arabian Gulf coastal region and continuing to the west.

ARABIAN GULF COASTAL REGION A strip of the Arabian Peninsula bordering the western and southern parts of the Arabian Gulf, between Kuwait on the north and the Trucial Coast on the south, is distinguished by low relief and relatively plentiful water. This is the region in which Aramco first discovered oil and in which most of the company's installations are located.

The general trend of the Arabian Gulf coast line in this region does not seem particularly irregular on the average page-size map, but the detailed configuration of the coast is extremely irregular. The shore is generally low and sandy. The sea for some distance from the coast is relatively shallow and full of shoals. In many places the waterfront shifts back and forth over several miles, depending on the tide and wind direction. Shallow fords connect some islands with the mainland at low tide. Under some conditions coastal salt flats are covered by the sea for miles inland. Sand spits often change their form as the result of wind and waves.

Salt flats, called *sabkhahs*, are common in this region. They occur in depressions where there are water seepages and along the low coast line. Water is found within a few feet of the surface of these flats. Because of evaporation, salt is deposited on the surface, and usually an impure mixture of salt and sand forms a crust a few inches deep. Occasionally a layer of almost pure salt is mined for local consumption.

The flat surface of the *sabkhahs* is maintained at the level to which moisture rises above the static water level. Below the moisture level the sand, silt and dust are damp and fixed in place, but above the moisture level they dry out and blow away, leaving a flat surface. The surface is firm in dry weather and sometimes cracks into countless hard, warped, irregular pieces. The smooth, dry surfaces can be excellent for automobile driving, but rains turn the *sabkhahs* into impassable morasses. After a short period of drying they may form a deceptively dry crust through which vehicles break to become mired in the mud below.

From Jubail northward to Kuwait Bay the region consists primarily of low, rolling plains covered with a thin mantle of sand. The sand supports a growth of bushes and grass varying from sparse to fairly dense. The roots hold the sand in hummocks, forming terrain called *'afjah* or *dikakah*. Such terrain can be extremely difficult for motor vehicles. West of Kuwait this bumpy terrain merges with the Dibdibah gravel plains. Through the center of the gravel plains, the great valley of al-Batin runs

A sabkhah *or salt flat near the Arabian Gulf, being crossed by an Aramco car in the pioneering days.*

A section of the highly irregular coast of the Arabian Gulf, where land and water merge into each other.

209

A bumpy area of dikakah, *where the sand is held by bushes and grass, with a* sabkhah *and an escarpment in the background.*

A belt of drifting sand piled up into large dunes on top of a sabkhah *in the Jafurah area on the Dhahran-Abqaiq road.*

northeast to the channels of the Tigris and the Euphrates in southern Iraq.

From Jubail southward there is a fairly wide belt of drifting sand often piled up into large dunes. This sand belt widens to the south and merges with the sand area known as the Jafurah, which in turn runs into the great sand area of the Rub' al-Khali. Abqaiq lies in, and Dhahran and Ras Tanura lie adjacent to, the northern portion of this sand-covered area. Consequently much of the area in which Aramco operates is distinguished by picturesque, but troublesome, sand dunes. The coastal areas not covered with sand are either bare, rocky terrain, as in the vicinity of Dhahran, or *sabkhahs.*

The sands of the Jafurah lie upon flat gravel plains. The plains, sometimes called *hadabahs,* appear east of the sands as far as an escarpment running south from the vicinity of al-'Uqayr. To the west of the sands, the plains spread out in broad, gravelly sheets from the oasis of al-Hasa in the north to an area some distance south of the oasis of Yabrin.

Wadi al-Miyah (Valley of the Waters), northwest of Qatif and inland from Jubail, is a basin rather than a stream channel. It takes its name from the numerous springs and wells found within its confines.

No part of this coastal region is more than a few hundred feet above sea level. The elevation of the region as a whole increases gradually from the coast toward the interior of the peninsula at the rate of about five feet per mile.

SUMMAN PLATEAU

SUMMAN PLATEAU Between the coastal strip and the great belt of sand known as the Dahna is a plateau called the Summan, a hard rock plain from 50 to 150 miles wide. Near the Dahna the Summan is fairly flat, but to the east old stream channels and other forms of erosion have cut the plateau into irregular terrain. Isolated buttes and mesas, as well as extensive tablelands, project prominently into the coastal lowlands. In part of this region, west of Abqaiq and the oasis of al-Hasa, Aramco has discovered the great Ghawar oil field. The Arabic word *ghawar* refers to the caves and shelters formed by erosion in the walls of many rocky features of the area.

The elevation of the Summan averages about 800 feet at its eastern edge and about 1,300 feet at its western margin adjoining the Dahna sands. Thus its westward rise is from three to four feet per mile. The surface of the Summan plateau is generally barren. After rain some vegetation springs up in sandy depressions such as the one in which the Aramco community of 'Udhailiyah, in the center of the Ghawar oil field, is situated.

The term *jabal* is applied loosely by the Arabs to hills, buttes, mesas, ridges and mountains. Other terms in use are *dil'* and *hazm*, although the latter usually is used for a rise lower than a *jabal*. *Abraq* (plural *burqan*, from which Kuwait's great oil field, Burgan, takes its name) and *barqa* are usually applied to hills whose sides are banked with sand. A promontory or headland of an escarpment is called *khashm*, an Arabic word for nose.

THE DAHNA One of the distinctive geographical features of Saudi Arabia is the long, narrow belt of sand known as the Dahna. It extends approximately 800 miles in a great arc from the Great Nafud in the north to the Rub' al-Khali in the south. The sands of the Dahna are from medium to fine in grain. The color, because of iron oxide (hematite) stains, approaches a deep reddish orange, especially in the morning and late afternoon.

The Dahna is a favorite grazing ground of the Bedouins in winter and spring. Water is scarce and the Bedouins who herd camels there get along with only a little of it for weeks. Camels do not require water while grazing in green grass and bushes and the Bedouins live mainly on the camels' milk.

In 1957 Aramco discovered oil in the Dahna at Khurais, almost due east of Riyadh and closer to the capital than to Aramco headquarters at Dhahran.

ESCARPMENT REGION West of the sands of the Dahna is the heart of Najd. This region is about 200 miles wide and is dominated by several steep, west-facing escarpments with gentle eastern slopes. The Tuwayq Escarpment (Upper Jurassic limestone), 500 miles long, and the 'Aramah Escarpment (Upper Cretaceous limestone), extending for a shorter distance, are the most prominent topographical features.

The top of the Tuwayq Escarpment has an average elevation of 2,800 feet above sea level with a maximum elevation of about 3,500 feet. The top of the escarpment is about 800 feet above the level of the plains to the west. The 'Aramah Escarpment, about 1,800 feet above sea level, is less conspicuous because it is only about 400 feet higher than the plain to the west of it.

The remaining escarpments, which are roughly parallel to the two dominant ones, are lower and not so long. Some of these escarpments, however,

Typical 'Asir terrain as seen from 10,000-foot elevation.

Wind and water erosion carved this stone statue at al-'Ula.

appear to be major elevations when contrasted with the adjacent featureless plains.

NORTHERN SAUDI ARABIA The northern region of Saudi Arabia, lying between the Great Nafud and the Jordan and Iraq borders, is part of the great Syrian Desert from a geographical point of view. This region is a land of gravel and rock plains along with lava beds.

The maximum elevations in this region are found on the plateau between the northern extremity of the Great Nafud and the junction of the borders of Saudi Arabia, Jordan and Iraq. This plateau attains an elevation of 2,900 feet and forms the divide between the drainage to the Euphrates on the east and the drainage to Wadi as-Sirhan on the west. A series of valleys running northeastwards into Iraq is known as al-Widyan, and the terrain through which they pass is scarred by the many tributaries of these water courses. Wadi as-Sirhan, the basin of which is not a water course, is a great depression, 200 miles long, from twenty to thirty miles wide, and 1,000 feet below the elevation of the adjoining plateau region.

For thousands of years one of the most important trade routes connecting the Mediterranean and central Arabia passed through Wadi as-Sirhan and the oasis of al-Jawf (Jawf Ibn 'Amir). With the construction of the trans-Arabian pipeline through this region, the principal overland artery of trade shifted to the highway paralleling the pipeline.

An 'irq area in the Rub' al-Khali, with sand masses heaped up to form long parallel veins.

A forbidding area of the Rub' al-Khali where dunes in the sand mountains rise to heights of 500 to 800 feet.

214

New towns have sprung up along this route. These communities depend on deep water wells.

GREAT SAND AREAS Saudi Arabia contains several other broad stretches of sand-covered land. The Great Nafud in the north is an expanse of sand covering approximately 22,000 square miles and consisting of rolling sand dunes supporting sparse vegetation. It contains a few watering places and affords good grazing for camels, sheep and goats during the winter and spring. As in the case of the Dahna, the sand is reddish in color due to an iron oxide stain.

South of the Great Nafud are other large stretches of sand in addition to the great arc of the Dahna. These stretches lie west of the Tuwayq Escarpment.

In the southern part of Saudi Arabia is the immense sand body of the Rub' al-Khali or Empty Quarter. This sand body occupies a basin bordered by the mountains of Oman on the east, the plateau behind the coastal escarpments on the south, and the foothills of the mountains of Yemen and 'Asir on the west. The Rub' al-Khali is approximately 750 miles long and has a maximum width of nearly 400 miles. It covers an area of about 250,000 square miles, nearly the size of Texas, and is the largest continuous body of sand in the world.

Aramco exploration parties have been examining the Rub' al-Khali for the past three decades. In the course of their work they have penetrated every corner of this region. It was not until this century that the region was crossed by travelers other than hardy Bedouins. Bertram Thomas, the first Western explorer to traverse the Rub' al-Khali, made his trip in 1931 from Salalah on the Arabian Sea to the peninsula of Qatar. In 1932 H. St. John B. Philby explored the central and northwestern portions, which he described in his book *The Empty Quarter*. Wilfred Thesiger, another Englishman, made several trips through unexplored parts of the Rub' al-Khali from 1945 on, first as a member of the Middle East Anti-Locust Unit and later as an independent traveler.

A comparatively recent lava bed, characteristic of various areas of western Arabia.

A range of mountains in the Hijaz, rising boldly from the coastal plain.

The sands of the Rub' al-Khali, like those of other sand regions in Saudi Arabia, are not all of one type. Some areas are covered by comparatively stabilized sand sheets. Across other areas, mobile dunes move with the prevailing wind. Dunes may be star-shaped, dome-shaped or crescent-shaped. Masses of sand sometimes form long single or parallel veins *('irq,* plural *'uruq).* Sand mountains of complex arrangement attain heights of 500 to 800 feet.

Parts of the Rub' al-Khali are uninhabited except during the infrequent rains when Bedouins move in to take advantage of the pasturage. Other parts support scattered nomads, especially along the regular north-south crossing which follows a belt of water wells between Longitudes 50° E and 52° E. Bedouins also frequent the northeastern section of the Rub' al-Khali, which contains many wells of salty water satisfactory for the watering of camels.

Nafud is the term used for a sand region in the northern part of Saudi Arabia and *ramlah* is the word used in the south. The word *'irq* usually means a single vein of sand, but sometimes it is used for an extended region containing many examples of this formation. What is known to Westerners as the Great Nafud is called simply *an-Nafud,* the Nafud, by the Bedouins. The whole area of the Rub' al-Khali is known to its inhabitants as *ar-Ramlah* or *ar-Rimal* (the plural of *ramlah).*

CENTRAL PLATEAU REGION Within the arc formed by the Great Nafud and the Tuwayq Escarpment is a broad central plateau about 300 miles wide. Most of this area is part of the ancient land mass of Arabia over which the sea did not deposit the layers of sediments which make up the surface of eastern Arabia or in which any such rocks have been removed by erosion. The rocks of the central plateau region are igneous and metamorphic. Over its western half there are several extensive lava beds of comparatively recent age.

The elevations of the central plateau region vary from 3,500 to 4,500 feet, although there are depressions as low as 3,000 feet and ridges higher than 6,000 feet. The region is sparsely populated except in the north between the valley of Wadi ar-Rumah and the southern edge of the Great Nafud. In the vicinity of the ranges of Aja and Salma, together known as Jabal Shammar, lies the great oasis of Hayil with its scores of dependent towns and villages.

The central plateau east of the coastal mountain ranges has a gentle, gradual slope toward the east. The continental divide, or line of separation between drainage toward the Red Sea and drainage toward the Arabian Gulf, is in the western part of the country. Short streams of high gradient have carved deep gorges in the steep-walled western flank of the coastal range. Longer patterns of drainage have been developed on the gentler eastern slopes. Of the latter the greatest is Wadi ar-Rumah, which through its extension, al-Batin, runs to the Arabian Gulf basin near Basra. The three large valleys of Ranyah, Bishah and Tathlith, which join to form Wadi ad-Dawasir, are also typical examples of drainage down the eastern slopes.

WESTERN ARABIA Along the eastern shore of the Red Sea is a coastal plain confined within a narrow space by mountains dropping sharply toward the sea. The plain is called Tihamah. Sometimes the plain is subdivided into Tihamat al-Hijaz, Tihamat 'Asir and Tihamat al-Yaman.

The mountains rise boldly from the coastal plain with something of a gap in the neighborhood of Mecca. Between the Gulf of Aqaba and Mecca these mountains are seldom higher than 7,000 feet and generally do not exceed 4,000 feet. In 'Asir and Yemen they are much higher. Southeast of Mecca several peaks are more than 8,000 feet high. The elevations continue to rise to the south and reach their highest point, about 12,000 feet, in a summit west of San'a, the capital of Yemen. The height of the mountains of 'Asir and Yemen and their proximity to the monsoons of the Indian Ocean bring these areas the most abundant rainfall of any section of the Arabian Peninsula and enable them to support the densest populations.

The abrupt western drop of the coastal mountain ranges is the result of a break, or fault, in the crust of the earth. The Red Sea fills the gap formed when a great block slipped downward in relation to the land masses on either side.

MOUNTAINS IN SOUTHERN ARABIA High mountains fringe the southwestern margin of the Arabian Peninsula. Near the Gulf of Aden the average elevation is from 6,000 to 8,000 feet, while one peak north of the town of al-Mukalla rises more than 11,000 feet. Eastward the elevations decrease to 3,000 feet in Dhufar, except for a 5,500-foot peak north of Murbat.

The mountains of south Arabia and Dhufar are composed essentially of sedimentary rocks dipping gently northward into the Rub' al-Khali basin. The southern slopes are irregular and precipitous. The abrupt termination of these mountains on the south is thought to have been caused when great blocks of the rocky surface dropped along cracks in the earth's crust.

A lowland plateau about 150 miles long occurs between the eastern extension of the mountains of Dhufar and the southern part of the ranges of Oman. In this area the average elevation is about 500 feet.

The mountains of Oman known as al-Hajar have a conspicuously rugged topography. The highest elevations reach 10,000 feet or more in the central massif of al-Jabal al-Akhdar (the Green Mountain). The mountain chain sweeps along an arc roughly parallel to the Gulf of Oman, with steep slopes both seaward and towards the inland plateau. The mountains are similar to the Iranian ranges in structure, topography and geology. They are very unlike the mountains on the western and southern sides of the Arabian Peninsula, which are characterized by steep slopes on the seaward side and gentle slopes toward the interior.

A field of alfalfa nudges the mountains outside of al-Mustaniya, a village lying in the Wadi Najran.

218

the 'Asir Province, watered by monsoon rains, terraced fields of wheat and barley climb up the highlands in the as-Sawda area.

FLAGS,
MONEY AND STAMPS

The people of Saudi Arabia have ever before them the reminders of their heritage in the form of emblems which appear on their flags, public buildings, money, books and postage stamps. Three of the most common symbols are the palm tree, the sword and the Muslim Creed.

The date palm, which traditionally supplied the main agricultural crop of Saudi Arabia, is emblematic of vitality and growth.

The sword, always unsheathed, symbolizes strength rooted in faith.

The Muslim Creed, translated as: "There is no god but God; Muhammad is the Messenger of God," is the first pillar of Islam.

The national flag bears two of these emblems: the sword and the creed. It was adopted by 'Abd al-'Aziz in 1926. The emblems are printed on both sides and the flag looks the same from either side. The royal standard shows a palm tree and crossed swords. This combination occurs frequently in other contexts, including coinage and paper money.

The first money of the House of Sa'ud was a copper and nickel coin, called the *qirsh*, issued about the time of the capture of Jiddah in the name of 'Abd al-'Aziz, King of the Hijaz and Sultan of Najd. This coin circulated along with the British gold sovereign, the Turkish silver *majidi*, the Maria Theresa dollar, the Indian rupee and other foreign coinage, as well as the gold dinar, silver riyal and copper qirsh struck by the Hashimite Government of the Hijaz.

On January 24, 1928, Saudi Arabia established an independent monetary system based on the Saudi riyal, a silver coin about the size of a U. S. silver dollar and valued at one-tenth of a British sovereign. In 1936 a new riyal coin about the size of a U. S. half dollar was issued. This coin weighed 11.66 grams and was eventually valued at approximately 3.75 Saudi riyals to the U. S. dollar. New half-riyal and quarter-riyal silver coins and one-qirsh, half-qirsh and quarter-qirsh cupronickel coins also were issued. By the late Nineteen Fifties the value of the silver content of the silver coins had became considerably more than their value as coins, and

The Saudi Arabian flag bears the Arabic inscription: "There is no god but God; Muhammad is the Messenger of God."

they disappeared from circulation. They were officially demonetized in December, 1959. The cupronickel coins were withdrawn from circulation in 1958 and demonetized in the following year. They were replaced by new cupronickel coins in one-qirsh, two-qirsh and four-qirsh denominations.

In 1952 the government established the Saudi Arabian Monetary Agency to strengthen and stabilize the country's currency, to centralize government receipts and payments and to control disbursements authorized under the government's budget.

In the same year the Monetary Agency issued the Saudi sovereign, a gold coin of the same weight and approximate fineness as the British sovereign and with a par value of forty Saudi riyals. Following the discovery of a large number of counterfeit

The royal standard displays crossed swords and date palm.

Cupronickel coins are used within Saudi Arabia. Both sides are shown of the four, two and one qirsh coins.

Some of the Saudi Arabian stamps. The one at upper left commemorated the accession to the throne of King Faysal.

Saudi sovereigns, a new sovereign of the same size and weight but of a different design was issued in January, 1958. Both types of sovereigns were later demonetized.

For many years Saudi Arabia issued no paper currency. The original charter of the Monetary Agency, in fact, forbade it to do so. Large transactions had to be carried out with gold or large quantities of silver riyals and occasionally by foreign banknotes such as Indian rupees, U. S. dollars and Egyptian pounds. In 1953, however, the Monetary Agency issued paper notes called "pilgrim receipts." It was announced that these receipts were issued primarily to relieve pilgrims of the necessity of carrying large sums in heavy silver coins, but the receipts soon circulated throughout the kingdom and gained the virtual status of official paper currency.

A new series of pilgrim receipts in one, five and ten-riyal denominations was issued beginning in 1954.

At the beginning of 1960, the Saudi Arabian Government revalued the riyal, fixing its value in terms of gold at the equivalent of 4.5 riyals to the U. S. dollar and insuring stability of the riyal by providing one hundred percent backing in gold and foreign currency. At the time it was announced that henceforth the riyal would contain twenty qirsh rather than twenty-two and that the qirsh would be divided into five *halalah*. Thus the currency, in effect, was put on a decimal basis for the first time.

Saudi Arabia joined the International Monetary Fund in 1957, and in March, 1961, accepted the International Monetary Fund's obligation to make the Saudi riyal a fully convertible currency.

In June, 1961, the Monetary Agency issued an official paper currency in denominations of one, five, ten, fifty and one hundred riyals. The pilgrim receipts remained in circulation until 1963.

The traditional symbols of the palm tree, the sword and the creed also recur on the country's postage stamps. Saudi Arabia, as a member of the

Saudi Arab riyal notes, top to bottom, 100, fifty and ten.

Universal Postal Union and the Arab Postal Union, maintains postal contact with most nations. Mail service between Saudi Arabia and other countries relies heavily on air communications routed through Jiddah and Dhahran.

Beginning in 1916, the Hashimite Kingdom of the Hijaz had issued postage stamps for a number of years before the Saudi conquest. The first Saudi stamps for Najd were issued in 1925. In the following year a combined Saudi issue for Najd and the Hijaz appeared. The first stamps issued for the Kingdom of Saudi Arabia appeared in 1934. Postage stamps for regular and airmail use are now issued in various denominations and a number of commemorative issues have appeared. A four-qirsh stamp, commemorating King Faysal's accession to the throne, bears his picture and was issued in late 1964.

223

Part 5

The Culture

and

Customs of

the Arabs

THE RELIGION
OF ISLAM

Islam is the religious faith of about 500,000,000 people living in lands stretching from the west coast of Africa to the southwest Pacific. It is the predominant faith in North Africa, the Middle East, Pakistan and Indonesia.

The religion of Islam is not a profound departure from the other religions which originated in the Middle East—Judaism and Christianity. The three religions have much in common.

The histories of all three religions contain some stories of fanaticism, intolerance and ruthlessness in dealing with heretics and infidels. Though unrepresentative and inaccurate, these stories often have been overemphasized by enemies and cynics, and so has it been with Islam. The image built up by medieval crusading propaganda still lingers, leaving Western people with false impressions of Islam and the Muslims.

Muslims believe fervently that theirs is the only true faith and that they are charged with spreading it throughout the world. Yet they have not been as intolerant of other religions as is commonly believed. Islam was spread widely as the result of conquests, but contrary to popular belief it was not generally imposed upon the conquered by terror or even by force. The conquerors were ardent missionaries. They offered new hope and a new faith in what was then a generally decadent and misgoverned world. Muslim missionaries also have made and are still making countless conversions in many countries never invaded by Muslim armies. In the countries conquered by the Arabs, communities of other faiths—Christian and Jewish, for example—were allowed to continue their separate religious existence.

As its Arabic name signifies, Islam is a religion of submission to the will of God. Man is viewed as an instrument for carrying out that will, which is supreme in governing all earthly affairs. One who submits himself unreservedly to God's will and obeys the precepts He has laid down for mankind is a Muslim, a follower of Islam.

The Arabs, as well as the Jews, regard Abraham as their patriarch. According to Arab tradition, the Arabs descended from Abraham's first son, Ishmael, while the Hebrews descended from his second son, Isaac. This tradition agrees with the account in the Book of Genesis. The Arabs sometimes are called Ishmaelites.

According to Muslims, elements of their religion were revealed through a long line of Prophets, including Abraham (Ibrahim), Moses (Musa) and Jesus ('Isa), but the full and final revelation was given to Muhammad and later was embodied in written form as the Quran. Muslims regard the Quran as the word of God Himself and therefore the chief source of Islamic doctrines and practices. For interpretation of the Quran and for guidance on matters not dealt with in that book, the Muslim refers to the Sunnah, the acts and sayings of the

Sample illuminated pages from a Quran which dates to the eighteenth century.

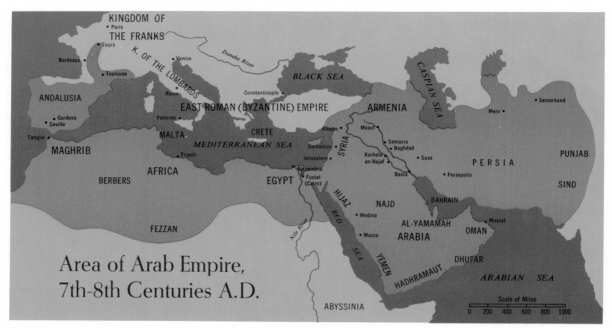

Area of Arab Empire,
7th-8th Centuries A.D.

The tremendous extent of the Arab empire of more than 1,000 years ago (above), stretching in all directions beyond Arabia's borders, bears a remarkable resemblance to the present areas of Islamic predominance (below).

Islam today is the religious faith of about five hundred million people living in a vast area, including North Africa, the Middle East, Pakistan and Indonesia, stretching from the Atlantic Ocean to the southwest Pacific.

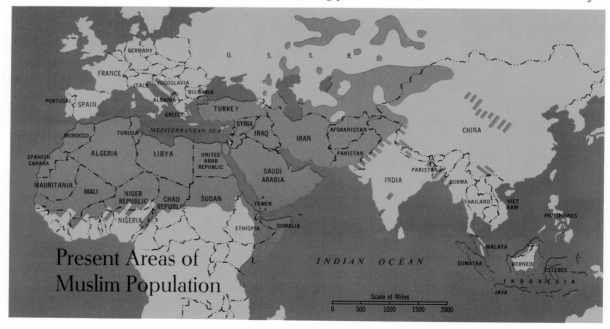

Present Areas of
Muslim Population

230

Prophet, which constitute a vast body of written traditions known as the *Hadith*.

Islam pervades the whole life of the community of its faithful. In a Muslim country such as Saudi Arabia, which recognizes the law of Islam as its fundamental code, religious law (the *Shari'ah*) prevails in numerous matters which in other states fall within the province of civil law.

Early in its history, Islam was split into two great segments, the Sunnite and the Shi'ite. Each segment developed its own legal systems. Four great schools arose within the Sunnite form of Islam. Each of them still has a multitude of followers. The founders of the four schools were:

Abu Hanifah . . . . THE HANAFITE SCHOOL
Malik ibn Anas . . . . THE MALIKITE SCHOOL
Ash-Shafi'i . . . . THE SHAFI'ITE SCHOOL
Ahmad ibn Hanbal . . . . . . THE HANBALITE SCHOOL

The Hanbalite school, the latest of the four to be founded, is the principal one in the Kingdom of Saudi Arabia. The others also are recognized and respected in the kingdom. A recent qadi, or religious judge, of Dhahran, for example, was a Malikite.

Although *Shari'ah* law governing questions of human relations and conduct has been elaborately developed, the Islamic religion itself is extremely simple and personal. There are no rites or ceremonies performed by priests or ministers. Indeed, there are no priests or ministers or congregations like those in Christian churches. Muslims spend much time discussing religion, and men who are well versed and eloquent may acquire great influence. Such men, of whom Shaykh Muhammad ibn 'Abd al-Wahhab was an outstanding example, might be considered preachers. There are imams who lead believers in prayer at the mosque and who deliver a sermon at the Friday noon prayers, and there are qadis as religious judges, but the religious concept is one of direct relationship between the individual and God without any earthly intercessor or intermediary. The simple ceremonies of the prayers and pilgrimage are performed by each person as an individual, although joining with others in worship or the Meccan rites is deemed to be meritorious.

The mosques, many of which are imposing and beautiful, are sanctified places for Muslims to pray. There is no instrumental or vocal music. The leader of the prayers simply chants verses of the Quran. The religion of a good Muslim pervades every hour of his life. There are few moments in an ordinary conversation which do not contain references to God. God is always present and controls everything.

Five primary duties, known as the five pillars of the faith, are required of a Muslim.

The first pillar, *the profession of faith*, consists of repeating the basic formula, which is a euphonious utterance in Arabic, *La ilaha illa Allah*—"There is no god but God," to which is added, "Muhammad is the Messenger of God." This entire formula is inscribed in graceful Arabic letters on the green flag of the Kingdom of Saudi Arabia.

The second pillar of the faith is *prayer*. Muslims pray five times a day—before dawn, at midday, in the latter part of the afternoon, at sunset and in the evening. The washing that precedes the prayer, the words of the worshipers, the number of bows and other parts of the ritual are set out in detail. The worshipers face toward the Ka'bah, the House of God in Mecca. Prayer is ordinarily a private affair to be performed singly or in groups wherever Muslims chance to be at the appointed hour. Every Friday at midday, however, congregational prayers are held in the mosques and all men are expected to be present. Friday, rather than Sunday, is the weekly day of rest in Saudi Arabia.

The third pillar of the faith is *zakah*, freely translated as obligatory alms. This includes the obligatory religious tax paid to the government for charitable works, *zakah* proper, as well as personal and voluntary gifts of alms to the needy, *sadaqah*. Islam recognizes that the lot of men in life varies and endeavors to lessen the differences that divide men by requiring the rich to devote a share of their substance to the welfare of the poor.

231

THE FAST OF RAMADAN *Fasting*, the fourth pillar of Islam, is prescribed for Muslims throughout Ramadan, the ninth month of the Muslim year. For every day of this month, complete abstinence from food and drink, as well as continence in other respects, is enjoined from the moment before dawn when a white thread can be distinguished from a black until the setting of the sun. The purpose of fasting is to lead men to a deeper and richer perception of God and the obligations of human creatures in the service of their Maker. The fast of Ramadan produces in the community of Islam a spiritual unity and a sense of equality.

The last ten days of Ramadan are regarded as particularly sacred, for one of the nights of these days—no man knows which one—is the Night of Power, the anniversary of the night on which the Prophet Muhammad received his first revelation from God.

The first three days of Shawwal, the succeeding

This highly ornamented mihrab *shows the* qiblah *or direction of Mecca toward which Muslims everywhere face when praying.*

Muslim pilgrims in the state of purity known as ihram, *wearing seamless white cloth garments, face the Ka'bah in the Sacred Mosque in Mecca.*

month, are holidays for celebrating the Feast of the Breaking of the Fast, *'Id al-Fitr*, one of the two great festivals of the Muslim year.

THE PILGRIMAGE TO MECCA The *hajj*, or pilgrimage to Mecca, is set apart from the other four pillars of Islam because it requires a Muslim to perform this act of piety only if he has the means. A Muslim of the purest faith may live and die without ever being able to go to Mecca. But the merit is great for one who goes, for the Prophet Muhammad said in effect that the reward of paradise awaits one who makes a pilgrimage acceptable to God.

In addition to the value of the pilgrimage as an individual act, the institution exercises a strong social influence. The Prophet said: "The believers in their love and affection and sympathy for each other are like the body: if one member complains the whole body remains awake and feverish." The pilgrimage annually gives the members of the body of Islam a chance to come together and become

acquainted with each other. The pilgrim is encouraged to associate himself with companions from the hour in which he begins his journey. The Prophet frowned upon traveling in solitude. He is reported to have said: "One is a devil, two are devils, but three make a party."

In accordance with the Quran, the preliminary ceremonies of the pilgrimage may be performed during the months of Shawwal (which follows Ramadan) and Dhu al-Qa'dah, or during the succeeding first ten days of Dhu al-Hijjah, the last month of the Muslim year, but the climactic ceremonies of the hajj must be performed on the ninth and tenth days of Dhu al-Hijjah.

This is the time when pilgrims from all points of the Muslim world ordinarily assemble in Mecca by the hundreds of thousands. Islam also recognizes the merit of the *'umrah*, or lesser pilgrimage, which may be made at any other time of the year and in which most of the ceremonies of the hajj may be performed.

When the pilgrim is ready to leave his house, he

233

recites the prayer for the journey: "O God, Thou art my Companion on the journey, and Thou art the One who remains with my people. O God, roll up the earth for us...." At the door of the house another prayer is said, beginning: "In the name of God, I place my trust in God." Upon boarding whatever conveyance he is using, the pilgrim repeats "*Allah akbar*" ("God is greatest") three times.

In recent years, increasing numbers of pilgrims have been arriving by air; in 1967, about one third of the 316,000 foreign pilgrims came by air, another third by sea and the remainder overland.

At a designated point on each principal road or route, the pilgrims enter into a state of purity known as *ihram* and don the dress bearing the same name. They clip their nails, shave or cut their hair, bathe, discard headgear and exchange shoes for sandals, since neither the head nor the feet may be covered. The dress consists of two long pieces of white seamless cloth, one wound about the waist and the other around the shoulders. These simple garments make all men equal as they give homage to their Creator.

As the pilgrim dons his seamless garments, he says the Prayer of Intent: "O God, I have dedicated myself to Thee and I intend to make the pilgrimage." He then cries out: "*Labbayka*" ("Here I am at Your service"). This cry is made frequently during the pilgrimage. The Muslim in *ihram* is forbidden to indulge in any pleasures of the flesh, to use perfumes, to wear garments with seams, to clip his nails or cut his hair, to hunt (though fishing is permitted), or to cut, uproot or destroy any trees or plants growing in sacred territory.

The great majority of the foreign pilgrims enter the country at Jiddah, where they may spend a few days before proceeding to Mecca. In Jiddah pilgrims are assigned in groups to their *mutawwifs*, professional guides responsible for the spiritual and material welfare of the pilgrims in their charge.

A group of pilgrims from Pakistan, in ihram *and protected by umbrellas against the burning heat of the sun.*

234

Pilgrims at prayer in the Great Mosque at Medina, a sacred shrine to Muslims and the burial place of the Prophet.

The *mutawwifs* and their assistants arrange lodgings for the pilgrims, advise them in their religious rites and assist in any ways they can. They represent an old and important profession in Mecca.

In former years the majority of the pilgrims traveled from Jiddah to Mecca in litters on camelback. Buses and automobiles long ago replaced the picturesque camel trains over this forty-six mile route. Two markers (al-'Alamayn) a few miles from Mecca denote the boundary of the sacred territory beyond which non-Muslims may not pass.

The pilgrims enter Mecca preferably on foot and preferably, although not necessarily, in the daytime. As soon as possible they begin the pilgrimage ceremonies.

The most sacred place of the Holy City is the Ka'bah, a stone building, cubical in shape and about forty-five feet high, which stands in the great courtyard of the Sacred Mosque. It is shrouded in a covering of black silk, beautifully embroidered with inscriptions in ornamental Arabic characters. Set in the southeast corner of the Ka'bah is the sacred Black Stone which is believed to have been sent down by God from heaven in ancient times as a sign to men. It is about twelve inches in diameter, black with a reddish hue, and surrounded by a silver collar. Over the centuries the kisses of countless pilgrims have worn it smooth. If the crowds about the stone are too great, the pilgrim may touch the stone with a stick and kiss the stick or even salute the stone with his hands and kiss his hands.

In tracing their ancestry back to the patriarch Abraham, the Arabs believe that Abraham and Ishmael built the Ka'bah. In the courtyard of the Great Mosque is the Station of Abraham, which is believed to contain the stone upon which Abraham and Ishmael stood while building the shrine. Water from the nearby well of Zamzam is believed to have saved the life of Ishmael as a child.

Chapters 16 and 21 of the Book of Genesis tell the Biblical form of the story. Hagar, the Egyptian handmaiden of Abraham's wife, Sarah, bore him a son (Ishmael) after Sarah had despaired of having any children. In her old age, however, Sarah was blessed with a son (Isaac) and refused to harbor Hagar and Ishmael in the household any longer. The Lord told Abraham to "hearken unto her voice," but not to worry about this son, "for in Isaac shall thy seed be called. And also of the son of the bondwoman will I make a nation, because he is thy seed." Accordingly, Abraham sent Hagar and Ishmael into the wilderness with bread and a bottle of water, which soon ran out. In her despair, and unable to bear the sight of his final suffering, Hagar placed the child in a bush. Then Gabriel, the Angel of God, said unto her: "What aileth thee, Hagar? Fear not; for God hath heard the voice of the lad where he is. Arise, lift up the lad, and hold him in thine hand; for I will make him a great nation. And God opened her eyes, and she saw a well of water; and she went, and filled the bottle with water, and gave the lad drink."

According to the Muslim version of the story, the place in the wilderness where this incident occurred is within the present site of Mecca. Before the Angel Gabriel appeared, Hagar had run back and forth seven times between two hills, called as-Safa and al-Marwah, in her search for water. The well that Gabriel showed her was the well of Zamzam, from which pilgrims now drink as one of the rites of the pilgrimage ceremony.

The well in time became filled in, but according to tradition it was rediscovered and reopened by the grandfather of the Prophet Muhammad, who in turn was told in a vision that it would furnish water to all pilgrims. The well is held in great reverence. According to a tradition of the Prophet, "Fever comes from the boiling of Hell, but the water of Zamzam will cool it." Another Arab proverb enumerates the five acts of virtue: "Looking into the Quran, looking at the Ka'bah, looking up to one's parents, looking into Zamzam and looking the world in the face."

In following the regular ceremony, the pilgrims circle the Ka'bah seven times, three times running, four times slowly, kissing the stone and saluting the Yemenite (southern) corner each time. They then visit the Station of Abraham and say a prayer,

236

after which they may visit other sacred spots, including the well of Zamzam. The next rite is the running between as-Safa and al-Marwah in commemoration of Hagar's desperate search for water before Zamzam was revealed to her. Seven times the pilgrims go along the street, known as the Course, between the two knolls, a distance of 1,465 feet, walking most of the way but running at each end.

On the ninth day of Dhu al-Hijjah is the Standing on 'Arafat, which brings the great pilgrimage to a climax. 'Arafat is a plain about twelve miles east of Mecca. Some of the pilgrims go on foot, as Muhammad said that every step of a man who walks is a hundred times better than the step of a mount bearing a rider. The pilgrims spend the night before the Standing on 'Arafat in a village known as Mina which, with 'Arafat, is associated with a belief about Adam and Eve. It was at Mina that Adam made a wish to see Eve, who was then at Jiddah, and it was at 'Arafat that he met her.

The plain of 'Arafat is roughly circular. Toward the northern end stands a rocky hill, Jabal ar-Rahmah (the Mount of Mercy). On this plain the pilgrims remain until sunset, facing toward Mecca and repeating prayers. Many weep as they pray, for the Prophet told his followers: "The best of prayers is the prayer of the Day of 'Arafat." The

Pilgrims, carrying their flags, gather on Mount of Mercy.

Pilgrims' tents line the plain of 'Arafat and fill the village of Mina on the night before the Standing on Mount 'Arafat.

The Station of Abraham (foreground), in the courtyard of the Great Mosque in Mecca, is believed to contain the stone upon which the patriarch Abraham and his son Ishmael stood while constructing the Ka'bah (background).

most desirable place to be is near the Mount of Mercy. It is better to be mounted than to stand, as the Prophet remained on his camel during this part of his farewell pilgrimage.

Soon after sunset the pilgrims start to return to Mecca, headed by the King or his deputy. Early on the morning of the tenth of Dhu al-Hijjah, the day of the Feast of the Sacrifice *('Id al-Adha)*, they move on to Mina. In this village there are three stone pillars, representing three devils. The stoning of these pillars is among the final rites of the pilgrimage. Each pilgrim throws seven pebbles at the devil nearest Mecca. Following this rite, each pilgrim offers a sacrifice, traditionally a sheep, in commemoration of God's sparing Abraham the sacrifice of his son, who is Isaac in the Biblical story, but identified by the Arabs as Ishmael. The meat must be shared with the needy of Mecca.

The final rite on the day of the feast is the shaving or cutting of the hair, which symbolizes the end of the state of *ihram*. The pilgrim now lays aside his *ihram* dress for ordinary clothing.

The three days following the day of the feast are called the Days of the Drying of Meat. Two acts, following the example of the Prophet, are expected of the pilgrim during this time. He should spend the night at Mina and should stone the pillars representing the devils. This time all three are stoned.

The pilgrim then makes a final visit to the Ka'bah, which is regarded by the Arabs as "the noblest spot on earth, which God has chosen."

Although to do so is not obligatory as part of the pilgrimage, many pilgrims visit Medina and the tomb of the Prophet either before or after the visit to Mecca. The tomb is in the Great Mosque of Medina, one of the holiest shrines of Islam. The city also contains many other places associated with incidents in Muhammad's life. In a sense it is a great historical museum of the early days of Islam.

One of the final rites of the pilgrimage is the stoning of the three pillars, located in Mina, which represent devils.

DEVELOPMENT
OF ARABIC LITERATURE

Arabic is one of the Semitic languages, which are believed to be descended from a common mother tongue called Proto-Semitic. The Arabs did not begin to record their language in writing until long after other Semitic peoples, such as the Hebrews, had developed extensive written literatures. However, Arabic preserved better than any other Semitic language the original forms of Proto-Semitic.

The fact that Arabic has survived with little change for many centuries and over a vast area is due in part to the veneration by Muslims of the language of the Quran and in part to an effort by Arabic writers to preserve the language of the early years of Islam.

The alphabets of the Semitic languages, including Arabic, are derived from the same source as the Roman alphabet. In spite of this common origin, the Arabic alphabet now differs greatly from the Roman. This difference is most apparent in the form of the letters and in the fact that Arabic is written from right to left.

Another important difference is that all twenty-eight letters of the Arabic alphabet are consonants. The short vowel sounds—a, i, and u—can be indicated in the written language by a system of small diacritical marks placed above and below the consonants, but these marks ordinarily are not used. That the absence of these marks is not an insurmountable difficulty in reading Arabic can be seen by writing an English sentence with its consonants only: "Ths sntnc cn b rd wth lttl dffclty."

This emphasis on consonants is connected with another characteristic that distinguishes Arabic and the other Semitic languages from English. This is the system of consonant roots, by which a group of consonants (usually three) forms a root having a basic meaning.

For example, the consonant group *k-t-b* is connected with the idea of writing. By doubling one of the letters of this group, or by adding other consonants or vowels to it, various Arabic words are formed connected with the basic meaning of writing. *Kātib* is a writer, ma*ktab* is the place where he writes (his desk or his office), ma*ktūb* is the thing written by him (a letter), and *kitāb*ah is the act of writing. These changes in the root follow a definite pattern, and one or more changes can be applied to every root in the language. Thus, by adding *ā* between the first and second letters of the root and *i* between the second and third, Arabic forms words referring to the doer of an action. In this way we get *rākib*, one who rides; *qātil*, one who kills; *sākin*, one who resides.

This method of word formation not only greatly enlarges the vocabulary of Arabic but also makes it possible to guess at the meaning of many unfamiliar words.

BEGINNING OF ARABIC LITERATURE It is not known just when classical Arabic developed as a spoken language, but Byzantine sources of the fifth century record the fame of Arabic poetry. The writing of Arabic grew slowly and was not widely practiced until after the death of the Prophet Muhammad.

The Arabs of ancient Arabia were divided culturally as well as geographically into South Arabians and North Arabians. The South Arabians developed their own alphabet which has been preserved chiefly in thousands of religious and memorial inscriptions. Today a modified form of this alphabet

This page of the Maqamat *of al-Hariri is typical of the style of illustration developed in Iraq in the thirteenth century.*

Calligraphy and geometrical design are the basis of Arabic art, as in this thirteenth-century Syrian mosque lamp.

242

Rug design, as in this sixteenth century prayer rug, is one of the fine arts of Persia.

The calligraphy of the Quran, as in this manuscript of the fourteenth century, is a fine art of the Arabs.

is used for Amharic, the official language of Ethiopia.

The North Arabian alphabet appears to have been derived from the Nabataean, which in turn was based on Aramaic, the Semitic language most widely used for commercial and literary purposes in the Middle East at the time of Christ. The Nabataeans were North Arabians who founded a small but wealthy kingdom between the Gulf of Aqaba and Damascus with its capital at Petra. Although their speech was similar to classical Arabic, their language was written in a modified Aramaic alphabet.

The earliest surviving example of pure Arabic writing appears in an inscription dated 512 found at Zabad, Syria. This inscription includes Syriac, Greek and Arabic texts. It is clear that the Arabic alphabet was used in northern Arabia and probably in the Hijaz during the latter part of the sixth century.

The literature of the Arabs is perhaps their greatest artistic monument. The nomad Arab, with his great need for mobility, concentrated most of his artistic impulses on oral literature. Poetry com-

prised the largest and most important part of this pre-Islamic Arabic literature, although there is little doubt that the Arabs possessed also a substantial body of prose in the form of fables, proverbs and war stories. The poetry conveyed the heroic characteristics of early Bedouin life—courage, loyalty, love and blood revenge—and expressed the pride and fears of the people in a pungent and easily remembered form.

It is almost impossible to produce a translation of Arabic poetry which gives the non-Arab reader a just idea of the original. A few quotations, however, may be used to illustrate several characteristics of this early poetry. The first quotation is from Taabbata Sharran's "Song of Vengeance," in which the famous robber-poet describes the revenge he has taken against the tribe of Hudhayl for the death of his uncle.

O'er the fallen of Hudhayl stands screaming
The hyena; see the wolf's teeth gleaming!
Dawn will hear the flap of wings, will discover
Vultures treading corpses, too gorged to hover.

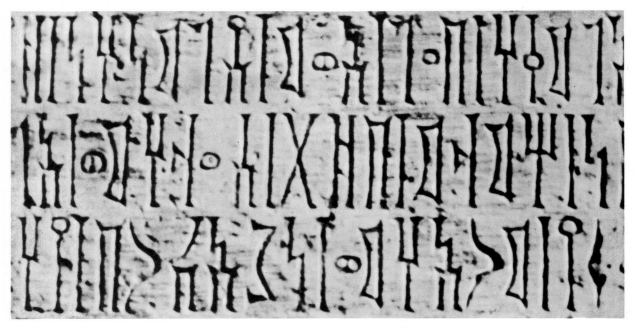

An inscription found at Marib in southern Arabia, in the temple of 'Ilumquh, the ancient Sabaean moon god.

Another poet, in strong contrast to the ferocity of this vengeful verse, writes of his love for his children:

Our children among us going,
Our very hearts they be;
The wind upon them blowing
Would banish sleep from me.

A third poet emphasizes the place of tribal pride and honor:

With the sword will I wash my shame away,
*Let God's doom bring on me what it may!**

The form and subject matter of pre-Islamic poetry were firmly fixed even in its earliest examples, and its style has been followed until modern times. The most important of the forms is the *qasidah* or ode. This is a poem of about sixty lines with each line ending in the same rhyme. Its pattern calls for a love preface, a soliloquy on a deserted campground, a recollection of hunting or war prowess, and an appeal for generosity to the person to whom the poem is addressed.

If such a style of poetry seems narrow and sterile to Western literary taste, the explanation of its appeal must be sought in the melody of the Arabic language. To the Arab ear, the sound of Arabic words skillfully used has a sonorous, almost hypnotic effect in which the specific meaning often is secondary. It is this sensual appeal, coupled with overtones of ancient magic, that gives Arabic literature, ancient and modern, its stature among the arts and the poet his high place in Arab society.

THE QURAN IN ARABIC LITERATURE The Quran, the sacred book of Islam, is the oldest existing book in the Arabic language. For Muslims, the essential fact of the Quran is that it is not the composition of the Prophet Muhammad but the Word of God as revealed to Muhammad through the Angel Gabriel. The original text of the Quran is believed to be with God in heaven, and the revelation sent down to Muhammad is a copy of this in Arabic. The style of the Quran is so peculiarly Arabic that much of its excellence is bound to be lost in the process of translation. One cannot appreciate the power and beauty of the Quran unless he knows Arabic, and he cannot understand it to the fullest extent unless he is a master of the language.

The Quran was not written down as a whole until after the death of Muhammad. It was the custom for the Prophet's companions to commit the Prophet's revelations to memory as he recited them. When the first text of the Quran was assembled in 633, the year following the death of the Prophet, the material for it was taken from the men who knew it by heart and from their notes. The text was revised in 651 and this revised text became the authoritative one.

The style of the Quran falls into two categories. In the earlier chapters, revealed while the Prophet was in Mecca, the revelations are powerful, emotional verses warning the Arabs of divine retribution should they reject the guidance of the revelations. The language of these verses fits the mood of the context admirably. It is a type of early Arabic rhetoric known as *saj'* in which words rhyme at short intervals, although there is no regular meter as there is in Arabic poetry. The later chapters of the Quran, revealed after the *hijrah* to Medina, consist largely of prose in which the details of Islam are divulged against a backdrop of stories and pious homilies.

It is difficult to overestimate the influence of the Quran on later Arabic literature. The book was so powerful in style that it became a model of unquestioned authority. The weight borne by the language of the Quran in the revelation of Islam is most strongly indicated in the Quran itself. In one verse, doubters of its authenticity are challenged to produce anything like it. Muslim scholars are unanimous in interpreting this challenge as a defiance to equal the Quran either in content or in language

---

These and other translations of Arabic verse quoted later are taken from Reynold A. Nicholson's A Literary History of the Arabs (Cambridge University Press, 1930.)

and style. Such linguistic pride did not sound out of place to the Arab ear, and the challenge has never been met.

The Quran is not only unique as an Arabic literary work but also unsurpassed as a medium for spreading knowledge of the Arabic language across the world. After the death of Muhammad, the religion of Islam followed the expansion of the Arabs westward to the Atlantic and eastward toward China, and with Islam went the Arabic Quran. Islam was soon adopted by the majority of the inhabitants in the conquered territories, and even in non-Arab areas Arabic became the language both of religion and of government.

During the two centuries after the death of Muhammad, scholars codified the language of the Quran. They established the grammar of classical Arabic, which has remained the language of almost all subsequent Arabic literature. By painstaking research they standardized Arabic letters, spelling and pronunciation. They also recorded and published much of the oral literature that had existed among Arabs for many hundreds of years.

From the death of Muhammad in 632 until the death of his son-in-law, 'Ali, in 661, the Muslims for the most part were sternly engaged in the consolidation of Islam in the Arabian Peninsula and the conquest of neighboring lands. Poetry, the chief form of literature in Arabia at that time, was discouraged. Its place was filled by the recitation of the Quran and the narration of the *Hadith*, the record of the acts and sayings of the Prophet.

UMAYYAD AGE In 661 the dynasty of the Umayyads assumed leadership of the Muslims, transferring the caliphate to Damascus. An era of courtly elegance and chivalry emerged, blending old Arab customs with those of the more sophisticated civilizations of the north, the Byzantine and the Persian. In the midst of a growing Muslim empire which spread within a century from southern France to the borders of China, men of Arab blood were a privileged class. Poetry flourished once more and the poet became a leading figure in the imperial court and the tribal gathering. Only in the Holy Cities of Mecca and Medina was the revival of

Various styles of Arabic calligraphy for the phrase "Kingdom of Saudi Arabia": Ruq'ah, *normally used in handwriting...*

*...*Diwani, *an especially ornamental and stylized form...*

*...*Thuluth, *a decorative style used for headlines and titles.*

248

chivalric literature restrained for some time to come.

The *qasidah*, the standard poetic form, was too rigid in style for the new sophistication. Parts of the *qasidah*, however, provided the basis for several new styles of poetry which evolved. Chief among these was the romantic verse growing out of the *nasib*, the love prelude to the *qasidah*. The most brilliant exponent of this verse was 'Umar ibn Abi Rabi'ah, who wrote:

Gently she moved in the calmness of beauty,
Moved as the bough to the light breeze of morning,
Dazzled my eyes as they gazed, till before me
All was a mist and confusion of figures.
Ne'er had I sought her, and ne'er had she sought me;
Fated the love, and the hour, and the meeting.

These love lyrics of simple, unpretentious tenderness are in striking contrast both to the raw vigor of pre-Islamic verse and to the florid sentimentality of later love songs.

There are few remains of the literary activity of this period because oral instruction was the practice and because there were strong feelings against recording anything but the Quran. Moreover, the successors to the Umayyads, the Abbasids, destroyed such records as there were in an effort to expunge the memory of what they considered a disgraceful period.

Surviving literary relics of the period usually were preserved only as parts of later books. They indicate that studies of the Quran and the Traditions were developed to the point where they formed the bases for the disciplines of theology, jurisprudence and history.

ABBASID AGE In 750 a new dynasty, the Abbasids, took over the leadership of the Muslims and moved the caliphate to Baghdad. The rise of the Abbasids was backed by two groups—those non-Arab Muslims who resented their second-class status under an ultra-Arab rule and those Arabs who considered the Umayyads religious backsliders and usurpers of the caliphate. Accordingly the new dynasty encouraged the talents of such non-Arab people as the Persians and fostered theological studies. Aided by lavish patronage from the court, the infant science and literature of the Umayyads matured in a period of tremendous intellectual activity. This Golden Age, as it is often called, may be divided into four literary periods.

Period of Literary Development (750-813): The orthodox position of the Abbasid caliphate demanded administrative conformity with religious law. Two magistral codifications helped meet this need. The first was the collection of Traditions of the Prophet and his Companions compiled by a practicing judge, Malik ibn Anas. The second was a handbook of practical administration by Abu Yusuf, the chief judge of the Caliph Harun ar-Rashid.

History grew into a full-fledged discipline, though at first it was limited in the main to the history of Islam. An important biography of the Prophet was compiled by Ibn Ishaq. A monograph on the Prophet's military expeditions was written by al-Waqidi. Numerous short studies of Islamic history, which have survived only as excerpts in other books, were produced by al-Madaini.

In poetry a new style was developed in which farfetched similes were employed. The Persians, an increasing number of whom were writing Arabic poetry, added a touch of delicacy and urbanity which had been lacking. There were two outstanding poets during this period. One was Abu Nuwas, the half-Persian companion of Harun ar-Rashid in many of the tales of *The Arabian Nights*. The other was an Arab, Abu al-'Atahiyah, who was the first to cast the earnest and reflective thoughts of his verse into the language of the people.

Period of Hellenistic Influence (813-847): During the reigns of the Caliph al-Mamun and his two successors, Persian converts to Islam dominated the literary field. They drew upon the Hellenic heritage left by centuries of Greek and Roman occupation in the Middle East. There followed a period of intellectual inquiry and controversy unmatched in the subsequent history of Islam. A major question was the part to be played by Greek logic in solving

The Golden Mosque of Khadhimain on the Tigris River at Baghdad is the architectural glory of the Abbasid Caliphate.

Al-Azhar University in Cairo, the most famous
center of Islamic studies, established by the
Fatimids in the latter part of the tenth century.

The great colonnade of the Umayyad Mosque in
Damascus, built at the time this city was the site of
the caliphate of the growing Muslim empire.

Muslim theological problems. The Caliph al-Mamun officially supported the group inspired by Greek philosophy, known as the Mu'tazilites, and imposed restrictions on the conservative, orthodox theologians. The most famous opponent of the Mu'tazilites was Ahmad ibn Hanbal, the founder of the school of Islamic law which is followed today by the House of Sa'ud.

Writers in the natural sciences attained standards not surpassed in Europe until the sixteenth century. The first scientific writers were translators of Greek and Indian works, but later Muslim scientists developed their own theories and methods. Arabic works of this period on medicine, optics, astronomy, mathematics and alchemy were translated into Latin and used in Europe for centuries.

Period of Orthodox Reaction (847-945): Under the Caliph al-Mutawakkil, the orthodox Muslim theologians won out over those inspired by Greek

The tomb built outside Baghdad by the Caliph Harun ar-Rashid for his wife Zubaidah during the Abbasid age.

thought. Religious writing turned back to the task of systematizing the laws and history of Islam. Two new collections of the Traditions of the Prophet and his Companions, which have remained second only to the Quran in their importance to Islam, were written by al-Bukhari and a scholar named Muslim. The Traditions were carefully culled on the basis of their degree of authenticity and were arranged by subject matter for the first time. Another work of great erudition was at-Tabari's commentary on the Quran, which became the foundation of orthodox Quranic science.

During this period, Ibn Qutaybah, a prolific essayist, wrote a ten-volume compendium which set a pattern followed by other writers. Each volume dealt with a separate subject—such as religion, war, sovereignty, friendship—and was interspersed with quotations from the Quran, history and other sources.

History became a mature study in the ninth century with al-Baladhuri's *History of the Conquests*, written in the form of a narrative rather than a simple chronicle of events. At the same time geographical studies came into existence. Writers such as Ibn Hawqal and al-Maqdisi combined the results of their extensive travels with references to earlier studies and related fields.

This period produced the greatest of the medieval doctors, ar-Razi, known in Europe as Rhazes, whose works became known widely through Latin translations. He did pioneer research on smallpox and published careful case studies.

Period of Patronage by Several Courts (945-1055): During the ninth century the caliphate began to depend on Turkish mercenaries. By the middle of the tenth century the sprawling empire had been broken up into smaller states paying lip service to the central government, and the orthodox leaders of Islam had lost their once-powerful position. Literary activity at the capitals of several of the smaller states had a secondary resurgence which recalled the brilliance of the finest days of Baghdad.

The court at Aleppo supported the poetic genius of al-Mutanabbi, who returned to the Arab

The Mosque of Muhammad 'Ali, which was built in Cairo by the ruler of Egypt in the early years of the nineteenth century.

spirit of the Umayyad poets for his inspiration:

The desert knows me well, the night, the mounted men,
The battle and the sword, the paper and the pen.

In Iraq literature was patronized generously by Persian viziers who built several excellent libraries. The court at Baghdad was interested principally in entertainment. The first editions of what eventually became *The Arabian Nights* date from this period.

Eastern Persian courts at Bukhara and Ghaznah rivaled the Aleppo court in the talent of their writers. Persian scientists like Ibn Sina, known in Europe as Avicenna, considered themselves philosophers, and their scientific studies were usually included in encyclopedias on logic, science and theology.

The Fatimid court at Cairo and the descendants of the Umayyads in Spain cultivated the literary attainments of many gifted scholars and writers. The famous works of the Muslim East were well known in Spain. It is probably through Spain that Europe received most of the Muslim science later translated into Latin.

FROM THE ABBASID CALIPHATE TO 1700 The Seljuk Turks dominated the shadowy Abbasid caliphate from 1055 to 1258, a period of internal strife and of wars with the Crusaders, when the lack of stability had its effect on literature and the other arts. Nevertheless, a number of brilliant men managed to make themselves heard and on occasion influenced the course of events. One of them, al-Ghazzali, recorded in a series of books his attempt to overcome his own skepticism. His theological works helped bring the vigorous elements of per-

253

sonal religious experience into the structure of orthodoxy.

Several histories of this period are known today in the West primarily because they dealt with the Crusades and the life of Saladin. The most eminent historian was Ibn al-Athir, whose *Complete History* in twelve volumes comes close to living up to its name.

New types of poetry became popular in this period. An Egyptian poet of Meccan origin, Baha ad-Din Zuhayr, wrote with a simplicity of style that gives his verse a Western flavor. In Spain poets composed works in the colloquial language. This vogue never spread to the East but greatly influenced the poetry of medieval France and Italy.

The Mongols smashed the feeble remains of the caliphate of Baghdad in 1258. Centers of learning were razed. Important literature virtually ceased being produced except in North Africa and in Egypt, where the Mameluke dynasties held off the Mongol hordes. In 1517 the Ottoman Turks finally brought most of the former caliphate again under one rule, but the Turks never inspired a literary revival of Arabic.

Much of the literature of Mameluke Egypt was confined to history and geography, although the best of a vast number of popular stories were added to the earlier tales collected in *The Arabian Nights.*

One of the most penetrating and original thinkers of medieval Islam was the North African Ibn Khaldun. His reputation stems largely from the introduction to his *History of the Arabs, Persians and Berbers.* In it he decries digests of books as "harmful not only to style but also to understanding," comments upon the manner in which the vanquished invariably strive to imitate their conquerors, indicates a grasp of what has become known as the optimum tax rate, points out that knowledge of grammar does not constitute knowledge of a language, emphasizes the necessity of studying the group as well as the individual and discusses the nature of the social bonds uniting individuals into groups.

Here and there in the Arabic world sparks of literary genius flared briefly, but in general literature went into an eclipse from which it did not emerge until the eighteenth century.

MODERN AGE (1700 TO THE PRESENT) At first glance it would almost appear that Arabic literature had lost life in the eighteenth century. The Turkish regime usually favored Turkish and Persian writing. Arabic literary work had not come to a complete halt, however, and the quiet activity of writers in the eighteenth century contributed to an amazing revival of Arabic literature in the nineteenth century. These writers were religious scholars and had a solid foundation in Arabic grammar and a good knowledge of the Arabic classics. Although their work followed traditional lines, they tended to show dissatisfaction with the low moral state of Arab society. In Arabia, for example, Muhammad ibn 'Abd al-Wahhab sought the moral regeneration of his people by his interpretation of the religious tracts of Ibn Taymiyah, a medieval disciple of Ibn Hanbal.

Arabic literature in the nineteenth century became the voice of many reform movements, with the writers divided by their approaches into traditionalists and modernists. The traditionalists sought to revitalize the Arab world by eliminating its faults through a return to the purity and simplicity of the original ways of the Arabs. The modernists sought to imbue the Arab community with new energy by adopting some of the ideas of Western culture.

In Cairo and Beirut the impact of Western culture was an obvious and major factor in the literary revival of the nineteenth century. In both cities a circle of active men translated Western literature into Arabic. By degrees translation was coupled with some imitation with the result that Arabic works were published which differed radically from the Arabic classics in language, style and spirit. These modernists won immediate popularity.

The unorthodox modernist approach, despite its popular success, did not go unchallenged by the traditional literary school. The traditionalists, invigorated to a large extent by competition with the modernists, produced a growing body of literature in the old style, concentrating on history, religion and language. Al-Jabarti's history of Egypt, written during this period, compares favorably with the best medieval histories.

The importance of the nineteenth century, a period of transition, lies more in overall literary accomplishment than in individual masterpieces. The experimentation of this period, however, laid the foundation for the fresh, polished literature of the twentieth century. The intellectual activity of the nineteenth century was aided tremendously by the introduction of private and official printing presses in Cairo and Beirut.

The first school of writers to combine the best aspects of the modernists and the traditionalists was led late in the nineteenth century by Butrus al-Bustani of Lebanon. His most famous works are his comprehensive dictionary of modern and classical Arabic and his encyclopedia, the first of a Western type in Arabic. Al-Bustani's work was carried on by a son and a nephew, among others.

It remained for a young Muslim shaykh, al-Manfaluti, to close the gap between the modernists and the traditionalists. In 1910 his essays called *an-Nazarat* were published. So transcendent was the appeal of his easy style that this book became, as it remains, a favorite Arabic work.

Arabic writers are traditionally more at home in verse than in prose, and the most famous of the twentieth-century poets were the Egyptians Ahmad Shawqi and Hafiz Ibrahim. Among the Syrians living in the United States, new styles of poetry were developed, based in part on English and American literature, which have had a certain vogue in the Middle East.

A notable Arabic novel was Muhammad Husayn Haykal's *Zaynab*, published in 1914, which was the first Arabic fiction to compete with translations from Western languages. Before that time, the Syrian author, Jurji Zaydan, had written somewhat stiff historical novels, which were followed by the more polished ones of Muhammad Farid Abu Hadid. Other writers, such as 'Abbas al-'Aqqad,

Islamic Cultural Center in Washington, the most important mosque and center of Islamic studies in the United States.

turned out histories of early Islam which had great popular appeal.

A recent trend in Arabic literature has been the increasing use of autobiography in various literary forms. The most famous work of personal experience is a series of delightful sketches of the life and early education of Dr. Taha Husayn, a blind Egyptian scholar.

The deeply ingrained tradition of oral literature, especially popular poetry, served the Saudi Arabs adequately for a long time, and they were not influenced at first by modern literary trends. In recent years, however, they have taken part in the literary revival. The output of books and magazines has multiplied. Old histories are being republished or rewritten. Poetry still holds its high place and is being issued in books of popular and classical verse.

255

INDO-ARABIC
NUMERALS

The system of numeration employed throughout the greater part of the world today was devised, as far as is known, in India at an early date and transmitted to the West by the Arabs along with other cultural riches. The term Arabic numerals is not quite fair to the Indian contribution; they might more properly be called Indo-Arabic.

After conquering the Middle East in the early age of Islam, the Arabs began to assimilate the cultures of the peoples they had subdued. One of the great centers of learning was Baghdad, where Arab, Greek, Persian, Jewish and other scholars found sponsorship at the court of the Abbasid caliphs. There they pooled their cultural heritages in a working mental exchange. An Indian scholar is reported to have appeared in Baghdad in the year 771, toward the close of the caliphate of al-Mansur, bringing with him a treatise on astronomy. This treatise was possibly the first contact the scholars of Baghdad had with the numerical system evolved by the Indians.

Until that time the various cultures (Egyptian, Greek, Roman and others) used their own numerals in a manner similar to that of the Romans. Thus, the number 323 was expressed like this:

Egyptian	999 ∩∩ III
Greek	HHH △△ III
Roman	CCC XX III

The Egyptians actually wrote them from right to left. They are here set down from left to right to call attention to the similarities of the systems.

The Indian contribution was to substitute a single sign (in this case "ㅈ," meaning "3," and "ㄹ," meaning "2") indicating the number of signs in each cluster of similar signs. In this manner the Indians would render Roman CCC XX III as:

$$\overset{\overset{\displaystyle ㅈ}{\downarrow}}{\underset{\underset{\displaystyle 3}{\uparrow}}{CCC}} \quad \overset{\overset{\displaystyle ㄹ}{\downarrow}}{\underset{\underset{\displaystyle 2}{\uparrow}}{XX}} \quad \overset{\overset{\displaystyle ㅈ}{\downarrow}}{\underset{\underset{\displaystyle 3}{\uparrow}}{III}}$$

This new way of writing numbers was economical but not flawless. The Roman numeral CCC II, for instance, presented a problem. If a 3 and a 2 respectively were substituted for the Roman clusters CCC and II, the written result was 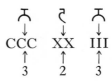 . Clearly, the number intended was not thirty-two but three hundred and two. The Arab scholars perceived that a sign representing "nothing" or "naught" was required because the *place* of a sign gave as much information as its unitary value did. The *place* had to be shown even if the sign which showed it indicated a unitary value of "nothing." It is believed to have been the Arabs who filled this need by

256

Development of Arabic Numerals

Modern Arabic (western)	1	2	3	4	5	6	7	8	9	0
Early Arabic (western)	١	2	≥	٣ع	9	6	7	8	9	0
Arabic letters used as numerals	ا	ب	ج	د	ه	و	ز	ح	ط	ي
Modern Arabic (eastern)	١	٢	٣	٤	٥	٦	٧	٨	٩	٠
Early Arabic (eastern)	١	٢	٣	۴	٥	٧	٧	٨	٩	٠
Early Devanagari (Indian)		ट	ᅐ	ᒍ	ப	ᗺ	ᇁ	४	ᔔ	
Later Devanagari (10th Century Sanskrit)	१	२	३	४	५	६	७	८	९	०

inventing the zero. Now the new system could show neatly the difference between XXX II (32) and CCC II (302).

If the origin of this new method was Indian, it is not at all certain that the original shapes of the Arabic numerals also were Indian. In fact, it seems quite possible that the Arab scholars used their own numerals but manipulated them in the Indian way. The Indian way had the advantage of using much smaller clusters of symbols and greatly simplifying written computations. The modern forms of the individual numerals in both eastern Arabic and western Arabic (European) appear to have evolved from letters of the Arabic alphabet.

The Semites and Greeks traditionally assigned numerical values to their letters and used them as numerals. This alphabetical system is still used by the Arabs much as we use Roman numerals in numbering paragraphs in contracts and legal documents.

The new mathematical principles on which the Indo-Arabic numerals were based greatly simplified arithmetic. Their adoption in Europe began in the tenth century after an Arabic mathematical treatise was translated by a Spanish scholar. Before long the system was being used in all European universities. Modern science owes a great debt to those imaginative Arab scholars.

ISLAMIC CALENDAR
AND HOLIDAYS

Saudi Arabia uses the Islamic calendar, initiated by the second caliph, 'Umar ibn al-Khattab, more than 1,300 years ago. The first year of the Islamic calendar was the year of the Prophet Muhammad's flight, or *hijrah*, from Mecca to Medina (622). The Western method of designating Islamic dates is by the abbreviation A. H., for Anno Hegirae. The first day of A. H. 1387 corresponded to April 11, 1967.

The Islamic calendar is based on the lunar, rather than the solar year, and contains twelve months. A lunar month is the time between two successive new moons, about $29\frac{1}{2}$ days, and the basic length of a lunar year is 354 days ($12 \times 29\frac{1}{2} = 354$), eleven days shorter than the normal Gregorian year. The months of the Islamic year normally contain twenty-nine and thirty days alternately. To adjust for a slight overlap, an additional day is added eleven times in every cycle of thirty years, making eleven leap years of 355 days each for every nineteen normal years. One hundred years of the Islamic calendar approximately equal ninety-seven years of the Gregorian calendar used in the West.

Unlike Gregorian months, the months of the Islamic year have no relation to the season and make a complete circuit of the seasons once about every thirty-three Gregorian years.

The twelve months of the Islamic year are:

    Muharram
    Safar
    Rabi' al-Awwal (Rabi' I)
    Rabi' ath-Thani (Rabi' II)
    Jumada al-Ula (Jumada I)
    Jumada al-Akhirah or ath-Thaniyah
      (Jumada II)
    Rajab
    Sha'ban
    Ramadan
    Shawwal
    Dhu al-Qa'dah
    Dhu al-Hijjah

The ninth month, Ramadan, is a month of fasting. According to Islamic law, the month begins with the sighting of the new moon and ends with the sighting of the next new moon. Saudi Arabia relies upon the testimony of one witness for news of the new moon of Ramadan. When this news is confirmed it is broadcast immediately throughout the kingdom. Consequently, the exact length of Ramadan depends to a considerable extent upon weather conditions at the beginning and end of the month. Without complete records of the number of days thus attributed to Ramadan each year, the corresponding Gregorian dates used in historical studies may contain slight inaccuracies, usually no more than a couple of days.

The Islamic system follows the ancient convention by which each day is considered to begin at sunset. Thus the night precedes the day. What Westerners would call Sunday night, Muslims refer to as Monday night (better translated as the eve of Monday). A similar usage is preserved in such English phrases as Christmas Eve and New Year's Eve.

The Saudi Arabian Government considers two religious occasions and one secular date as official national holidays. The more important of the religious holidays is the Feast of the Sacrifice (*'Id al-Adha*), beginning on the tenth of Dhu al-Hijjah and lasting four days. The second is the Feast of the Breaking of the Fast (*'Id al-Fitr*), occurring on the first three days of Shawwal, the month following Ramadan.

Saudi Arabia celebrates National Day, commemorating the unification of the country under the new name of the Kingdom of Saudi Arabia in September, 1932. This is the only official holiday in Saudi Arabia not determined by the Islamic calendar. National Day falls on the first day of the month of Libra in the solar (zodiacal) calendar, corresponding more or less to September 23 in the Gregorian calendar. A date corresponding to a Gregorian date was presumably picked for the convenience of foreign governments and their diplomats. It is customary for them to send formal congratulatory messages to the Government of Saudi Arabia and for Saudi diplomats to hold receptions on National Day.

Various other Islamic occasions are celebrated by Muslims outside Saudi Arabia. The first day of Muharram is New Year's Day. The twelfth of Rabi' I is the Prophet Muhammad's birthday. The twenty-seventh of Rajab is the Night of the Ascent, the anniversary of the night on which the Prophet is believed to have been miraculously transported to Jerusalem and thence to heaven. The fifteenth of Sha'ban is the Night of Decrees, when the guardian angels are believed to receive from God the tablets on which is written the fate of their charges during the year to come. The twenty-seventh of Ramadan is celebrated as the Night of Power. In addition, the Shi'ites observe a number of other occasions, connected mainly with events in the lives of the Caliph 'Ali and his descendants.

The solar calendar is used in Saudi Arabia by farmers, who require fixed seasonal dates for planting and harvesting.

١٣٨٧
1387

ذوالقعـــدة
DHU AL-QA'DAH

الجمعـة F	الخميس T	الأربعاء W	الثلاثاء T	الاثنين M	الأحـد S	السَّبت S
٤ 4	٣ 3	٢ 2	١ 1			
١١ 11	١٠ 10	٩ 9	٨ 8	٧ 7	٦ 6	٥ 5
١٨ 18	١٧ 17	١٦ 16	١٥ 15	١٤ 14	١٣ 13	١٢ 12
٢٥ 25	٢٤ 24	٢٣ 23	٢٢ 22	٢١ 21	٢٠ 20	١٩ 19
	٣٠ 30	٢٩ 29	٢٨ 28	٢٧ 27	٢٦ 26	

An Arabic calendar (above) for the month of Dhu al-Qa'dah, A. H. 1387, reads from right to left with Saturday as the first day of the week. The dates correspond to those shown in the Gregorian calendar (below) for January/February, 1968.

JANUARY/FEBRUARY 1968

S	M	T	W	T	F	S
		30	31	1	2	3
4	5	6	7	8	9	10
11	12	13	14	15	16	17
18	19	20	21	22	23	24
25	26	27	28			

SOCIAL CUSTOMS

Arab manners, courtesies, mores and customs are rooted in the habits of centuries. Some of them are peculiar to the Arabs, others they share with people living in adjacent regions. Thus, for example, the Arabs share a preference for cooking with oil and a love of bargaining in the market place with all of the people of the Mediterranean basin. The religion of Islam not only determines the way of life of its Arab adherents; it is also the religion of and, therefore, a major cultural influence on millions of non-Arabs in Asia and Africa.

Many customs in Saudi Arabia are undergoing rapid changes, although the changes are distributed unevenly from the standpoints of geography and of the various ranks of society. Most men still wear the traditional Arab robes. Others, who wear Western clothes, particularly at work, sometimes modify their dress and actions in the presence of their elders or on occasions, such as appearing at the Royal Court, where other traditions are still the rule.

Foreigners who live or intend to live in Saudi Arabia should familiarize themselves with the local customs. Unfortunately, much of what is written about the manners and customs of the Arabs tends to accentuate romantic and picturesque actions, many of which are no longer as important as they once were. The honored guest, for example, no longer needs to be prepared to eat the eye of a whole-cooked sheep. No guide could ever prepare the newcomer to Arabia for the diversity of customs between the mountains of 'Asir and the coasts of the Arabian Gulf, between the tents of the Bedouins and the modern homes of Jiddah and Dhahran.

The newcomer, however, can take comfort in the knowledge that most Arabs he will meet will have had far more experience in associating with foreigners than he has had with Arabs. Furthermore, the foreigner can hardly go wrong in Saudi Arabia if his relations with Arabs are characterized by that universal courtesy which springs primarily from a consideration for others and a respect for their feelings, customs and beliefs.

FAMILY RELATIONS The position of women in Arabia is different from what it is in Western countries, but nothing is changing more radically than women's place in society. Until the Royal Proclamation of October 23, 1959, providing for the establishment of government schools for girls, the education of girls was almost exclusively a family matter. There were classes where girls learned to read and recite the Quran in virtually all villages and towns. There were also a few small modern private schools for girls. Some well-to-do men arranged to have their daughters educated abroad. Within five years of the opening of government girls' schools, more than 40,000 girls were enrolled. Notwithstanding the rapid expansion of this program, the demand for girls' schools continues to exceed the supply.

For centuries the women of Arabia lived in extreme privacy and were not seen by men other than their husbands and close male relatives. In the houses of rich and poor and in the tents of the Bedouins, the women had separate quarters (the *harim*) into which only those men who were immediate members of the family were permitted.

Girl students carry out experiments in the science laboratory at the Dar al-Hanan (Home of Mercy) orphanage in Jiddah.

When women went outside their homes, they were heavily veiled and shrouded in black. Perhaps because the girls of 'Asir assumed the veil somewhat later than those of central Arabia and because women of all ages in 'Asir traditionally worked in the fields beside the men of the family, the women of 'Asir have long been considered remarkably unrestricted by the standards of the rest of the country. In some Bedouin tribes, particularly those in the extreme northern and southern portions of Saudi Arabia, the veiling of women was not as rigid as in other areas. The veil and the *harim* have not disappeared, but exceptions to the rule become more common every year. Accordingly, mixed social gatherings, dinners or parties are more common than they once were.

Marriage relations are governed by an elaborate system of religious law. A man is permitted to have four wives and can divorce any of them relatively simply, but not without assuming certain obligations, such as provision for the children. Islam greatly enhanced the status of women in Arabia by limiting for the first time the number of wives a man might have, imposing restrictions on divorce and insuring the rights of women to property and a share in the inheritance from father or husband. Polygamy and divorce have been on the decline for many years. Polygamy, always infrequent among younger families for obvious reasons, is increasingly rare among Arabs of all ages.

The sense of family unity extends to grandparents, aunts, uncles and cousins. Many households include relatives from outside the immediate

261

family who do not have their own homes. Large households, consisting of what sociologists call an "extended family," were once the rule. However, increasing numbers of Saudi Arabs are living in smaller home units consisting of only husband, wife and children. This does not mean that these smaller units do not retain extremely close ties with their other relatives. Even in the large and modern towns of Cairo and Beirut, large family groups share a kind of cohesion and loyalty which is no longer a feature of American culture.

The tight kinship system of the old days was perpetuated by the preference for first cousins to marry one another. Nowadays, a girl's education and other criteria are becoming more important than who her father is. As a result, future husbands, girls themselves and parents are increasingly demanding more and better girls' education.

RANKS OF SOCIETY Saudi Arabian society is basically democratic, and wealth, success and education cut across the boundaries of hereditary position. Everyone has the opportunity to better himself through merit and learning. The government actively encourages social mobility not only by providing free education at all levels, both at home and abroad, but also by paying monthly subsidies to students in vocational schools and in institutions of higher learning. Some men who today hold responsible positions in the government are descendants of slaves. The large influx of Africans in the past through the slave trade and pilgrimage has resulted in a small proportion of Negroes in the population, but there are no social distinctions founded on color.

In 1962 King Faysal, while Crown Prince and President of the Council of Ministers, took the opportunity during an outline of his government's program to announce the "absolute abolition of slavery and the manumission of slaves." His father had already started the process in 1936 with a decree forbiding the further import of slaves.

The development of the oil industry in the Eastern Province has given impetus to a general expansion of commerce and business. Commercial growth has been instrumental in creating an influential middle class which continues to grow as the number of productive ventures increases. In similar fashion, the spread of education is helping to add to the middle class a growing number of public servants, businessmen and members of the professions. These educated young Saudi Arabs are contributing not only to the further development of their own country but also to the shaping of events in the entire Middle East.

The influence of the harsh desert environment poses problems of survival resulting in a highly individualistic society, and one that has developed a deep sense of equality among all men. Such a society demands strong leadership for the welfare of the community. Although the King and his ministers and the amirs of provinces and towns wield great power, their offices and councils are remarkably open to all citizens, regardless of wealth or station. Everyone is free to petition the King for the redress of grievances, and he daily gives his personal attention to a number of complaints that in other lands would never be allowed to come to the attention of the ruler.

The *sayyids* and *sharifs*, or descendants of the Prophet Muhammad, are held in high esteem regardless of the extent of their worldly goods. Some social distinctions exist among the Bedouins, but they are few and will in time become meaningless. Certain tribes are regarded as socially inferior to others. One is the Sulabah, a tribe of nomads who wander over northern Arabia supporting themselves by hunting and acting as craftsmen and tinkers for other Bedouins. As the tribesmen settle in and around existing urban centers, they place greater emphasis on achievements as determining each other's status and less emphasis on ancestry.

HOSPITALITY The Arabs are justifiably famous for their hospitality. A guest, whether rich or poor, city dweller or desert Bedouin, is treated with courtesy and graciousness in the home of his Arab host. Even an enemy is assured of safety and courtesy while he enjoys the status of a guest. The standards of hospitality are set by custom, but the Arab applies them with a spontaneity and warmth which truly reflect his keen enjoyment in entertaining his guest.

The wayfarer in the desert can always be assured of food and lodging in a Bedouin camp, even though the hosts may have too little for themselves. Bedouins whose food supply is low may try to avoid visitors by keeping away from ordinary routes of travel, but they would not think of refusing food and water to any stranger who happened to present himself.

The most common gesture of hospitality among all Arabs, whether they are entertaining each other or foreign visitors, is the serving of coffee. In the cities, especially in summer, the visitor may well be offered a choice between coffee and a cold soft drink.

The making of coffee starts with the roasting of green beans. The beans are broken up with a brass mortar and pestle, the source of the musical ringing so familiar in town and camp. Usually cardamom is mixed with the coffee to give the drink spice. Sometimes cloves or saffron is added for a different flavor. The coffee is served from brass pots having long spouts stuffed with fiber for straining.

Coffee cups are small and without handles, like Chinese teacups, and are only about a quarter filled at each serving. The server proceeds around the circle of guests in the order of their rank, pouring as many drinks as each desires. The guest indicates that he has had enough by shaking the cup and handing it back to the server. Although some say it is good form to accept one cup or three, but never two or more than three, there is no firm rule. Small glasses of hot tea frequently are served to guests after coffee. The tea is always sweetened, and mint or milk is sometimes added. When coffee is followed by tea, it is customary to offer guests yet another round or two

of coffee. Audible sipping of coffee or other hot drinks and sounds of gratification while eating are not impolite. They indicate to the host how much the guest is enjoying himself.

In the towns, coffee houses are the most popular gathering places. They are usually outside with tables in or near the street. There men come to drink coffee, tea or soft drinks, to smoke hubble-bubble pipes and to talk.

As in most places in the world, an invitation to dinner is the most common way of extending more than passing hospitality. Most Arabs with whom foreigners come in contact are likely to serve a meal in much the same manner as dinners are served in the West. A few specifically Middle Eastern dishes might be featured, but not necessarily so. Only on rare occasions will the foreigner have the opportunity to partake of the traditional Arab feast, although not uncommonly such a meal is served at an Arab picnic or beach party.

The Arab feast can be an elaborate affair. If the group is large and the guests are important, the main dish may be a young camel, although oftener it is one or more sheep. The sheep are boiled or roasted whole and served atop a mound of steaming, buttered rice on large copper or brass trays. There are many side dishes, including chicken, fruits, vegetables, pastries and sweets.

The feast is laid out on mats or carpets spread on the ground or floor and the guests assemble around it. Conventional tables and chairs are sometimes used, at least in towns, and the customary fare is frequently supplemented by American and European dishes. Knives, forks and spoons may be used, but in the desert the guests tear off chunks of meat and dip into the rice and other dishes with their right hands. To use the left hand for eating is considered bad form.

At such a traditional feast the host frequently does not eat with his guests but spends his time making sure that each one is amply served. When a guest has eaten his fill, he says a word of thanks to God (*bismillah*) and leans back or rises. Water, soap and towels are provided for washing hands. Rose water or cologne is poured over the hands. The first group of guests usually makes a minor impression upon the supply of food. It is followed in relays by persons of lesser rank, down to the servants.

Guests do not linger long after one of these traditional feasts. After dinner, coffee is served and often a burner of fuming incense is passed around for the guests to inhale and waft into their beards and clothes. This final rite of hospitality is a sign that the guests may take their leave. A common Arabic saying is *la qu'ud ba'd al-'ud*, there is no sitting after the incense.

SOCIAL ETIQUETTE Conventional good manners and consideration for the customs and beliefs of others prevail in Saudi Arabia as elsewhere. The Arabs are good-humored, kind and informal, as they expect others to be. They are not likely to take offense at social blunders by foreigners which arise not from intent but from ignorance of customs. Handshaking on meeting and parting is more customary than in America but not more so than in Germany. Wisecracking and barnyard humor, which are acceptable at certain times and places in America, are generally inappropriate in Saudi Arabia.

It is perfectly proper for an Arab to wear something on his head indoors. He should not be urged to uncover his head, indoors or outdoors.

It is customary for the host to accompany his visitor to the door of his office or to the street or to a waiting car. The Arab's protest that his host remain comfortably in office or living room is largely formal.

Salutations—The foreigner will do well to learn a few simple Arabic salutations and the correct responses. A few of the common polite exchanges are listed below:

Statement	Meaning	Use
is-salaam 'alaykum	Peace be upon you.	Universal Arab greeting.
wa-'alaykum is-salaam	And upon you be peace.	(The reply.)
sabaaн il-khayr	Morning of goodness.	Good morning.
sabaaн in-nuwr	Morning of light.	(The reply.)
masaa' il-khayr	Evening of goodness.	Good evening or afternoon.
masaa' in-nuwr	Evening of light.	(The reply.)
kayf нaalak?	How are you?	
тayyib, il-нamdu lillaah!	Fine, praise be to God!	
min faдlak	Please.	Used when requesting a thing or service.
tafaддal	Please.	Offering a thing or service.
mashkuwr (*or* shukran *or* ashkurak)	Thank you.	
mamnuwn	You're welcome.	
fiy amaan illaah	(Go) in the care of God.	Good-by.
fiy amaan il-kariym	(Go) in the care of The Generous One.	(The reply.)

264

An Arab picnic is served on rugs in a grove of trees with huge trays of meat and rice in the center. The main course is dipped from the trays and side dishes serve other foods. The host stands to see that his guests are well served.

Conversation—In social conversations or in opening business conversations, there is a give-and-take of good-humored small talk often centering on the health and well-being of the other party. Weather does not vary much from day to day and does not ordinarily afford a subject of conversation. One normally inquires about the health of his companion and perhaps about his father and brothers (but not about female relatives), his work or anything else in which he is interested. The use of flowery language is habitual in such conversations, but does not indicate any lack of sincerity.

In conversing with Arabs or supervising their work, one should not show impatience, preoccupation with other affairs or undue haste. A common Arab proverb says: "Haste comes from the devil." Impatience is considered a sign of bad manners or a lack of self-confidence. Naturally the pace of the conversation or the work should not lag, but there is a distinction between alertness in keeping things moving and a show of anxiety and impatience. In entertaining visitors, the host should never terminate a conversation abruptly or seem to be dismissing a guest, no matter how busy he may be.

Arabs are not always ready to discuss religion, politics or family affairs with strangers. When a measure of friendship has been established, religion or politics may be discussed freely, but among older and more conservative Arabs family affairs ordinarily remain a private matter. In discussing politics, which Arabs enjoy, it is well to remember that Saudi Arabs consider themselves part of the larger Arab world. They share the feelings of all other Arabs concerning Palestine and the Arab search for unity.

Caution should be used in expressing admiration for any of an Arab's possessions, for the visitor may be embarrassed by having the object offered to him then and there as a present. This is an ancient and still common custom.

266

Eating and Drinking—Coffee or some other refreshment is normally served by the host promptly upon the arrival of a guest. Some Arabs smoke, so cigarettes may be offered on occasion to Arab guests. No one, however, smokes in the presence of the King or members of the royal family unless permission has been given to do so.

Muslims are forbidden to drink alcohol and to eat meat from pigs. One must be careful not to offer them any food containing pork, ham or bacon. The fact that some Muslims do not strictly adhere to these dietary regulations should not be used as an excuse for gravely offending any of the greater number in Saudi Arabia who do.

Dress—Male foreigners in Saudi Arabia usually wear the same styles of clothes they would wear in their own countries. Dress is generally informal, consisting for the most part of shirts and slacks, particularly during the hot months. Ties and jackets are usual at social functions during the winter.

Foreign women generally dress as they would in the countries they come from, although their sports clothes and bathing suits are more conservative than they might be in some Western countries. Extreme and tight-fitting dresses, shorts and slacks are not considered appropriate apparel on the street or in other public places. Bikinis are not considered acceptable swimming or beach attire.

Religion—Muslims fast during the holy month of Ramadan, when they cannot eat, drink or smoke from before dawn until sunset. It is a courtesy during this month not to eat, drink or smoke in the presence of those who are fasting. Smoking should be avoided in the streets of Saudi Arabian towns during Ramadan.

The non-Muslim should never show undue curiosity or lack of respect when Muslims are in the act of praying. He should not walk across rugs or other spots set aside for prayer and he should not walk immediately in front of a Muslim at prayer.

BOOKS FOR
FURTHER READING

Of the authors who have written about Arabia in the English language, four deserve special recommendation—Doughty, Philby, Dickson and Thesiger.

Charles M. Doughty's *Travels in Arabia Deserta*, a classic of literature as well as of travel, stands without a peer for its portrayal of the traditional life of Arabia and of the Arabs of the desert. Doughty was in Arabia about a century ago, so his observations do not apply—at least on the surface—to the modern aspects of Saudi Arabia. Yet, for much of the country and for much that lies below the surface, his shrewd and penetrating remarks are timeless. The style, being the creation of an extremely individualistic man who was above all else a poet, is difficult and demanding, but perseverance will reward the reader who has a true interest in Arabia. The edition listed in the bibliography contains an introduction by T. E. Lawrence.

After Doughty there is none to compare with H. St. John B. Philby. He went to Arabia during World War I, and in the following forty years Philby traveled farther and was first in more places than any other explorer in the history of the peninsula. His books are freighted with information that has stood the scrutiny of later investigators with the time and training for more specialized studies.

The Heart of Arabia and *Arabia of the Wahhabis* give the story of Philby's earliest years in Arabia, when he became intimate with King 'Abd al-'Aziz Al Sa'ud and crossed the peninsula and explored much of central Arabia. *The Empty Quarter* tells of his penetration into the Rub' al-Khali, a famous feat even though his exploit was a few months later than that of Bertram Thomas, who has recorded his journey in an entertaining book entitled *Arabia Felix*. In *Sheba's Daughters* Philby describes the overland trip he made from Najran to Hadhramaut through a region containing ruins of cities which he took to have been associated with the Sheba of the Old Testament and Arabic legend. *The Land of Midian* contains descriptions of the ancient centers of Khaybar and Tayma in northwestern Saudi Arabia. *A Pilgrim in Arabia* has chapters on the Meccan pilgrimage and the cities of Medina and Riyadh. *Saudi Arabia* is an excellent summary of the history of the peninsula from the rise of the House of Sa'ud in the eighteenth century to 1954. *Arabian Jubilee*, written to celebrate the fiftieth anniversary of the accession of King 'Abd al-'Aziz, contains much information on the King and the kingdom not found elsewhere in English.

Arabian Days is the first installment of Philby's salty autobiography. It is continued in his *Forty Years in the Wilderness*. In *Arabian Oil Ventures* Philby tells three stories: the first is about an abortive oil concession in the Hijaz, the second is of the winning and losing by Major Frank Holmes of a concession covering most of the land from which Aramco now produces oil, and the third concerns Philby's part in the negotiation of what became Aramco's concession.

H. R. P. Dickson, first a British political officer and later in charge of government relations for the Kuwait Oil Company, wrote only two books, *The Arab of the Desert* and *Kuwait and Her Neighbours*. They are profusely illustrated and full of marvelous things about people and places in eastern Arabia.

Wilfred Thesiger's *Arabian Sands* is the most fascinating book on Arabia published in this century. It is a record of his magnificent feats of travel in the sands and steppes of southern Arabia; it describes with great care and fondness the hardy people who live in these desolate regions, and it is illustrated with superb photographs by the author.

267

Thesiger has a penchant for areas ignored by others. After giving up exploration of the empty places of the Rub' al-Khali, he focused his talents on the Arabs living in the marshes of southern Iraq, about whom he has also written.

D. G. Hogarth's *The Penetration of Arabia* and R. H. Kiernan's *The Unveiling of Arabia* are surveys setting forth the accomplishments of Western travelers in the peninsula. Hogarth's book is in many respects the better of the two. Kiernan's has the advantage of being more recent and of containing more extensive excerpts from the writings of the travelers themselves. Both may be followed as guides to a large part of the literature on Arabia in Western languages.

Books like K. S. Twitchell's *Saudi Arabia* and Richard Sanger's *The Arabian Peninsula* are somewhat dated, but they do provide an introduction to the area. The same can be said of the excellent surveys of Middle Eastern history by Sydney N. Fisher, P. K. Hitti, G. E. Kirk, George Lenczowski and William Yale. *Caravan* by Carleton Coon, an anthropologist's view of the Middle East, and *The Middle East* by W. B. Fisher, a description of physical, social and regional geography, are less dated by events.

Much of the comparatively recent history of Saudi Arabia appears in biographies of King 'Abd al-'Aziz, such as H. C. Armstrong's *Lord of Arabia*, Kenneth William's *Ibn Sa'ud*, and the most recent, David Howarth's *The Desert King*. Gerald De Gaury, whose *Arabian Journey and Other Desert Travels* and *Arabia Phoenix* were pleasant glimpses of Arabia during World War II, has written the first biography in English of *Faisal, King of Saudi Arabia*.

Other good sources for facets of the history of Saudi Arabia are the reminiscenses of public servants whose duties have kept them for considerable time in the country. Such, for example, are *The Camels Must Go* by Sir Reader Bullard and *The Last of the Dragomans* by Sir Andrew Ryan, both men having served as British diplomats in Jiddah. *Faces in Shem* by Colonel D. van der

Meulen is a collection of essays on events in Arabia by a former Dutch diplomat in Jiddah. *F. D. R. Meets Ibn Sa'ud* by William A. Eddy is the record of the historic meeting of the American president and the Saudi king by the then American Minister to Saudi Arabia, who later became an Aramco official. *Arabian Days* by Hafiz Wahba is the work of a distinguished advisor to King 'Abd al-'Aziz, who was one of the first Arab members of Aramco's board of directors. *A Soldier with the Arabs* by Sir John Bagot Glubb provides glimpses of Arabia from the respectful point of view of an officer of soldiers in Iraq and Transjordan skirmishing with the Bedouin troops of King 'Abd al-'Aziz.

The Eastern Province is one of the most neglected parts of Saudi Arabia as far as material in English is concerned. In addition to the works of Dickson, there is Major R. E. Cheesman's *In Unknown Arabia* and F. S. Vidal's *The Oasis of al-Hasa*. The six volumes by the Czech scholar and explorer, Alois Musil, cover the northern portion of the peninsula in a detailed fashion. One may read about the Hijaz in two classics: T. E. Lawrence's *Seven Pillars of Wisdom* and Sir Richard Burton's *Personal Narrative of a Pilgrimage to Al-Madinah and Meccah*. Burton was also responsible for a complete, entertaining and instructive translation of *The Thousand Nights and a Night*, usually referred to as *The Arabian Nights*.

Little material is available on the natural history of Arabia, outside of learned journals. Colonel Richard Meinertzhagen has published a handsome volume on *Birds of Arabia*. W. R. Brown's *The Horse of the Desert* describes the Arabian thoroughbred. Violet Dickson (Mrs. H. R. P. Dickson) has used her many years in Kuwait and neighboring areas to study and record the native flowers, which she describes in *Wild Flowers of Kuwait and Bahrain*. Guy Mountfort portrays the wildlife of Jordan in *Portrait of a Desert*, much of which is applicable to Saudi Arabia, in a most attractively written and illustrated volume.

For neighboring areas there are many good books. Colonel D. van der Meulen's *Aden to the*

Hadramaut and Harold Ingrams's *Arabia and the Isles* are among the best about the southern fringe of the peninsula. Sir Charles Belgrave, for many years advisor to the Ruler of Bahrain, writes of his experiences in *Personal Column*, and his son James Belgrave has produced a handy little guide and reference work, *Welcome to Bahrain*. Sir Arnold Wilson's *The Persian Gulf* is a history of the waters off Arabia's eastern coast. Alan Villier's *Sons of Sinbad* tells of the Arab sailors who ply the sea lanes between Zanzibar, India and the ports of Arabia. Sir Rupert Hay gives an authoritative survey of the situation in the Nineteen Fifties of many of the little states adjoining Saudi Arabia in *The Persian Gulf States*.

Philip Hitti's books *History of Syria (Including Lebanon and Palestine)* and *Lebanon in History* provide background on the area through which passes the trans-Arabian pipeline. The modern history of Iraq is particularly well covered in Brigadier S. H. Longrigg's *Four Centuries of Modern Iraq* and *Iraq, 1900 to 1950*, and in Majid Khadduri's *Independent Iraq*.

More general works dealing with the area as a whole include *Background of the Middle East*, a symposium edited by Ernest Jackh with chapters by specialists on different phases of the history of the Middle East. Other worthwhile collections of articles by specialists are *The Modern Middle East*, edited by Richard N. Nolte, and the American Assembly's *The United States and the Middle East*, edited by Georgiana G. Stevens.

A good introduction to the Middle Eastern oil business is David Finnie's *Desert Enterprise*, but Brigadier Longrigg's *Oil in the Middle East* is the standard text on the subject. George Lenczowski's *Oil and State in the Middle East* deals with some of the economic and political problems encountered by Aramco and other oil companies operating in the Middle East. Even more up-to-date and specialized is the work by J. E. Hartshorn published as *Politics and World Oil Economics* in the United States and as *Oil Companies and Governments* in England.

No bibliography of Arabia is complete without some references to Islam. The Quran has been rendered into Western tongues many times. Of English editions there are two which may serve as an introduction: Pickthall's version, *The Meaning of the Glorious Qur'an*, by a convert to Islam, and A. J. Arberry's *The Koran Interpreted*, by a distinguished orientalist and poet at Cambridge University. A. Guillaume's *Islam*, Sir Hamilton Gibb's *Mohammedanism* and *Modern Trends in Islam*, and Wilfred Cantwell Smith's *Islam in Modern History* are excellent résumés of the religion of Arabia by Western scholars. *The Eternal Message of Muhammad* by Abdel Rahman Azzam is an excellent résumé by a Muslim. The great German scholar, Carl Brockelmann, has written *History of the Islamic People*, which extends beyond the Arab people to some of the non-Arab lands on the outer fringes of Islam.

Julian Huxley composed *From an Antique Land* for the armchair traveler interested particularly in historic sites in the Middle East. Wendell Phillips's *Qataban and Sheba* concerns an archaeological expedition to an ancient center of civilization in southwestern Arabia. Recommended to the scholar and valuable for its extensive bibliography is R. Bayly Winder's *Saudi Arabia in the Nineteenth Century*.

An unusually successful introduction to the literature and thought of the Arabs is Eric Schroeder's *Muhammad's People: a Tale by Anthology*. James Kritzeck's *Anthology of Islamic Literature from the Rise of Islam to Modern Times* is another good selection. Arberry's *Modern Arabic Poetry* gives the flavor of the contemporary Arab's favorite literary form.

Of books on Islamic art and architecture and on the oriental rug there is no end. A good book with which to start is Maurice S. Dimand's *A Handbook of Muhammadan Art*. Other respected authorities, whose writings are inevitably well illustrated, are Arnold, Dilley, Ettinghausen, Grube, Hill, Jacobsen, Kuhnel, Lane and Wilson. Some of their books are cited in the following list, a list which does not purport to be more than an introduction to the vast number of works on Arabia and the Middle East.

Antonius, George. *The Arab Awakening.* New York: Lippincott, 1939.

Arabian Nights. Many editions. Most famous translations by Burton and Lane.

Arberry, Arthur J. *Modern Arabic Poetry.* London: Taylor's Foreign Press, 1950.

...... *The Koran Interpreted.* 2 vols. London: Allen & Unwin, 1955.

Armstrong, H. C. *Lord of Arabia.* Beirut: Khayyat, 1954.

Arnold, Sir Thomas W. *Painting in Islam.* New York: Dover, 1965.

Azzam, Abdel Rahman. *The Eternal Message of Muhammad.* New York: Devin-Adair, 1964.

Belgrave, Sir Charles D. *Personal Column.* London: Hutchinson, 1960.

Belgrave, James H. D. *Welcome to Bahrain.* London: The Augustan Press, 1965.

Brockelmann, Carl. *History of the Islamic Peoples.* New York: Putnam's, 1947.

Brown, W. R. *The Horse of the Desert.* New York: Macmillan, 1948 (c. 1929).

Bullard, Sir Reader. *The Camels Must Go.* London: Faber, 1961.

Burton, Sir Richard F. *Personal Narrative of a Pilgrimage to Al-Madinah and Meccah.* London: Bell, 1898, and other editions.

Cheesman, R. E. *In Unknown Arabia.* London: Macmillan, 1926.

Coon, Carleton Stevens, *Caravan: The Story of the Middle East.* New York: Holt, 1951.

De Gaury, Gerald. *Arabia Phoenix.* London: Harrap, 1946.

...... *Arabian Journey and Other Desert Travels.* London: Harrap, 1950.

...... *Faisal, King of Saudi Arabia.* London: Arthur Barker, 1966.

Dickson, H. R. P. *Kuwait and Her Neighbours.* London: Allen & Unwin, 1956.

...... *The Arab of the Desert.* London: Hodder and Stoughton, 1957.

Dickson, Violet. *Wild Flowers of Kuwait and Bahrain.* London: Allen & Unwin, 1955.

Dilley, Arthur U. and Dimand, M. S. *Oriental Rugs and Carpets: A Comprehensive Survey.* Philadelphia: Lippincott, 1965.

Dimand, Maurice S. *A Handbook of Muhammadan Art.* New York: The Metropolitan Museum of Art, 1958.

Doughty, C. M. *Travels in Arabia Deserta.* New York: Random House, 1946. London: Jonathan Cape, 1964.

Eddy, William A. *F. D. R. Meets Ibn Saud.* American Friends of the Middle East, 1954.

Ettinghausen, Richard. *Arab Painting.* (Skira Art Book.) Cleveland: World, 1962.

Finnie, David H. *Desert Enterprise.* Cambridge, Mass.: Harvard University Press, (1958).

Fisher, Sydney N. *The Middle East, a History.* New York: Knopf, 1959.

Fisher, W. B. *The Middle East; A Physical, Social, and Regional Geography.* 4th rev. ed. London: Methuen, 1961.

Gibb, Sir Hamilton A. R. *Modern Trends in Islam.* Chicago: University of Chicago Press, (1947).

...... *Mohammedanism.* London and New York: Oxford University Press, 1953.

Glubb, Sir John Bagot. *A Soldier with the Arabs.* London: Hodder and Stoughton, 1957.

Grube, Ernest. *The World of Islam.* (Landmarks of the World's Art Series.) New York: McGraw-Hill, 1967.

Guillaume, A. *Islam.* 2nd ed. Harmondsworth, England: Penguin Books, 1956.

Hartshorn, J. E. *Politics and World Oil Economics.* New York: Praeger, 1962.

...... *Oil Companies and Governments.* 2nd rev. ed. London: Faber and Faber, 1967.

Hay, Sir Rupert. *The Persian Gulf States.* Washington: Middle East Institute, 1959.

Hill, Derek and Grabar, Oleg. *Islamic Architecture and Its Decoration.* Chicago: University of Chicago Press, 1964.

Hitti, P. K. *The Arabs; a Short History.* Princeton, N. J.: Princeton University Press, 1949.

...... *History of Syria (including Lebanon and Palestine).* New York: Macmillan, 1951.

...... *History of the Arabs.* 7th ed. London: Macmillan, 1961.

...... *Lebanon in History, from the Earliest Times to the Present.* 2nd ed. New York: St. Martin's Press, 1962.

Hogarth, D. G. *The Penetration of Arabia.* New York: F. A. Stokes, 1904.

Howarth, David. *The Desert King.* London: Collins, 1964.

Huxley, Julian S. *From an Antique Land.* 2nd rev. ed. New York: Harper & Row, 1967.

Ingrams, W. Harold. *Arabia and the Isles.* 3rd rev. ed. London: Murray, 1966.

Jackh, Ernest (ed.). *Background of the Middle East.* Ithaca, N. Y.: Cornell University Press, 1952.

Jacobsen, Charles W. *Oriental Rugs; a Complete Guide.* Rutland, Vt.: Tuttle, 1962.

Khadduri, Majid. *Independent Iraq.* 2nd ed. London: Oxford University Press, 1960.

Kiernan, R. H. *The Unveiling of Arabia.* London: Harrap, 1937.

Kirk, G. E. *Short History of the Middle East.* 4th ed. London: Methuen, 1959.

Kritzeck, James. *Anthology of Islamic Literature from the Rise of Islam to Modern Times.* New York: Holt, Rinehart and Winston, 1964.

Kuhnel, Ernst. *Islamic Art and Architecture.* London: Bell, 1966.

Lane, Arthur. *Islamic Pottery from the Ninth to Fourteenth Centuries A. D.* London: Faber, 1956.

Lawrence, T. E. *Seven Pillars of Wisdom.* Garden City: Doubleday, 1935.

Lenczowski, George. *Oil and State in the Middle East.* Ithaca, N. Y.: Cornell University Press, 1960.

...... *The Middle East in World Affairs.* Ithaca, N. Y.: Cornell University Press, 1962.

Longrigg, Stephen H. *Four Centuries of Modern Iraq.* Oxford: The Clarendon Press, 1925.

...... *Iraq, 1900 to 1950.* London: Benn, 1958.

...... *Oil in the Middle East.* 2nd ed. New York: Oxford University Press, 1961.

...... *The Middle East; a Social Geography.* London: Duckworth, 1963.

Meinertzhagen, Richard. *The Birds of Arabia.* Edinburgh: Oliver & Boyd, 1954.

Meulen, D. van der. *Aden to the Hadramaut, a Journey in South Arabia.* London: Murray, 1947.

...... *Faces in Shem.* London: J. Murray, 1961.

Mountfort, Guy. *Portrait of a Desert.* London: Collins, 1965.

Musil, Alois. *The Northern Heğâz.* New York: American Geographical Society, 1926.

...... *Arabia Deserta.* New York: American Geographical Society, 1927.

. . . . . . *The Middle Euphrates*. New York: American Geographical Society, 1927.

. . . . . . *The Manners and Customs of the Rwala Bedouins*. New York: American Geographical Society, 1928.

. . . . . . *Northern Neğd*. New York: American Geographical Society, 1928.

. . . . . . *Palmyrena*. New York: American Geographical Society, 1928.

. . . . . . *In the Arabian Desert*. ed. K. M. Wright. New York: Liveright, 1930.

Nolte, Richard H. (ed.). *The Modern Middle East*. New York: Atherton Press, 1963.

Philby, H. St. John B. *The Heart of Arabia*. London: Constable, 1922.

. . . . . . *Arabia of the Wahhabis*. London: Constable, 1928.

. . . . . . *The Empty Quarter*. New York: Henry Holt, 1933.

. . . . . . *Sheba's Daughters*. London: Methuen, 1939.

. . . . . . *A Pilgrim in Arabia*. London: Hale, 1946.

. . . . . . *Arabian Days*. London: Hale, 1948.

. . . . . . *Arabian Highlands*. Ithaca, N. Y.: Cornell University Press, 1952.

. . . . . . *Arabian Jubilee*. London: Hale, 1952.

. . . . . . *Saudi Arabia*. London: Benn, 1955.

. . . . . . *Forty Years in the Wilderness*. London: R. Hale, 1959.

. . . . . . *The Land of Midian*. London: Benn, 1957.

. . . . . . *Arabian Oil Ventures*. Washington: Middle East Institute, 1964.

Pickthall, M. *The Meaning of the Glorious Qur'an*. New York: New American Library, 1953.

Phillips, Wendell. *Qataban and Sheba*. New York: Harcourt, Brace, 1955.

Sanger, Richard. *The Arabian Peninsula*. Ithaca: Cornell University Press, 1954.

Shroeder, Eric. *Muhammad's People: A Tale by Anthology*. Portland, Maine: Bond Wheelwright, 1955.

Smith, Wilfred Cantwell. *Islam in Modern History*. Princeton: Princeton University Press, 1957.

Thesiger, Wilfred. *Arabian Sands*. New York: Dutton, 1959.

Thomas, Bertram. *Arabia Felix*. New York: Scribner's, 1932.

. . . . . . *The Arabs*. London: Butterworth, 1937.

Twitchell, K. S. *Saudi Arabia*. 3rd ed. Princeton, N. J.: Princeton University Press, 1958.

Vidal, F. S. *The Oasis of al-Hasa*. Arabian American Oil Company, 1955.

Villiers, Alan. *Sons of Sinbad*. New York: Scribner's, 1940.

Wahba, Hafiz. *Arabian Days*. London: Arthur Barker, 1964.

Williams, Kenneth. *Ibn Sa'ud*. London: Cape, 1933.

Wilson, Sir Arnold. *The Persian Gulf*. London: Allen & Unwin, 1954.

Wilson, Ralph Pinder. *Islamic Art*. London: Benn, 1957.

Winder, R. Bayly. *Saudi Arabia in the Nineteenth Century*. New York: St. Martin's Press, 1965.

Yale, William. *The Near East: A Modern History*. Ann Arbor, Mich.: University of Michigan Press, 1958.

Index

The Arabic definite article al- and the word Al, meaning
"Family of," are disregarded in the alphabetizing of this index.

DATE DUE

~~OCT 18 '75~~			
JUN 28 1979			
NOV 30 1994			
OCT 1 5 1996			
OCT 3 1 1996			